Gregory L. Moss

Purdue University

Lab Manual: A Design Approach

to accompany

DIGITAL SYSTEMS: PRINCIPLES AND APPLICATIONS

Tenth Edition

By Ronald J. Tocci, Neal S. Widmer, & Gregory L. Moss

PEARSON

Prentice
Hall

Upper Saddle River, New Jersey
Columbus, Ohio

Director of Development: Vern Anthony
Production Editor: Stephen C. Robb
Design Coordinator: Diane Ernsberger
Cover Designer: Linda Sorrells Smith
Cover art: Getty One
Production Manager: Matt Ottenweller
Marketing Manager: Ben Leonard

This book was set in Times Roman by Gregory L. Moss. It was printed and bound by Bind Rite Graphics. The cover was printed by Coral Graphic Services, Inc.

MAX+PLUS II and Quartus II software screens are reprinted courtesy of Altera Corporation.

Altera is a trademark and service mark of Altera Corporation in the United States and other countries. Altera products are the intellectual property of Altera Corporation and are protected by copyright laws and one or more U.S. and foreign patents and patent applications.

Pearson Education Ltd.
Pearson Education Singapore Pte. Ltd.
Pearson Education Canada, Ltd.
Pearson Education—Japan

Pearson Education Australia Pty. Limited
Pearson Education North Asia Ltd.
Pearson Educación de Mexico, S.A. de C.V.
Pearson Education Malaysia Pte. Ltd.

10 9 8 7 6 5 4 3 2 1

ISBN 0-13-188138-8

CONTENTS

To my family,
Marita, David, and Ryan

PREFACE

This laboratory manual is written for students in an introductory digital electronics course that emphasizes logic circuit analysis, applications, and design. This lab manual, which accompanies the tenth edition of *Digital Systems: Principles and Applications* by Ronald J. Tocci, Neal S. Widmer, and Gregory L. Moss, has been extensively revised but continues the digital logic design approach for new students that has been presented in previous editions. Introductory projects provide student practice in circuit construction, testing, and operational analysis using standard logic devices. The concepts of common digital functions are presented using both medium-scale integration (MSI) chips and programmable logic devices (PLDs), with an emphasis on the latter. The lab assignments consist of circuit projects that range from investigating basic logic concepts to synthesizing circuits for new applications. The projects are intended to challenge all students and to provide them with some directed laboratory experience that develops insight into digital principles, applications, and techniques of logic circuit analysis and design.

In addition to covering standard digital logic devices and functions, this lab manual also extensively explores digital system implementation using complex programmable logic devices (CPLDs) or field programmable gate arrays (FPGAs). PLD programming is performed with MAX+PLUS II or Quartus II, two industry-leading digital system development packages from Altera Corporation. Detailed step-by-step tutorials on the procedures for using each of these software packages are presented on a CD-ROM that is included in this manual. MAX+PLUS II is a mature software package that is perhaps easier for beginning students to learn, whereas Quartus II provides more features for the benefit of advanced students. With either MAX+PLUS II or Quartus II, hierarchical digital designs can be entered using schematics and hardware description languages (HDLs). This lab manual actually supports two HDL languages, VHDL and AHDL. VHDL is an industry-standard language and has the advantage that it can be used with other development system software, but it is a bit more difficult to master. AHDL, on the other hand, is a proprietary language from Altera that is quite similar to VHDL but has several features that make hardware design easier for beginners. A major objective of this manual is to provide the greatest possible flexibility to fit your course goals. The development software also provides design verification through circuit simulation and timing analysis. A compiled digital design can be downloaded at a student's lab station directly to a target CPLD or FPGA device via the parallel port on a personal computer. The Student Version of MAX+PLUS II and the Web Edition of Quartus II are also included on the CD-ROM in this lab manual.

The lab manual is divided into 23 major topical units, with each unit containing an introductory discussion of the digital topic addressed, several applications, and a variety of laboratory projects. Many examples of alternative design solutions are given in several of the lab units. Introductory units on combinational logic circuits and sequential logic circuits target using standard logic devices for pedagogical reasons and because such devices are still found in industry. The PLD development software is introduced using schematic capture design entry and is followed by units that discuss writing HDL code for combinational and sequential circuits. Introductions to each of the two HDL languages are given in separate lab manual units. Later lab units that deal with common digital functions, such as decoders, encoders, multiplexers, counters, and shift registers, each have a variety of lab projects that use standard digital devices or PLDs and a mix of schematic and HDL design entry. Both HDL language solutions to examples are given, and they are clearly labeled with AHDL or VHDL.

The applications-oriented lab projects are designed to provide beginning students with extensive experience in the analysis and design of digital logic circuits. The manual provides an extensive selection of projects for either a two-semester introductory digital course sequence or, by reducing the breadth of topics covered, a single-semester digital course. The sequencing of topics follows the textbook by Tocci, Widmer, and Moss. However, the lab manual is designed for flexibility by including many different lab projects with varying levels of difficulty. To provide more depth, some lab units may be assigned over more than one laboratory period. There is no expectation that any course would have sufficient time for students to perform all of the laboratory projects provided. Rather, instructors can select and rearrange the topics and projects to fit their particular course objectives. Likewise, two HDLs are presented so that a school can decide which language approach can best suit its program goals.

Personal computers and electronic design automation software have changed how digital systems are designed and developed in industry today. Programmable logic devices and logic circuit development software are popular and extremely important digital technologies. These technologies need to be included in the educational experience of future electronics personnel. Accordingly, the custom implementation of logic circuits using CPLDs or FPGAs is emphasized in this manual.

There are several relatively low-cost prototyping boards for Altera PLDs that can be utilized in the digital laboratory. Photographs of example training boards are shown on page vii. Pictured are Altera, RSR, and DeVry boards that contain an EPM7128SLC84 chip. The HVW board has a smaller EPM7064SLC44 chip. The Altera UP2 board also has a large Flex 10K family chip, and the Altera UP3 board contains an EP1C6Q240C8. Each of these boards is programmed via the parallel port of a standard PC.

A list of laboratory equipment, integrated circuits, and other necessary components is found in the Equipment List on pages viii–ix. Only standard digital integrated circuit part numbers (74XX) are listed. Either TTL or CMOS families can be used for the standard logic device projects (but note that mixing CMOS and TTL devices in a single project may not work properly). Logic design today primarily uses CMOS technology, but TTL components may be used since they are readily available. Data sheets for most logic devices can be found on the *Texas Instruments* web site at http://www.ti.com. Data sheets for the Altera CPLD devices can be found on the web at http://www.altera.com.

I am very grateful to the Altera Corporation, whose continued support has helped to make this laboratory manual possible.

Gregory L. Moss

Example CPLD/FPGA prototyping boards (clockwise from top left): Altera Corporation UP2, HVW Technologies Intro-FPGA, DeVry University eSOC, Altera Corporation UP3, and RSR Electronics PLDT-2. (photographs by G. L. Moss)

EQUIPMENT LIST

Recommended Laboratory Equipment and Software

Digital breadboarding system
Power supply (5 V, 500 mA)
Logic probe
Digital multimeter
Oscilloscope (4-trace preferred, dual-trace minimum)
Frequency counter
Signal generator
Personal computer
Altera MAX+PLUS II or Quartus II development software
CPLD/FPGA training board with Altera EPM7128SLC84 (or other MAX 7000S family
    devices) or Altera EP1C6Q240C (or other Cyclone family devices)

Digital Integrated Circuits

Quantity	Part #	Logic families	Description
1	7400	ALS, LS, HC, HCT	Quad 2-input NAND
1	7402	ALS, LS, HC, HCT	Quad 2-input NOR
1	7404	ALS, LS, HC, HCT	Hex INVERTERs
1	7408	ALS, LS, HC, HCT	Quad 2-input AND
1	7410	ALS, LS, HC	Triple 3-input NAND
1	7411	ALS, LS, HC	Triple 3-input AND
1	7414	LS, HC, HCT	Hex Schmitt-trigger INVERTERs
1	7420	ALS, LS, HC	Dual 4-input NAND
1	7427	ALS, LS, HC	Triple 3-input NOR
1	7432	ALS, LS, HC, HCT	Quad 2-input OR
2	7447	LS	BCD-to-7-segment DECODER/DRIVER
2	7474	ALS, LS, HC, HCT	Dual D-type, positive-edge-triggered FLIP-FLOPs
1	7485	LS	4-bit MAGNITUDE COMPARATOR
1	7486	ALS, LS	Quad 2-input EXCLUSIVE-OR
2	74112	ALS, LS, HC	Dual JK, negative-edge-triggered FLIP-FLOPs
1	74138	ALS, LS, HC, HCT	3-line-to-8-line DECODER/DEMUX
1	74148	LS, HC	8-line-to-3-line priority ENCODER
1	74151	ALS, LS, HC	1-of-8 MULTIPLEXER
1	74157	LS, HC	Quad 2-line-to-1-line MULTIPLEXER
1	74160	ALS, LS, HC	Synchronous decade COUNTER
1	74161	ALS, LS, HC	Synchronous binary COUNTER
1	74163	ALS, LS, HC	Synchronous binary COUNTER

Quantity	Part #	Logic families	Description
1	74166	ALS, LS, HC	8-bit SHIFT REGISTER (PISO)
1	74175	LS	Quad D-type FLIP-FLOPs with clear
1	74190	ALS, LS, HC, HCT	Synchronous up/down decade COUNTER
1	74221	LS	Dual MONOSTABLE MULTIVIBRATOR
1	74244	ALS, LS, HC, HCT	Octal 3-state BUFFER
1	74375	LS	4-bit bistable LATCH
2	2114		Static RAM (1K × 4) [9114]

Linear Integrated Circuits

1	NE555	Timer	
1	AD557	8-bit digital-to-analog converter	
1	ADC0804	8-bit analog-to-digital converter	

Miscellaneous Components

MAN72 (or equivalent) common-anode, 7-segment LED display (×2)

Resistors (1/4 watt):

330 Ω (×14)	1.0 kΩ (×10)	1.1 kΩ
1.3 kΩ	2.0 kΩ	3.3 kΩ
10 kΩ (×2)	27 kΩ	33 kΩ
47 kΩ	62 kΩ	68 kΩ
72 kΩ	82 kΩ	

Capacitors:

10 µf	0.1 µf	0.01 µf (×8)
0.001 µf	0.0047 µf	150 pf

Potentiometers (10-turn):

10 kΩ

Rectifier diode: 1N4001 (×2)

SPDT switch

Grayhill 84BB1-003 (or equivalent) Keypad (4 × 4 matrix)

INTRODUCTION TO DIGITAL TEST EQUIPMENT

Objective

- To describe the function and operation of a typical digital breadboarding and testing system.

Suggested Parts		
7404	7408	7432

Digital Test Equipment

Typical breadboarding and testing equipment used with digital circuits is shown in Fig. 1-1. Included are a power supply, lamp monitors, logic switches, pulsers, clock, breadboarding sockets, and a logic probe.

Power supply

The power supply typically provides a regulated +5 V DC voltage to be used to power TTL or CMOS integrated circuits. Note that some units may also contain additional fixed voltages or a variable DC power source for other types of circuits.

Lamp monitors

The lamp monitors indicate the voltage level at various points in the digital circuit being tested. The lamp monitors will light when a digital "high" voltage is applied to them.

Logic switches

The logic switches input either of the two logic levels (voltages) to the circuit being tested. A switch in the "down" position will provide a logic "low" voltage, while a switch in the "up" position will provide a logic "high" voltage.

Pushbuttons or pulsers

A pushbutton provides a momentary "bounce free" logic input to the test circuit. Pulsers that are provided on some testing systems produce a short duration (narrow) pulse or change in the logic level of the pulser's output.

Clock

The clock provides a variable frequency pulse waveform that can be used for the timing control of some digital circuits.

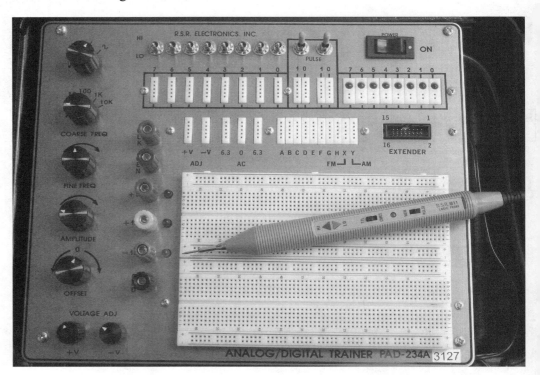

Fig. 1-1 Digital breadboarding and testing equipment (photograph by G. L. Moss)

Breadboarding sockets

Breadboarding sockets are very convenient devices on which circuits may be constructed for testing purposes. The socket contains a matrix of contacts that are used to interconnect the various components and wires needed to construct the digital circuit. The socket holes are small and only #30 to #22 solid "jumper" wires should be inserted into them. A photograph of a typical breadboarding socket is shown in Fig. 1-2. This style of socket is designed to breadboard DIP (dual-in-line package) type integrated circuits (ICs or chips). The illustrated socket has several separate electrical buses across the top and bottom of the board. For identification, a rectangle has been drawn around the top right bus in the photograph. Not all breadboarding sockets will have these buses or may have fewer of them. The buses will often be used to connect power and ground to **each** of the chips in the circuit. The chips will be inserted into the socket as shown in the photograph so that their pins will be parallel to and on either side of the center groove in the socket. Electrical connections are made to any pin by inserting wires into the set of vertical holes that line up with that pin. Another identifying rectangle has been drawn around the holes that will connect to the leftmost pin (pin #1) on the bottom side of the chip in the photograph. Fig. 1-3 is a photograph of an example digital circuit that has been constructed on a breadboarding socket.

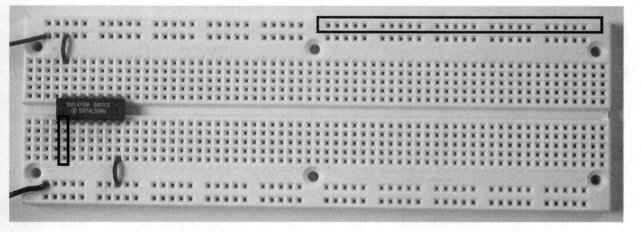

Fig. 1-2 Typical IC breadboarding socket (photograph by G. L. Moss)

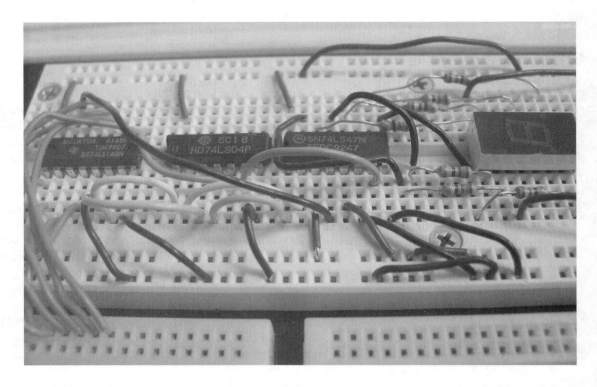

Fig. 1-3 A digital circuit wired on a breadboarding socket (photograph by G. L. Moss)

Notes on Test Equipment Operation

Measuring Voltage with a Digital Multi-Meter (DMM)

The potential difference or voltage between the positive and negative terminals of a battery or power supply connected to a circuit will cause current to flow through the circuit. The basic unit to measure potential difference is the volt (V). A potential difference or voltage drop occurs across the various devices in a circuit when current flows through them. The magnitude (and polarity with respect to a reference point in the circuit) of a potential difference is measured with an instrument called a voltmeter. You must be extremely careful when making voltage measurements since the measurement is made on a "live" (powered) circuit. The voltmeter test leads (probes) are placed across (in parallel with) the device or power source whose voltage is to be measured. The procedure to measure DC voltages using a typical digital voltmeter is:

(1) *Connect the test leads to the DMM*
(2) *Set the function switch to measure DC voltages*
(3) *Set the range switch for the maximum voltage anticipated (unless the meter is autoranging)*
(4) *Connect (or touch) the black test lead to the reference point of the circuit (or component)*
(5) *Connect (or touch) the red test lead to the point in the circuit where you wish to measure the voltage*
(6) *Read the voltage on the digital display*
(7) *Readjust the range setting if necessary for a proper reading*

Ask your lab instructor if you have any questions concerning the use of the DMM.

Measuring Logic Levels with a Logic Probe

The logic probe is an extremely handy and easy to use piece of digital test equipment. It is used to detect and display the logic levels at various test points within a circuit. To use a logic probe to test TTL circuits:

(1) *Connect the alligator clip leads to the power supply for the circuit being tested (red to +5 V and black to ground)*
(2) *Set the logic family switch to TTL*
(3) *Carefully touch the probe tip to the circuit node (normally a chip pin) to be tested (do not short any nodes together in the process)*
(4) *Note the logic level present at the test point by which the LED (HIGH or LOW) is illuminated*
(5) *If neither HIGH nor LOW is indicated, the proper logic voltage is not present at the test point*

Some logic probes also have a pulse detector (indicated on a separate LED) feature to indicate that the logic level at the test point is changing. Ask your lab instructor if you have any questions concerning the use of the logic probe.

Laboratory Projects

Investigate the features of the digital breadboarding and test system available in the laboratory by performing the following tasks with the unit. Carefully plug it into the AC outlet and turn on the power. Consult your lab instructor if you have any problems or questions concerning the laboratory procedures or equipment operation.

1.1   Measure and record the TTL **power supply** output voltage (with respect to ground) using a DMM. Remember that one of the most important safety precautions to observe in electronics is to avoid personal contact with any voltage source or component in a "live" circuit. You may need a short piece of jumper wire if the DMM's probes do not easily make electrical contact to the power supply connectors. Make sure that you are reading the TTL supply voltage if the unit has more than the single output supply. The TTL supply voltage should be between +4.75 V and +5.25 V DC. If you are unfamiliar with the use of the DMM, refer to the "Measuring Voltage with a Digital Multi-Meter (DMM)" section of this lab assignment.

Measured power supply voltage _____

1.2   Locate the **logic switches** on the digital tester. Determine the number of individual input switches available. Determine the number of wiring connection points available for each logic switch. Measure and record the voltage (with respect to ground) from a logic switch when it is placed in each of its two positions (up and down). In TTL logic, a "low" voltage will be approximately 0 V and a "high" will be approximately +5 V (actually anywhere from +2 V to +5 V).

Number of logic switches on digital tester _____

Number of wiring connections for each switch _____

Switch position	Voltage	Logic level
Up		
Down		

1.3   Record your observations when a **logic probe** is used to test the output from the logic switch in each of its two positions. What does it mean if both logic probe lights are off at the same time? You may need a short piece of jumper wire. See the "Measuring Logic Levels with a Logic Probe" section of this lab.

Switch position	Which LED on?	Logic level indicated
Up		
Down		

Both LEDs are off if _____

1.4   Locate the **lamp monitors** on the digital tester. Determine the number of individual lights available. Determine the number of wiring connection points available for each lamp monitor. Record your observations of the operation of the lamp monitors by connecting a jumper wire from one of the logic switches to a lamp monitor and then moving the switch between the two logic levels (high and low voltage). In positive logic, a high voltage is referred to as a "1" and a low voltage is referred to as a "0." How does the result from the lamp monitor compare to the logic probe's result?

Number of lamp monitors on digital tester _____

Number of wiring connections for each lamp _____

Switch output	0 or 1?	Lamp on or off?
High		
Low		

Compare operation of lamp monitor to logic probe. _____

_____

_____

1.5   Locate the **pushbuttons** or pulsers on the digital tester. Determine the number of individual momentary inputs available. Note the operation of a pushbutton or pulser by connecting it to an unused lamp monitor and then pressing and releasing the button or switch. Determine the "normal" output condition for one of the pushbuttons or pulsers. What output is produced if the pushbutton or pulser is "activated"? If your unit has pushbuttons with two complementary outputs available, connect each of the outputs to a separate, unused lamp monitor and then press and release the button. Describe the operation of a pushbutton or pulser.

Number of logic pushbuttons/pulsers on digital tester _____

Pushbutton	Logic level
Normal	
Activated	

Describe operation of pushbutton/pulser. _____

_____

1.6   Note the operation of the **clock** output by connecting it to the logic probe with the <u>clock set at its lowest frequency</u>. If your unit has a clock with two complementary outputs available, also connect each of the clock outputs to a separate, unused lamp monitor. Describe the clock operation by observing the lamp action. Describe the clock signal when the clock frequency is increased using a "fine" adjustment control and when using a "coarse" adjustment control. What is the logic probe telling you when both LEDs appear to be lit?

Describe clock operation at lowest frequency. _____

_____

Describe clock signal while increasing "fine" control. _____

_____

Describe clock signal while increasing "coarse" control. _____

_____

If both logic probe LEDs appear to be lit, it means that _____

_____

1.7   Investigate the internal connections of the **breadboarding socket** using the ohmmeter
function of the DMM. A typical breadboarding socket is illustrated in the following
diagram. There are four separate horizontal buses along the top and an additional four
separate buses along the bottom of this breadboard. One of the buses is highlighted in
the drawing to show the electrical connections for that bus. One set of vertical
connections for a single pin on an IC is also highlighted. Use some short wires and the
ohmmeter to determine the internal electrical conductor pattern for the breadboarding
socket. Make the resistance measurements indicated in the following table. Note: If
your breadboarding socket does not have bus strips available as illustrated, consult your
lab instructor for specific instructions.

From	To	Resistance
1	2	
1	3	
1	4	
A	B	
A	C	
A	D	

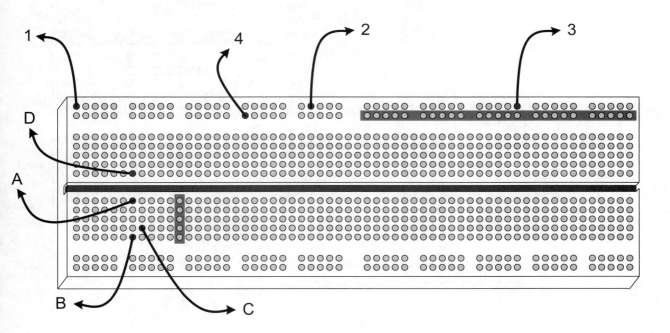

1.8   Construct the **logic circuit** shown in the following drawing on a breadboarding socket. A 74LS08 is used in the circuit. This chip contains **AND** gates. Two logic switches (A and B) are used to provide the inputs to the logic circuit (an AND gate). There are four input combinations possible with the two switches A and B. The output (X) from the logic circuit will be observed on a lamp monitor. Be sure to connect power (+5 V) and ground to the IC chip. <u>Complete</u> the table below to record the test results. <u>Describe</u> the necessary logic inputs to produce a high output for an AND gate.

A	B	X
0	0	
0	1	
1	0	
1	1	

Chip pin-out drawing

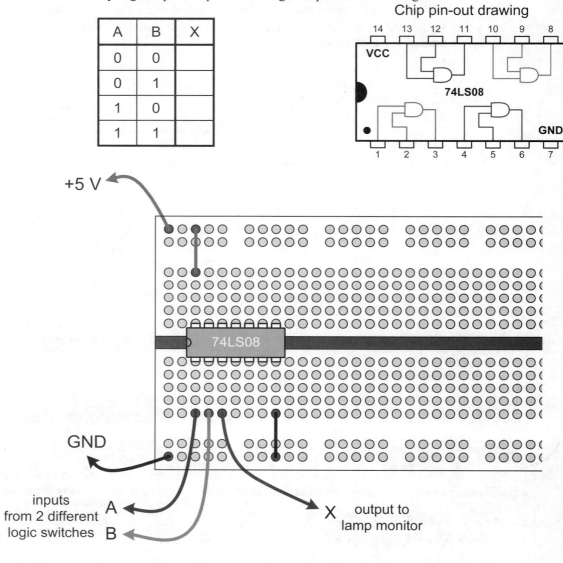

An AND gate produces a high output when _____

1.9　Construct the **logic circuit** shown in the following drawing on a breadboarding socket. A 74LS32 is used in the circuit. This chip contains **OR** gates. Two logic switches (A and B) are used to provide the inputs to the logic circuit (an OR gate). There are four input combinations possible with the two switches A and B. The output (X) from the logic circuit will be observed on a lamp monitor. Be sure to connect power (+5 V) and ground to the IC chip. Complete the table below to record the test results. Describe the necessary logic inputs to produce a high output for an OR gate.

A	B	X
0	0	
0	1	
1	0	
1	1	

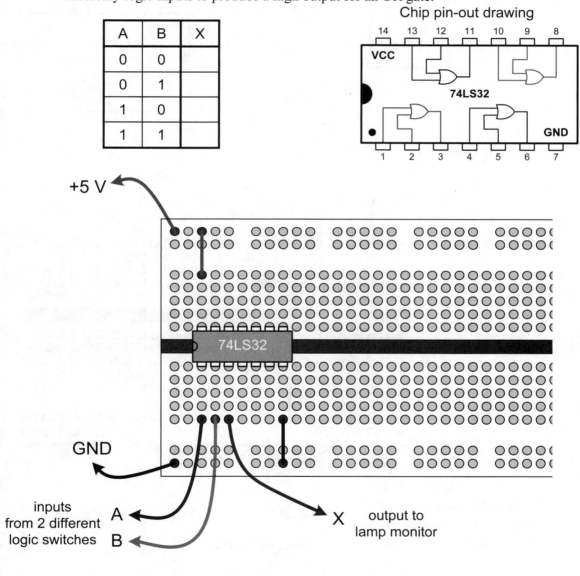

Chip pin-out drawing

An OR gate produces a high output when _____

1.10 Construct the **logic circuit** shown in the following drawing on a breadboarding socket.
A 74LS04 is used in the circuit. This chip contains **NOT** gates. One logic switch (A) is
used to provide the input to the logic circuit (a NOT gate). There are two input
combinations possible with switch A. The output (X) from the logic circuit will be
observed on a lamp monitor. Be sure to connect power (+5 V) and ground to the IC
chip. Complete the table below to record the test results. Describe the relationship
between the input and output for a NOT gate.

A	X
0	
1	

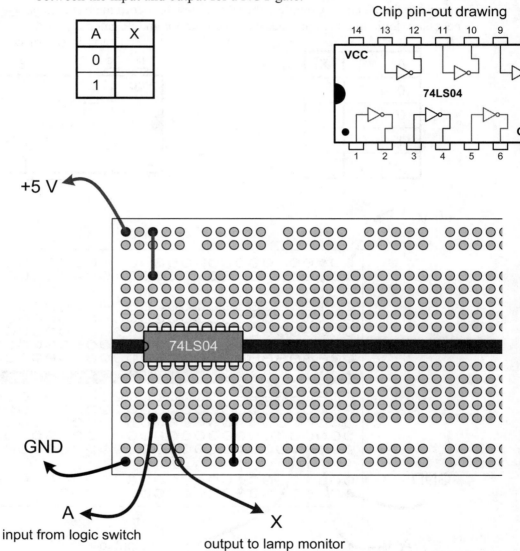

Chip pin-out drawing

Relationship between input and output for a NOT gate: _____

_____

BREADBOARDING COMBINATIONAL LOGIC CIRCUITS

Objectives

- To construct simple combinational logic circuits from a schematic.
- To test simple combinational logic circuits to determine the functional operation of the circuits.
- To identify common logic functions produced by various circuit configurations by the resulting truth table.
- To connect various gates together to create simple logic functions.

Suggested Parts					
7400	7402	7404	7408	7420	7427
7432					

Combinational Logic Circuits

Logic Gates

A logic gate is the simplest device used to construct digital circuits. The output voltage or logic level for each type of gate is a function of the applied input(s). Various types of logic gates are available (including inverters, ANDs, ORs, NANDs, and NORs), each with its own unique logic function. Logic circuits are constructed by interconnecting various logic gates together to implement a particular circuit function.

Truth Tables

The logic function for a single gate or a complete circuit using many gates can be easily represented in a logic truth table or a logic expression. The layout for 1- and 2-input variable truth tables is given in Fig. 2-1. Note: L = low logic level voltage and H = high logic level voltage.

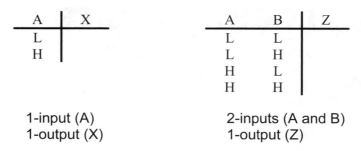

A	X
L	
H	

1-input (A)
1-output (X)

A	B	Z
L	L	
L	H	
H	L	
H	H	

2-inputs (A and B)
1-output (Z)

Fig. 2-1 Truth tables showing possible input combinations

Circuit Breadboarding

When constructing logic circuits, care should be taken to ensure that the parts are not damaged while breadboarding the circuit. Carefully insert the integrated circuit (IC) into the breadboarding socket so that the IC is straddling the center groove on the socket. Make sure that both rows of pins are correctly lined up with the holes in the breadboard, but be careful to avoid bending the IC pins any more than is necessary. The ICs can be safely removed by prying up each end with a screwdriver (or similar tool) or an IC puller. Do not insert or remove ICs with the power applied to the circuit.

A notch or dot at one end of the IC package is used to locate pin 1 of the chip, and the pin numbers then increase in a counterclockwise direction around the device as viewed from the top (see Fig. 2-2). Inserting all ICs with the same orientation for pin 1 will facilitate circuit wiring and troubleshooting.

Determine the pin-out information for <u>each</u> chip by consulting a data book or data sheet for the logic devices used (see Appendix for SSI device pin-outs). Notice that power and ground, inputs, and outputs are sometimes located on different pins for different part numbers. Label the pin numbers for each device on a logic circuit schematic to aid in wiring the circuit and in troubleshooting it later if necessary.

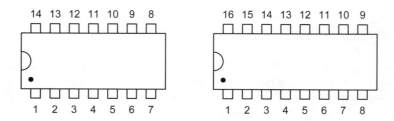

Fig. 2-2 IC pin numbering for 14- and 16-pin DIP packages (top view)

Systematically and carefully wire the circuit with the power off. Wiring errors are the most common source of circuit failure in breadboarding circuits. The jumper wires used to connect the circuit components together should have only about 1/4 inch of the insulation stripped from each end of the wire to avoid inadvertently shorting the wires together. Using short jumper wires will facilitate troubleshooting later if necessary. Double-check the wiring against the schematic diagram.

Circuit Testing and Troubleshooting

Verify that the power supply is correctly connected to the circuit before turning it on. Also make sure that the power supply voltage is the proper value (5 volts). Then, and only then, should you turn on the power to the circuit.

If the circuit does not function properly or if an IC gets very hot or starts smoking, turn off the power and all signals to the circuit immediately. Use the suggestions given in the troubleshooting checklist below to troubleshoot the malfunctioning circuit.

Troubleshooting Checklist

✔ *Do the parts used in the circuit match the schematic?*
✔ *Have the pin numbers been identified correctly in the schematic?*
✔ *Are the parts inserted correctly in the breadboard?*
✔ *Is the correct voltage supply being used to power the circuit?*
✔ *Is the power properly connected to each chip?*
✔ *Are there any wires shorted to one another?*
✔ *Is the circuit wired correctly?*
✔ *Has the circuit been analyzed correctly?*
✔ *Has the circuit been designed correctly?*

Breadboarded logic circuits can be manually tested using a digital test system like the one described in Unit 1. Connect a separate logic switch to each of the circuit's inputs and a lamp monitor to the circuit's output. Apply various input logic levels with the switches and monitor the output produced by the circuit with the lamp. List the resultant functional operation of the circuit in a truth table. Determine if the circuit is operating properly.

Example 2-1

Determine the logic expression and predict the theoretical operation for circuit L in Laboratory Project 2.1. Identify the common logic function produced by this circuit. Label the schematic with appropriate component part numbers and pin numbers and show how to wire this logic circuit on a breadboarding socket.

The logic circuit consists of a 4-input NAND gate with one input permanently connected to a high (5 volts). The logic expression for L is given below and the truth table is listed in Table 2-1. The logic function is simply a 3-input NAND. The extra, unused input on the gate is disabled by applying a logic high to it. The schematic is labeled with appropriate part numbers and pin numbers in Fig. 2-3. The drawing in Fig. 2-4 shows how to wire this circuit on a breadboard.

$$L = \overline{1 \cdot A \cdot B \cdot C} = \overline{A \cdot B \cdot C}$$

A	B	C	L
0	0	0	1
0	0	1	1
0	1	0	1
0	1	1	1
1	0	0	1
1	0	1	1
1	1	0	1
1	1	1	0

Table 2-1 Truth table prediction for Example 2-1

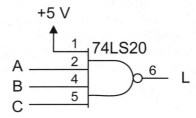

Fig. 2-3 Labeled schematic for Example 2-1

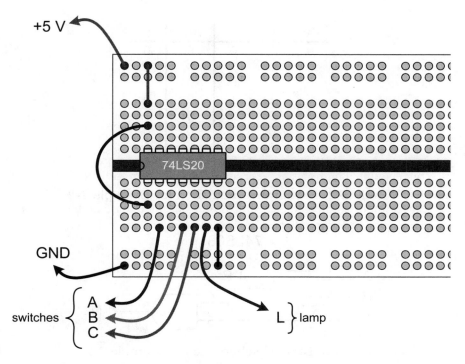

Fig. 2-4 Breadboard wiring of circuit L for Example 2-1

Example 2-2

Determine the logic expression and predict the theoretical operation for circuit **N** in Laboratory Project 2.1. Identify the common logic function produced by this circuit. Label the schematic with appropriate component part numbers and pin numbers and show how to wire this logic circuit on a breadboarding socket.

The logic circuit consists of two 2-input AND gates connected together. The logic expression for **N** is given below and the truth table is listed in Table 2-2. The logic function is simply a 3-input AND. The schematic is labeled with appropriate part numbers and pin numbers in Fig. 2-5. The logic function at the intermediate circuit node (output from the first AND gate) is also labeled in Fig. 2-5. The drawing in Fig. 2-6 shows how to wire this circuit on a breadboard.

$$N = (A \cdot B) \cdot C = A \cdot B \cdot C$$

A	B	C	A·B	N
0	0	0	0	0
0	0	1	0	0
0	1	0	0	0
0	1	1	0	0
1	0	0	0	0
1	0	1	0	0
1	1	0	1	0
1	1	1	1	1

Table 2-2 Truth table prediction for Example 2-2

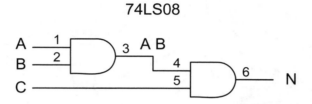

Fig. 2-5 Labeled schematic for Example 2-2

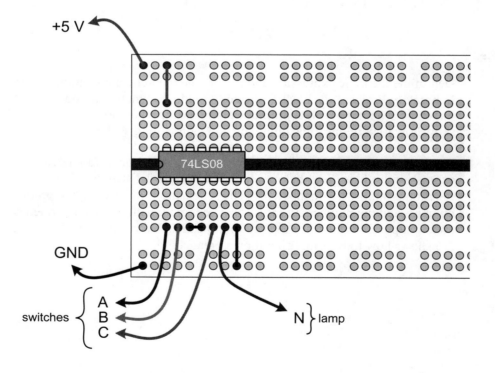

Fig. 2-6 Breadboard wiring of circuit N for Example 2-2

Example 2-3

Determine the logic expression and predict the theoretical operation for circuit Z in Laboratory Project 2.2. Identify the common logic function produced by this circuit. Label the schematic with appropriate component part numbers and pin numbers and show how to wire this logic circuit on a breadboarding socket.

The logic circuit consists of two 2-input NAND gates and one NOT gate. The logic expression for Z is given below and the truth table is listed in Table 2-3. The logic function is simply a 3-input NAND. The schematic is labeled with appropriate part numbers and pin numbers in Fig. 2-7. Intermediate circuit nodes are also labeled in Fig. 2-7. The drawing in Fig. 2-8 shows how to wire this circuit on a breadboard.

$$Z = \overline{\overline{\overline{A \cdot B}} \cdot C} = \overline{A \cdot B \cdot C}$$

A	B	C	$\overline{A \cdot B}$	$\overline{\overline{A \cdot B}}$	Z
0	0	0	1	0	1
0	0	1	1	0	1
0	1	0	1	0	1
0	1	1	1	0	1
1	0	0	1	0	1
1	0	1	1	0	1
1	1	0	0	1	1
1	1	1	0	1	0

Table 2-3 Truth table prediction for Example 2-3

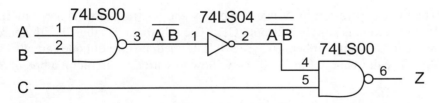

Fig. 2-7 Schematic for Example 2-3

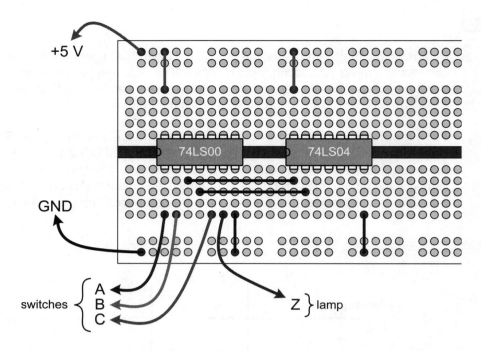

+5 V

74LS00   74LS04

GND

switches { A
           B
           C

Z } lamp

Fig. 2-8 Breadboard wiring of logic circuit in Example 2-3

Example 2-4

Determine the logic expression and predict the theoretical operation for circuit V in Laboratory Project 2.3. Identify the common logic function produced by this circuit. Label the schematic with appropriate component part numbers and pin numbers and show how to wire this logic circuit on a breadboarding socket.

The logic expression for V is given below and the truth table is listed in Table 2-4. The logic function is simply a 2-input OR. The schematic is labeled with appropriate part numbers and pin numbers in Fig. 2-9. Intermediate circuit nodes are also labeled in Fig. 2-9. The drawing in Fig. 2-10 shows how to wire this circuit on a breadboard.

$$V = (\overline{A} \cdot B + A \cdot B) + A \cdot \overline{B} = A + B$$

A	B	$\overline{A} \cdot B$	A·B	$A \cdot \overline{B}$	V
0	0	0	0	0	0
0	1	1	0	0	1
1	0	0	0	1	1
1	1	0	1	0	1

Table 2-4 Truth table prediction for Example 2-4

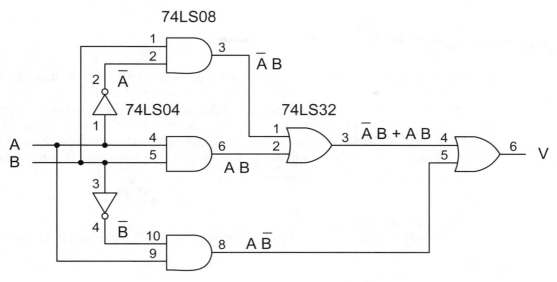

Fig. 2-9 Labeled schematic for Example 2-4

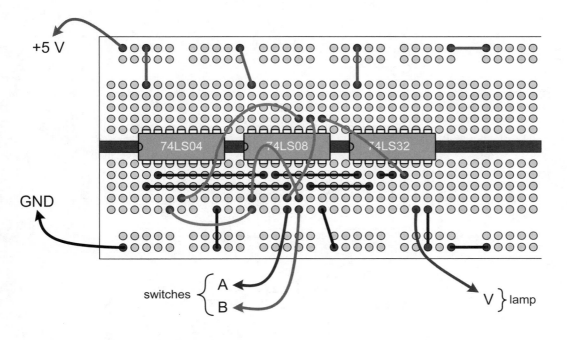

Fig. 2-10 Breadboard wiring of circuit V for Example 2-4

Laboratory Projects

Determine the logic expression for each of the following simple logic circuits. Analyze each circuit to predict its theoretical operation. Redraw the schematics for each circuit and label the schematics with appropriate component part numbers and pin numbers. Then construct and test each circuit to verify your predictions. Give the theoretical results and test results for each circuit in a logic truth table. Identify the common logic function produced by each circuit. Reconcile any differences between the predicted and test results. See the examples given in this unit.

2.1   One-chip logic circuits
Construct and test each of the following logic circuits. Each circuit will use only 1 chip.

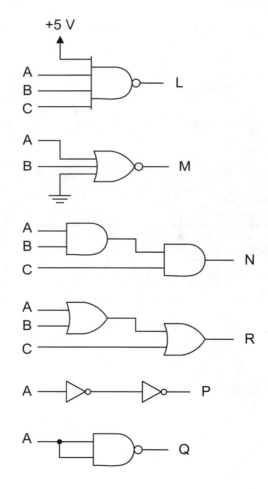

2.2 Two-chip logic circuits
Construct and test each of the following logic circuits. Each circuit will use 2 chips.

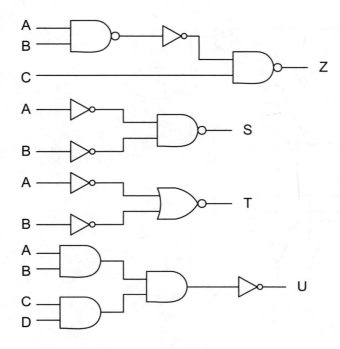

2.3   Three-chip logic circuits
        Construct and test each of the following logic circuits. Each circuit will use 3 chips.

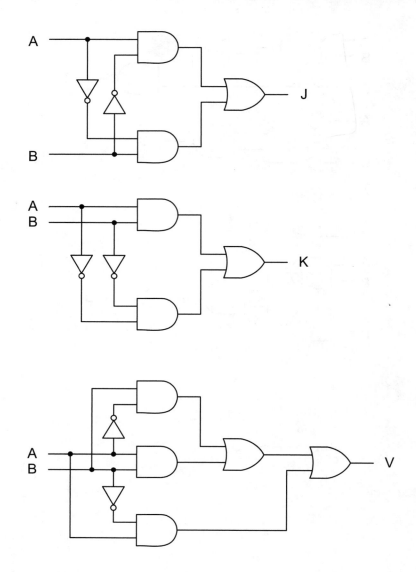

ANALYZING COMBINATIONAL LOGIC CIRCUITS

Objectives

- To analyze combinational logic circuits and predict their operation.
- To construct and test more complex combinational logic circuits.

Suggested Parts					
7400	7402	7404	7408	7410	7432
7486					

Combinational Logic Circuit Analysis

The theoretical operation of a combinational logic circuit can be predicted by analyzing the circuit's output for every possible input combination. The circuit analysis for each input combination is performed by determining the resultant output of each gate, working from the input side of the circuit to the output. We will later discover shortcuts to speed up the analysis process.

Logic circuits may be functionally equivalent. They may perform the same function (i.e., their logic truth tables are identical) but be constructed from different logic gates or interconnected in an entirely different manner. In fact we will find that often a complex logic circuit can be replaced with a much simpler one that performs the identical function.

Example 3-1

Analyze the circuit in Fig. 3-1 and determine its truth table.

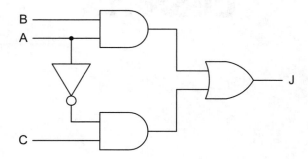

Fig. 3-1 Schematic for circuit analysis example

The logic expression for the given logic circuit is:

$$J = A B + \overline{A} C$$

Since the logic circuit has 3 input variables, a truth table (see Table 3-1) listing all 8 possible combinations is constructed. Create a separate output column in the truth table for each logic gate in the circuit and label the column to represent the gate function or output node name. The resultant output for every gate in the circuit can then be determined for each of the 8 possible input combinations. This gate output information is added to the truth table results for each of the logic gates.

A	B	C	$\overline{A}$	A B	$\overline{A}$ C	J
0	0	0	1	0	0	0
0	0	1	1	0	1	1
0	1	0	1	0	0	0
0	1	1	1	0	1	1
1	0	0	0	0	0	0
1	0	1	0	0	0	0
1	1	0	0	1	0	1
1	1	1	0	1	0	1

Table 3-1 Truth table analysis for example circuit

Laboratory Projects

Combinational circuit analysis and testing
Write the logic expression at each node for the following logic circuits and predict the circuit's theoretical operation with a truth table. Draw and label circuit schematics with appropriate part numbers and pin numbers. Then construct and test each circuit. Note any other observations.

3.1   Simple circuits

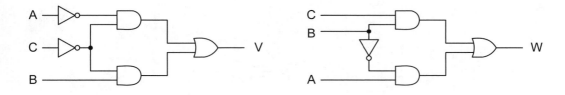

3.2   Equivalent circuits 1

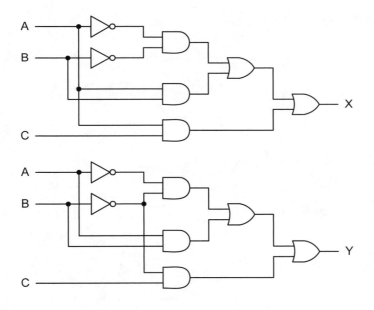

3.3 Equivalent circuits 2

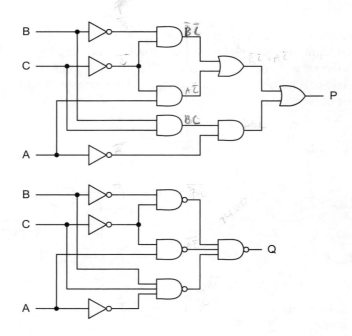

3.4 Exclusive-OR/NOR circuits

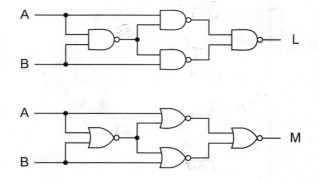

3.5 Multiple-output circuit (adder)

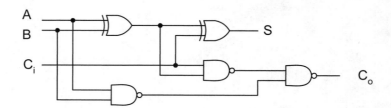

COMBINATIONAL CIRCUIT DESIGN WITH KARNAUGH MAPPING

Objectives

- To write standard sum-of-product (SOP) logic expressions for functions defined in given truth tables.
- To implement SOP logic expressions using standard AND/OR and NAND/NAND circuit configurations.
- To write simplified SOP logic expressions using Karnaugh mapping techniques.
- To design a combinational logic circuit that will perform a stated task by first defining the logic function with a truth table and then determining the simplified circuit solution using Karnaugh mapping.

Suggested Parts					
7400	7404	7408	7410	7420	7432

Combinational Circuit Design

SOP Expressions

The most commonly used format for writing logic expressions is a standard form called sum-of-product (SOP). SOP expressions can be quickly written from a truth table and they are easily implemented using a two-level (not counting inverters that may be needed) gate network. Conversely, these standard circuits that are used to implement SOP functions can be quickly analyzed just by inspection. A sum-of-product expression consists of two or more product (AND) terms that are ORed together. The SOP expression is obtained from a truth table by writing down all of the product terms (also called minterms) whose outputs are high for the desired function and then ORing them together. The resultant SOP expression can be directly implemented with either AND/OR or NAND/NAND circuit designs.

Karnaugh Mapping

The basic procedure for combinational logic circuit design is to develop first the truth table that defines the desired function and then from the table, write a simplified SOP expression. The expression can be simplified using various techniques (such as Boolean algebra, Karnaugh mapping, etc.). Karnaugh mapping is a simple and fast procedure for reducing SOP logic expressions and thereby also reducing the implemented circuit's complexity and cost. In Karnaugh mapping, the function is defined graphically. The relationships between the function's inputs and the output are plotted in a Karnaugh map (K map). This will be the same information that would be listed in the truth table for the function. The input variables must be labeled on the K map in a very systematic fashion. If the K map is not properly labeled, the function cannot be correctly simplified and the resulting design will be wrong. With K mapping, the function reduction is accomplished by forming appropriate groupings of 1s in the output. Then identify the common input variables for the group and write the indicated product term. Karnaugh mapping can best be applied to functions with 5 or fewer input variables.

Example 4-1

Design a combinational circuit that will indicate the majority result of 3 individuals voting.

First, define the problem in a truth table as shown in Table 4-1.

A	B	C	V
0	0	0	0
0	0	1	0
0	1	0	0
0	1	1	1
1	0	0	0
1	0	1	1
1	1	0	1
1	1	1	1

Table 4-1 Truth table for Example 4-1

The unsimplified SOP expression for Example 4-1 would be:

$$V = \overline{A} B C + A \overline{B} C + A B \overline{C} + A B C$$

The Karnaugh map for this function is plotted in Fig. 4-1.

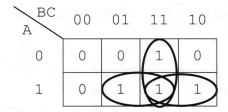

Fig. 4-1 Karnaugh map for Example 4-1

The simplified SOP expression for this function would be:

$$V = B C + A C + A B$$

The simplified SOP expression can be easily implemented with a NAND/NAND circuit arrangement using 2 chips (7400 and 7410). The circuit schematic for this solution is given in Fig. 4-2.

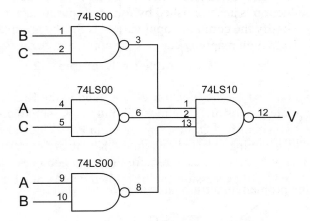

Fig. 4-2 Schematic for simplified SOP solution to Example 4-1

Example 4-2

Design a simplified logic circuit to implement the function W defined in the truth table given in Table 4-2.

A	B	C	D	W
0	0	0	0	0
0	0	0	1	1
0	0	1	0	1
0	0	1	1	1
0	1	0	0	0
0	1	0	1	0
0	1	1	0	0
0	1	1	1	0
1	0	0	0	1
1	0	0	1	1
1	0	1	0	0
1	0	1	1	0
1	1	0	0	0
1	1	0	1	0
1	1	1	0	0
1	1	1	1	0

Table 4-2 Truth table for Example 4-2

The output produced for the function W is plotted in the Karnaugh map in Fig. 4-3. Then appropriate groups of 1s are identified in the K map to create the SOP expression for W. The two simplified expressions given in Fig. 4-3 can be obtained with K mapping. The groupings of 1s shown in the K map are represented by the first equation. The two solutions each require the same number of gates or chips, and so either simplified SOP expression can be implemented. See Fig. 4-4 for the two solution schematics.

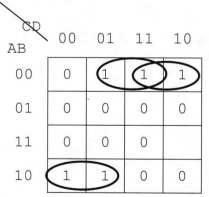

$$W = \overline{A}\,\overline{B}\,C + A\,\overline{B}\,\overline{C} + \overline{A}\,\overline{B}\,D = \overline{A}\,\overline{B}\,C + A\,\overline{B}\,\overline{C} + \overline{B}\,\overline{C}\,D$$

Fig. 4-3 Karnaugh map and simplified expressions for Example 4-2

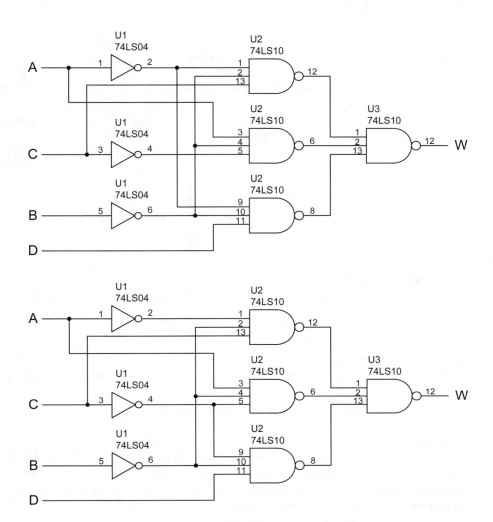

Fig. 4-4 Schematics for simplified SOP solutions to Example 4-2

Laboratory Projects

Design logic circuits to perform each of the following functions. Define the problem with a truth table and then use K mapping to write the simplified SOP expression. Draw and label the schematics to implement your simplified designs. Construct, test, and verify the operation of your design.

4.1   Two-input multiplexer
Design a circuit whose output (Y) is equivalent to one of two possible data inputs (A or B). A control input (S) selects either the data on the A input (if S is low) or the data on the B input (if S is high) to be routed to the single output line.

4.2   Three-bit equality detector
Design a 3-bit equality detector circuit that will output a low whenever the 3 input bits are <u>all</u> at the same logic level.

4.3   Greater than 9 detector
Design a circuit whose output will be high if the 4-bit data input is a value greater than 9.

4.4   Two-bit comparator
Design a comparator circuit to compare two 2-bit numbers (A1 A0 and B1 B0). The circuit will have two output signals: GE and LT. GE will be high to indicate that the 2-bit A value is equal to or greater than the 2-bit B value. LT will be high if A < B.

4.5   Alarm circuit
Design an alarm circuit to be used in a process control system. Temperature (T), pressure (P), flow (F), and level (L) of a fluid are each monitored by separate sensor circuits that produce a <u>high</u> logic output signal when the following indicated <u>physical</u> conditions exist:

> *high fluid temperature*
> *high fluid pressure*
> *low fluid flow rate*
> *low fluid level*

The alarm circuit output (A) should be <u>high</u> if any of the following <u>physical</u> conditions exist in the system:
  (1)   the pressure is high when the flow is low
  (2)   the temperature is high when either the pressure is high or the level is low

List the truth table inputs in the order T P F L. Be sure to identify the correct physical conditions for the alarm in the logic truth table.

4.6   Number detector
        Design a number detector circuit that will output a high if the 4-bit BCD input is 3, 5, or
        9. Assume that only valid BCD inputs will be applied to the detector circuit. Take
        advantage of "don't care" (for anything above 9) K mapping in your design.

4.7   Multiplier circuit
        Design a multiplier circuit that will output the product of any 2-bit number (0 through
        3) times a multiplier of 0, 1, or 2. Note that we "don't care" about the result if the
        multiplier is equal to 3.

SCHEMATIC CAPTURE OF COMBINATIONAL LOGIC CIRCUITS

Objectives

- To implement combinational logic circuits using programmable logic devices (PLDs) with MAX+PLUS II or Quartus II development system software.
- To perform design entry of combinational logic circuits using schematic capture with MAX+PLUS II or Quartus II.
- To simulate combinational logic circuits in MAX+PLUS II or Quartus II.

Suggested Parts

EPM7128S or EP1C6	74163

Programmable Logic Devices

With programmable logic devices (PLDs), logic circuit designers can go from a conceptual design to customized functional parts in a matter of minutes. A PLD is a digital IC that is capable of being programmed to provide a specific logical function. The PLD family of devices consists of a variety of device architectures and configurations. Many PLDs are based on the familiar AND/OR logic gate array in which the specific inputs to each AND gate are programmed to achieve the desired function. Sets of available AND gates in the PLD are internally connected to different OR gates to produce the needed outputs. The programmable AND/OR gate configuration is used to implement sum-of-product functions and, since the SOP form can be used to express any Boolean function, PLD designs are limited only by the number of terms available in the arrays. Many different PLD part numbers are available, providing a wide variety of choices in the number of inputs and outputs that are available, the number of product terms that can be handled, and the ability to produce registered outputs. The programmable flexibility of PLD devices typically allows circuit designers to replace many different standard SSI/MSI chips with a single PLD package. PLD devices are available for either one-time-only programming or are erasable and reprogrammable. High-capacity programmable logic devices contain the equivalent of at least hundreds of logic gates and flip-flops, and some families of PLDs contain thousands. Depending upon their specific architectural characteristics, these high-capacity PLDs are called complex programmable logic devices (CPLDs) or field programmable gate arrays (FPGAs).

The Altera EPM7128SLC84 is an example of an electrically erasable PLD (EEPLD or E^2PLD). The EPM7128S can be reprogrammed many times since it is electrically erasable. The old EEPLD configuration is erased automatically when it is reprogrammed for a new design. The EPM7128S contains 2500 useable gates arranged in 128 macrocells. In an 84-pin PLCC package this device can accommodate up to 64 user inputs and outputs. This chip can be programmed directly by the PC via a parallel port. The EPM7128S is a CMOS device and, as such, should be handled carefully. CMOS devices can be easily damaged by static electricity.

Altera CPLD/FPGA Development Software Tutorials

The general design procedure for implementing a logic circuit with a PLD is illustrated in Fig. 5-1. The design typically consists of Boolean equations, truth tables, and schematics that are entered into various computer files using appropriate development system software such as Altera's MAX+PLUS II or Quartus II. The Student Edition of MAX+PLUS II and the Web Edition of Quartus II are free versions of the commercial software and can be found on the accompanying CD-ROM for this lab manual. After installation of the hardware development software, you will need to request a software license from Altera via their web site at www.altera.com. These software packages contain all of the tools necessary to design and develop PLD solutions for logic circuit design. After design entry, the logic design is compiled using the computer software. In this step, the computer determines how to fit your design into a target PLD. The designer will then simulate the design with the computer software to verify that it satisfies the specifications. Any functional errors will require that the design be modified and appropriate design files changed. Design changes can be implemented simply by altering the design files. The updated design is recompiled and then re-simulated for verification. When the designer is satisfied that the design meets the specifications, a PLD is programmed with the design information and the prototype device is then ready to be tested in your application.

This unit will introduce Altera's development software using schematic capture for design entry. Two example design projects with step-by-step procedures are presented. The tutorial can be found on the accompanying CD-ROM in the Tutorials folder. The tutorials are written in two different formats for your convenience, as PowerPoint slides and in PDF format. The tutorial is designed to run in one window on your PC while either MAX+PLUS II or Quartus II is running in another window so that you can easily switch back and forth between the tutorial instructions and the actual software. The first example project, a logic circuit with several outputs, is developed using Karnaugh mapping techniques. Since it is a small circuit, it is implemented as a "flat design" (only one design entry file is used). The second example design is also a small project but it illustrates the use of hierarchical design techniques. The design is subdivided into two layers to make the design entry simple and convenient. Large designs can be more easily managed by subdividing the system into a hierarchical description of the design.

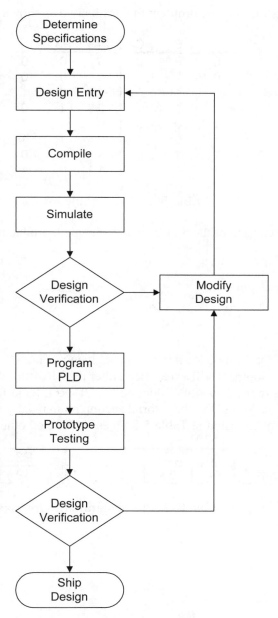

Fig. 5-1 Summary PLD design procedure

Example 5-1 (Tutorial)

Design a multiplier circuit that will output the product of any 3-bit input number (0 through 7) multiplied by the constant 3. Hint: This circuit will have several output bits and each of the outputs will have to be mapped separately. Each output bit represents a circuit that must be constructed.

First, define the problem in a truth table as shown in Table 5-1.

A	B	C	P4	P3	P2	P1	P0
0	0	0	0	0	0	0	0
0	0	1	0	0	0	1	1
0	1	0	0	0	1	1	0
0	1	1	0	1	0	0	1
1	0	0	0	1	1	0	0
1	0	1	0	1	1	1	1
1	1	0	1	0	0	1	0
1	1	1	1	0	1	0	1

Table 5-1 Truth table for Example 5-1

Next, each of the 5 outputs is K mapped, producing the following logic functions:

$$P4 = A\ B$$

$$P3 = A\ \overline{B} + \overline{A}\ B\ C$$

$$P2 = A\ \overline{B} + A\ C + \overline{A}\ B\ \overline{C}$$

$$P1 = \overline{B}\ C + B\ \overline{C}$$

$$P0 = C$$

The schematic for this design is given in Fig. 5-2. Depending upon your choice of development software, open either the MAXplus Schematic or Quartus Schematic file in the Tutorials folder on the CD-ROM and follow the step-by-step procedures. When you get to the tutorial section on manually assigning pin numbers, use the pin numbers listed in Table 5-2 unless instructed otherwise.

Signal	A	B	C	P4	P3	P2	P1	P0
Pin #	34	33	36	48	49	50	51	52

Table 5-2 Pin assignments for Example 5-1

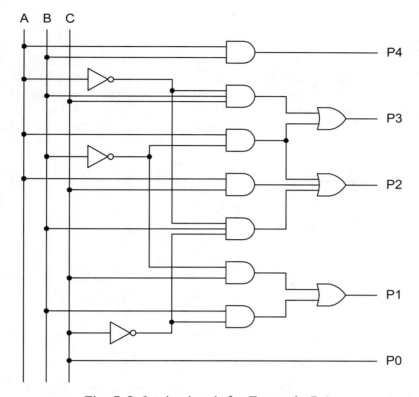

Fig. 5-2 Logic circuit for Example 5-1

Example 5-2 (Tutorial)

Design a 1-out-of-4 data selector circuit using a circuit design for a 1-out-of-2 data selector. A data selector uses a control input to select a single data input (from several choices) to be routed to the output of the circuit. See Fig. 5-3 and Table 5-3. If the control SEL is low, then output Y = D0; otherwise Y = D1. A data selector is also called a multiplexer.

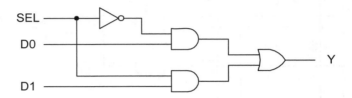

Fig. 5-3 1-out-of-2 data selector circuit for Example 5-2

SEL	Y
0	D0
1	D1

Table 5-3 Truth table for 1-out-of-2 data selector circuit

A 1-out-of-4 data selector can be constructed by combining two levels of the 1-out-of-2 data selector circuit design (see Fig. 5-4). This design can be easily implemented in a hierarchical fashion. Depending upon your choice of development software, open either the MAXplus Schematic or Quartus Schematic file in the Tutorials folder on the CD-ROM and follow the step-by-step procedures.

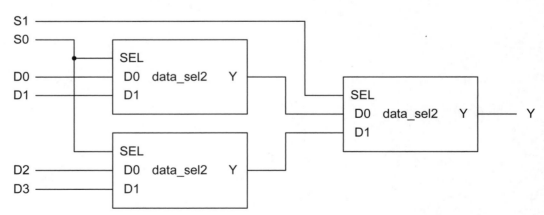

Fig. 5-4 Block diagram for 1-out-of-4 data selector circuit

Laboratory Projects

Construct and test each of the following designs in a PLD using MAX+PLUS II or Quartus II. Be sure to follow any special instructions given by your instructor.

5.1   Multiply-by-3 circuit
Test the design given in Example 5-1 (Tutorial).

5.2   1-out-of-4 data selector
Test the design given in Example 5-2 (Tutorial).

5.3   Elevator control
Design an elevator control system for a large building that has 5 elevators. Four of the elevators are turned on all of the time, while the fifth is activated only if a majority of the other 4 are being used (to save energy costs). The control system will have an input for each of the 4 primary elevators to indicate that that elevator is being used (with a logic "1"). A high output from the control system will activate the fifth elevator for its use.

5.4   Window detector
Design a circuit whose output will be low for all 4-bit input combinations that meet the following criteria:

$$4 < I < 11$$

where I represents the 4-bit input value.

5.5   Prime number detector
Design a 4-bit prime number detector circuit. The 4-bit input will allow the binary numbers for 0 through 15 to be applied to the circuit. The output should be high only if prime numbers (1, 2, 3, 5, 7, 11, 13) are being input to the detector circuit.

5.6   Multiplier circuit
Design a multiplier circuit that will output the product of any 2-bit number (0 through 3) times a multiplier of 0, 1, or 2. Note that we do not care about the result if the multiplier is equal to 3.

5.7   Digital switcher

Design a digital signal switching circuit that has two outputs (X and Y). For each of the two outputs, the circuit can select from two different signal sources (inputs A or B). The two input signals will be obtained from a binary counter chip, the 74163, as shown in the diagram below. The 74163 is being used as a 2-bit counter in this application. Use a low frequency such as 1 Hz for the CLOCK input to the counter. Do not forget to apply a high logic level to ENT, ENP, CLR, and LOAD inputs on the 74163, or the counter will not count. The input signal selection is controlled by the signals C and D. The two control signals will be obtained from two logic switches. The circuit function is described in the following truth table. Test your design using lights to monitor X and Y. If a dual-trace oscilloscope is available, increase the CLOCK frequency to approximately 1 kHz and monitor the two output signals (X and Y) on the scope. Use the counter output QC to trigger the oscilloscope. Hint: Expand the function table to show the 16 combinations that are possible with the four inputs D, C, B, and A and K map for each of the functions X and Y.

D	C	X	Y
0	0	A	B
0	1	A	A
1	0	B	B
1	1	B	A

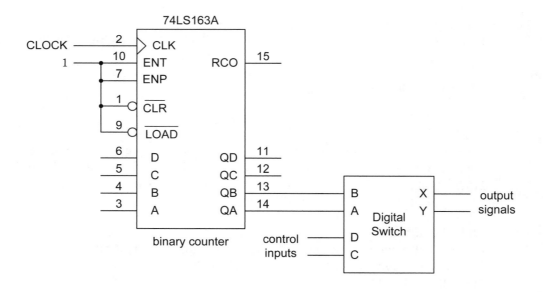

5.8   Binary number detector

Design a logic circuit that will detect (decode) which binary number is applied to the circuit. The binary number will consist of 4 bits, so there will be 16 possible input values (representing 0 through 15 in decimal) that can be applied. The number detector will also have an active-high enable control input named EN. Design this detector in a hierarchical fashion by first designing a 2-bit detector as shown in the following truth table and schematic. The 2-bit number is B A (A is the LSB) and the enable is G. The four outputs are active-high and are labeled Y0 through Y3.

G	B	A	Y0	Y1	Y2	Y3
1	0	0	1	0	0	0
1	0	1	0	1	0	0
1	1	0	0	0	1	0
1	1	1	0	0	0	1
0	X	X	0	0	0	0

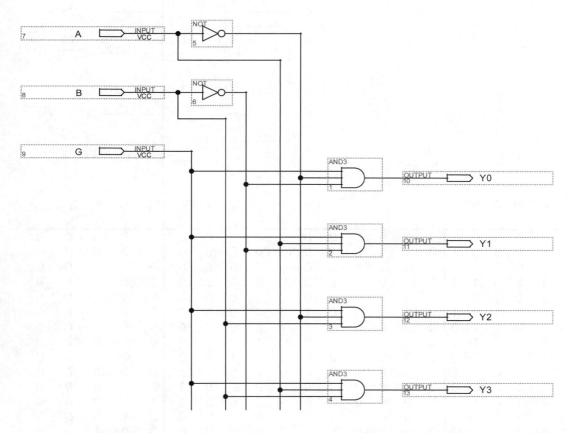

After drawing the schematic for this 2-bit detector, save and check the .gdf file and create a default symbol to be used in the next design level. Open a new .gdf file and enter the schematic for the <u>top level</u> of the 4-bit detector (see next page). The truth table for the 4-bit detector is given on the next page also. The 4-bit number is labeled

D C B A and the active-high enable is labeled EN. The outputs are labeled Y0 through Y15. Compile the top-level design and simulate the design.

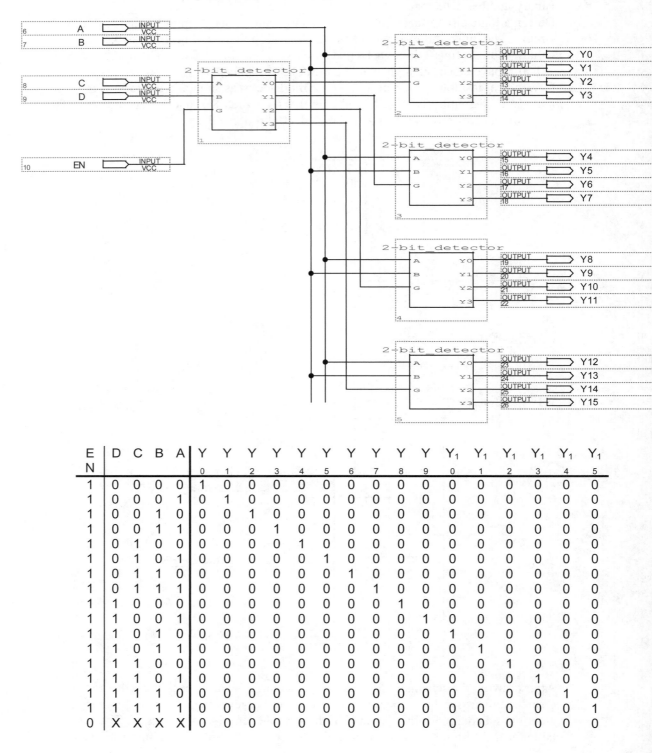

E N	D	C	B	A	Y0	Y1	Y2	Y3	Y4	Y5	Y6	Y7	Y8	Y9	Y_{10}	Y_{11}	Y_{12}	Y_{13}	Y_{14}	Y_{15}
1	0	0	0	0	1	0	0	0	0	0	0	0	0	0	0	0	0	0	0	0
1	0	0	0	1	0	1	0	0	0	0	0	0	0	0	0	0	0	0	0	0
1	0	0	1	0	0	0	1	0	0	0	0	0	0	0	0	0	0	0	0	0
1	0	0	1	1	0	0	0	1	0	0	0	0	0	0	0	0	0	0	0	0
1	0	1	0	0	0	0	0	0	1	0	0	0	0	0	0	0	0	0	0	0
1	0	1	0	1	0	0	0	0	0	1	0	0	0	0	0	0	0	0	0	0
1	0	1	1	0	0	0	0	0	0	0	1	0	0	0	0	0	0	0	0	0
1	0	1	1	1	0	0	0	0	0	0	0	1	0	0	0	0	0	0	0	0
1	1	0	0	0	0	0	0	0	0	0	0	0	1	0	0	0	0	0	0	0
1	1	0	0	1	0	0	0	0	0	0	0	0	0	1	0	0	0	0	0	0
1	1	0	1	0	0	0	0	0	0	0	0	0	0	0	1	0	0	0	0	0
1	1	0	1	1	0	0	0	0	0	0	0	0	0	0	0	1	0	0	0	0
1	1	1	0	0	0	0	0	0	0	0	0	0	0	0	0	0	1	0	0	0
1	1	1	0	1	0	0	0	0	0	0	0	0	0	0	0	0	0	1	0	0
1	1	1	1	0	0	0	0	0	0	0	0	0	0	0	0	0	0	0	1	0
1	1	1	1	1	0	0	0	0	0	0	0	0	0	0	0	0	0	0	0	1
0	X	X	X	X	0	0	0	0	0	0	0	0	0	0	0	0	0	0	0	0

5.9   2-bit comparator

Design a comparator circuit to compare the magnitudes of two 2-bit numbers (A1 A0 and B1 B0). The circuit will have three outputs AGTB, ALTB, and AEQB. AGTB will be high to indicate that the 2-bit A value is greater than the 2-bit B value. ALTB will be high to indicate that the 2-bit A value is less than the 2-bit B value. AEQB will be high if the two 2-bit values are equal. The truth table is shown below.

A1	A0	B1	B0	AGTB	ALTB	AEQB
0	0	0	0	0	0	1
0	0	0	1	0	1	0
0	0	1	0	0	1	0
0	0	1	1	0	1	0
0	1	0	0	1	0	0
0	1	0	1	0	0	1
0	1	1	0	0	1	0
0	1	1	1	0	1	0
1	0	0	0	1	0	0
1	0	0	1	1	0	0
1	0	1	0	0	0	1
1	0	1	1	0	1	0
1	1	0	0	1	0	0
1	1	0	1	1	0	0
1	1	1	0	1	0	0
1	1	1	1	0	0	1

AGTB function:
Use Karnaugh mapping to determine the simplified AGTB function. Draw the schematic for the AGTB function using the Graphic Editor. Save and Check. Create Default Symbol for AGTB.

ALTB function:
Use Karnaugh mapping to determine the simplified ALTB function. Draw the schematic for the ALTB function in a new file using the Graphic Editor. Note that the ALTB function is very similar to AGTB and that you may wish to create a copy of AGTB that is renamed ALTB and then is edited to produce the ALTB function. Save and Check. Create Default Symbol for ALTB.

AEQB function:
The XNOR function can be used to determine if two bits are equal. Use one XNOR gate to determine if the least significant bits (A0 and B0) are equivalent and a second XNOR gate to determine if the most significant bits (A1 and B1) are equivalent. Then the two 2-bit numbers will be equal in magnitude if the outputs of both XNOR gates are simultaneously high (i.e., AND the two XNOR outputs together for the AEQB function). Draw the schematic for the AEQB function in a new file using the Graphic Editor. Save and Check. Create Default Symbol for AEQB.

Top-level design file for a 2-bit magnitude comparator:
Place one of each of the three symbols in a new file using the Graphic Editor (see the top-level design file illustration). Compile your design from this top-level file.

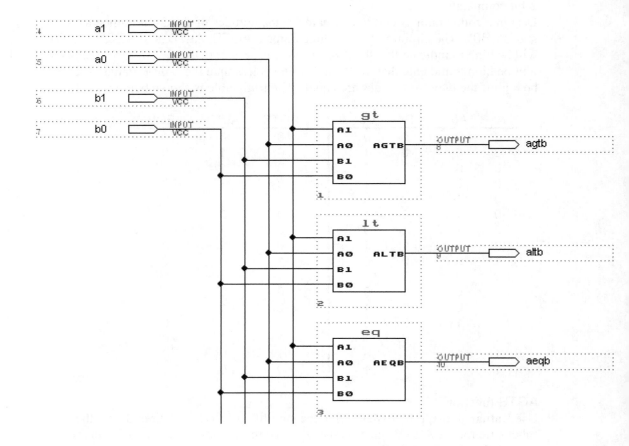

COMBINATIONAL CIRCUIT DESIGN WITH ALTERA HARDWARE DESCRIPTION LANGUAGE

Objectives

- To implement combinational logic circuits using programmable logic devices (PLDs) with MAX+PLUS II or Quartus II development system software.
- To perform the design entry of combinational logic circuits using Altera's AHDL.
- To simulate combinational logic circuits in MAX+PLUS II or Quartus II.

Suggested Part
  EPM7128S or EP1C6

<u>Altera Hardware Description Language</u>

Altera Hardware Description Language (AHDL) is a high-level language within MAX+PLUS II and Quartus II. With AHDL, a text design file (.tdf) can be created to describe any portion of a project's hierarchy. The AHDL language supports various design description techniques, including Boolean expressions, truth tables, and if/then and case statements. Each TDF file contains two required sections, a Subdesign section and a Logic section. The Subdesign section is used to declare the input and output ports for the design block. The Logic section will describe the logical operation of the block. It is important to recognize that AHDL is a concurrent language. This means that all behavior specified in the Logic section is evaluated at the same time rather than sequentially. There are additional optional TDF sections (e.g., Title, Constant, and Define statements and Variable section) that may also be included according to the needs of the application.

```
SUBDESIGN  simple_circuit
(
     a, b, c      :INPUT;
     y            :OUTPUT;
)
VARIABLE
     p            :NODE;
BEGIN
     p = a & !b;
     y = p # c;
END;
```

Fig. 6-1 AHDL design file for a simple circuit

A simple Text Design File for a combinational logic circuit is shown in Fig. 6-1. AHDL keywords are given in capital letters. The subdesign block, identified by SUBDESIGN, is followed by the name of the TDF (simple_circuit.tdf). The input and output signals (ports) for the subdesign are enclosed in parentheses and are labeled with INPUT and OUTPUT for the respective port type (signal direction). Multiple port names are separated by commas, a colon separates the port names from the port type, and a semicolon ends the logical line. The VARIABLE section is used to identify a buried NODE in the subdesign block. Buried node signals are not available outside the subdesign block. The logic section, sandwiched between BEGIN and END, describes the functionality for this block. The buried node p is the input a ANDed with NOT b. The subdesign output y is p ORed with input c.

AHDL text design files can be included in a project hierarchy together with other design file types (such as .gdf files). Breaking a design into smaller, more manageable blocks can be extremely helpful in creating larger systems. *A very important rule to remember when using multiple design blocks to define a system is that each design block must have a unique file name.* A built-in text editor allows the user to easily create and edit the TDF files. MAX+PLUS II and Quartus II treat TDF files the same as other design entry files. PLD design tasks such as syntax checking, accessing on-line help, compiling, and simulation are all available when using TDF files. Fundamental language elements of AHDL are summarized in Figs. 6-2a and 6-2b.

AHDL LANGUAGE ELEMENTS

Names
- Symbolic names specify internal and external nodes and groups, constants, state machine variables, state bits, state names, and instances
- Subdesign names are user-defined names for lower-level design files and must be the same as the TDF filename
- Port names are symbolic names that identify the input or output of a logic block
- Start with an alphabet character or slash unless quoted ' '
- Can contain numeric characters or underscore or dash (if quoted); cannot contain spaces
- Are not case sensitive
- May be up to 32 characters long
- Cannot contain any reserved keywords unless quoted

Reserved keywords

AND	FUNCTION	OUTPUT
ASSERT	GENERATE	PARAMETERS
BEGIN	GND	REPORT
BIDIR	HELP_ID	RETURNS
BITS	IF	SEGMENTS
BURIED	INCLUDE	SEVERITY
CASE	INPUT	STATES
CLIQUE	IS	SUBDESIGN
CONNECTED_PINS	LOG2	TABLE
CONSTANT	MACHINE	THEN
DEFAULTS	MOD	TITLE
DEFINE	NAND	TO
DESIGN	NODE	TRI_STATE_NODE
DEVICE	NOR	VARIABLE
DIV	NOT	VCC
ELSE	OF	WHEN
ELSIF	OPTIONS	WITH
END	OR	XNOR
FOR	OTHERS	XOR

Reserved identifiers

CARRY	JKFF	SRFF
CASCADE	JKFFE	SRFFE
CEIL	LATCH	TFF
DFF	LCELL	TFFE
DFFE	MCELL	TRI
EXP	MEMORY	USED
FLOOR	OPENDRN	WIRE
GLOBAL	SOFT	X

Fig. 6-2a Summary of AHDL language elements

AHDL LANGUAGE ELEMENTS

Symbols

% %	enclose comments
--	begin comments (to end of line)
( )	enclose port names in Subdesign section; enclose highest priority operations in Boolean and arithmetic expressions
[ ]	enclose the range of a group name
' '	enclose quoted symbolic names
" "	enclose digits in nondecimal numbers
.	separate symbolic names of variables from port names
..	separate MSB from LSB in a range
;	end AHDL statements and sections
,	separate members of sequential groups and lists
:	separate symbolic names from types in declarations
=	assign values in Boolean equations; assign values to state machine states
=>	separate inputs from outputs in truth table statements
+	addition operator
−	subtraction operator
==	numeric or string equality operator
!	NOT operator
!=	not equal to operator
>	greater than comparator
>=	greater than or equal to comparator
<	less than comparator
<=	less than or equal to comparator
&	AND operator
!&	NAND operator
$	XOR operator
!$	XNOR operator
#	OR operator
!#	NOR operator

Numbers

- Default base for numbers is decimal
- Binary values (series of 0's, 1's, X's) are enclosed in double quotes and prefixed with B
- Hexadecimal values (series from 0 to 9, A to F) are enclosed in double quotes and prefixed with H
- Numbers cannot be assigned to single nodes in Boolean equations; use VCC and GND

Fig. 6-2b Summary of AHDL language elements

Example 6-1 (Tutorial)

Design a comparator circuit to compare the magnitudes of two 2-bit numbers (A1 A0 and B1 B0). The circuit will have three output signals: GT, LT, and EQ. GT will be high to indicate that the 2-bit A value is greater than the 2-bit B value. LT will be high if the 2-bit A value is less than the 2-bit B value. EQ will be high if the two 2-bit values are equal. The desired 3-output function is defined in the truth table shown in Table 6-1.

A1	A0	B1	B0	GT	LT	EQ
0	0	0	0	0	0	1
0	0	0	1	0	1	0
0	0	1	0	0	1	0
0	0	1	1	0	1	0
0	1	0	0	1	0	0
0	1	0	1	0	0	1
0	1	1	0	0	1	0
0	1	1	1	0	1	0
1	0	0	0	1	0	0
1	0	0	1	1	0	0
1	0	1	0	0	0	1
1	0	1	1	0	1	0
1	1	0	0	1	0	0
1	1	0	1	1	0	0
1	1	1	0	1	0	0
1	1	1	1	0	0	1

Table 6-1 Truth table for Example 6-1

Four different solutions will be given. Each one is named 2bit_compare (with a .tdf file extension) and will produce the same desired output function. In all four solutions, the two 2-bit inputs are declared using AHDL group notation. A group is a collection of nodes that can be acted upon as a single unit. The group a[1..0] refers to the individual nodes a1 and a0. The group range is enclosed in brackets [ ]. The two dots separate the beginning and end of the inclusive range specified in the brackets. After a group has been defined, the entire group can be referenced as a[ ].

For the first solution, we will use Karnaugh mapping to determine the equations for GT and LT. Then EQ is determined as a function of GT and LT. These equations will be given in the Logic section of the TDF file. The equations are:

$$GT = A1\ \overline{B1} + A0\ \overline{B1}\ \overline{B0} + A1\ A0\ \overline{B0}$$

$$LT = \overline{A1}\ B1 + \overline{A0}\ B1\ B0 + \overline{A1}\ \overline{A0}\ B0$$

$$EQ = \overline{GT}\ \overline{LT}$$

These equations are written in the logic section of the AHDL design file between the keywords BEGIN and END. Each of the expressions ends with a semicolon. You should note that it was not necessary to simplify the logic expressions before writing the VHDL file since the compiler will simplify them for you, but it certainly saves a lot of typing!

```
SUBDESIGN 2bit_compare
(
      a[1..0], b[1..0]          :INPUT;
% a[1..0] and b[1..0] are the two, 2-bit inputs %
      gt, lt, eq                :OUTPUT;
)
% solution 1 %
BEGIN
            -- functions defined with Boolean expressions
      gt = a1 & !b1 # a0 & !b1 & !b0 # a1 & a0 & !b0;
      lt = !a1 & b1 # !a0 & b1 & b0 # !a1 & !a0 & b0;
      eq = !gt & !lt;
%     Boolean symbols
            &  AND
            #  OR
            !  NOT          %
END;
```

The second solution will also use Boolean expressions, but this time we will compare the values of the 2-bit numbers using greater than, less than, and equal to operations. If the comparison test is true, then the corresponding output will be high.

```
SUBDESIGN 2bit_compare
(
      a[1..0], b[1..0]          :INPUT;
      gt, lt, eq                :OUTPUT;
)
% solution 2 %
BEGIN
      gt = a[] > b[];           -- gt is high if a > b
      lt = a[] < b[];           -- lt is high if a < b
      eq = a[] == b[];          -- eq is high if a = b
END;
```

The third solution will use an IF/THEN statement in the Logic section to compare the values of the 2-bit numbers. If the expression following IF is true, the behavior following the keyword THEN will be applied. If the first expression is false, then the expression following ELSIF is evaluated. If the second expression is true, the behavior following the second THEN will be applied. If both of the test expressions are false, then the behavior following ELSE will be applied. Note that the IF/THEN/ELSIF statement will automatically establish a priority. The first expression that is evaluated to be true will determine the resulting behavior. Any test expressions after the first true one do not matter.

```
SUBDESIGN 2bit_compare
(
     a[1..0], b[1..0]          :INPUT;
     gt, lt, eq                :OUTPUT;
)
% solution 3 %
BEGIN
     IF      a[] > b[]          -- 1st expression tested
            THEN gt = VCC; lt = GND; eq = GND;
     ELSIF   a[] < b[]          -- 2nd expression tested
            THEN gt = GND; lt = VCC; eq = GND;
     ELSE         gt = GND; lt = GND; eq = VCC;
     END IF;
END;
```

The fourth solution will use a truth table to define the three outputs. The input and output signals are given on the first line after the keyword TABLE. Multiple input and output signals are separated by commas. The inputs and outputs are separated by the => symbol. The table ends with END TABLE.

```
SUBDESIGN 2bit_compare
(
     a[1..0], b[1..0]          :INPUT;
     gt, lt, eq                :OUTPUT;
)
% solution 4 %
BEGIN
     TABLE           -- truth table format
            a[],    b[]         =>     gt, lt, eq;
            B"00", B"00"        =>     0,  0,  1;
            B"00", B"01"        =>     0,  1,  0;
            B"00", B"10"        =>     0,  1,  0;
            B"00", B"11"        =>     0,  1,  0;
            B"01", B"00"        =>     1,  0,  0;
            B"01", B"01"        =>     0,  0,  1;
            B"01", B"10"        =>     0,  1,  0;
            B"01", B"11"        =>     0,  1,  0;
            B"10", B"00"        =>     1,  0,  0;
            B"10", B"01"        =>     1,  0,  0;
            B"10", B"10"        =>     0,  0,  1;
            B"10", B"11"        =>     0,  1,  0;
            B"11", B"00"        =>     1,  0,  0;
            B"11", B"01"        =>     1,  0,  0;
            B"11", B"10"        =>     1,  0,  0;
            B"11", B"11"        =>     0,  0,  1;
     END TABLE;
END;
```

See tutorial (on CD-ROM) for Example 6-1: MAXplus AHDL or Quartus AHDL

Example 6-2 (Tutorial)

Design and construct a 2421-BCD-to-5421-BCD code converter. The truth table for this design is given in Table 6-2. The inputs are labeled in[3..0] and the outputs are labeled out[3..0]. Note that in this situation, we care about only 10 of the 16 possible input combinations. The other 6 input combinations are listed at the bottom of the truth table and are labeled as "invalid." Each of the invalid input conditions should be given a default output value of 1111.

| Decimal | 2 | 4 | 2 | 1 | 5 | 4 | 2 | 1 | ← weights |
Value	in3	in2	in1	in0	out3	out2	out1	out0	← names
0	0	0	0	0	0	0	0	0	
1	0	0	0	1	0	0	0	1	
2	0	0	1	0	0	0	1	0	
3	0	0	1	1	0	0	1	1	
4	0	1	0	0	0	1	0	0	
5	1	0	1	1	1	0	0	0	
6	1	1	0	0	1	0	0	1	
7	1	1	0	1	1	0	1	0	
8	1	1	1	0	1	0	1	1	
9	1	1	1	1	1	1	0	0	
invalid	0	1	0	1	1	1	1	1	
invalid	0	1	1	0	1	1	1	1	
invalid	0	1	1	1	1	1	1	1	
invalid	1	0	0	0	1	1	1	1	
invalid	1	0	0	1	1	1	1	1	
invalid	1	0	1	0	1	1	1	1	

Table 6-2 Truth table for Example 6-2

Four AHDL solutions are given here. In each, the 4-bit input in[3..0] and 4-bit output out[3..0] are declared using AHDL group notation. All solutions produce the same results.

A truth table is used in the first TDF design file solution. The DEFAULTS statement is used to specify the output produced if the input combination is not listed in the table. An AHDL truth table is defined in the Logic section between the TABLE and END TABLE lines. The first line following TABLE declares the input and output variables, which are separated by the => symbol.

```
SUBDESIGN codes
(
      in[3..0]            :INPUT;
      out[3..0]           :OUTPUT;
)
% solution 1 %
BEGIN
      DEFAULTS
            out[] = B"1111";          -- default outputs
      END DEFAULTS;
      TABLE       -- truth table defines valid BCD inputs
            in[]         =>    out[];
        %     2421 BCD          5421 BCD      %
            B"0000"      =>    B"0000";
            B"0001"      =>    B"0001";
            B"0010"      =>    B"0010";
            B"0011"      =>    B"0011";
            B"0100"      =>    B"0100";
            B"1011"      =>    B"1000";
            B"1100"      =>    B"1001";
            B"1101"      =>    B"1010";
            B"1110"      =>    B"1011";
            B"1111"      =>    B"1100";
      END TABLE;
END;
```

The second solution uses an IF/THEN statement. Each of the IF or ELSIF lines in the TDF file tests for a different valid input combination using the equal to operator. The appropriate output behavior follows the corresponding THEN. If all of the tests fail (due to an invalid input code), then ELSE will produce the appropriate output behavior.

```
SUBDESIGN codes
(
      in[3..0]            :INPUT;
      out[3..0]           :OUTPUT;
)
% solution 2 %
BEGIN
            -- select appropriate output with IFs
      IF    in[] == B"0000"   THEN  out[] = B"0000";
      ELSIF in[] == B"0001"   THEN  out[] = B"0001";
      ELSIF in[] == B"0010"   THEN  out[] = B"0010";
      ELSIF in[] == B"0011"   THEN  out[] = B"0011";
      ELSIF in[] == B"0100"   THEN  out[] = B"0100";
      ELSIF in[] == B"1011"   THEN  out[] = B"1000";
      ELSIF in[] == B"1100"   THEN  out[] = B"1001";
      ELSIF in[] == B"1101"   THEN  out[] = B"1010";
      ELSIF in[] == B"1110"   THEN  out[] = B"1011";
      ELSIF in[] == B"1111"   THEN  out[] = B"1100";
      ELSE                          out[] = B"1111";
      END IF;
END;
```

The third solution uses a CASE statement to define the desired function. The input whose value is to be tested is sandwiched between the keywords CASE and IS. The valid input codes are listed after each WHEN choice, followed by the => symbol and the appropriate output behavior. The invalid input codes are covered by the WHEN OTHERS (for any input combination not already tested) clause.

```
SUBDESIGN codes
(
      in[3..0]              :INPUT;
      out[3..0]             :OUTPUT;
)
% solution 3 %
BEGIN
              -- selects appropriate output with CASE
      CASE in[]    IS
              WHEN B"0000"       =>     out[] = B"0000";
              WHEN B"0001"       =>     out[] = B"0001";
              WHEN B"0010"       =>     out[] = B"0010";
              WHEN B"0011"       =>     out[] = B"0011";
              WHEN B"0100"       =>     out[] = B"0100";
              WHEN B"1011"       =>     out[] = B"1000";
              WHEN B"1100"       =>     out[] = B"1001";
              WHEN B"1101"       =>     out[] = B"1010";
              WHEN B"1110"       =>     out[] = B"1011";
              WHEN B"1111"       =>     out[] = B"1100";
              WHEN OTHERS        =>     out[] = B"1111";
      END CASE;
END;
```

The fourth solution uses Boolean expressions derived with Karnaugh mapping. Notice that the circuit behavior is not obvious with this AHDL solution. Additionally, this technique requires a great deal more work by the designer!

```
SUBDESIGN codes
(
      in[3..0]              :INPUT;
      out[3..0]             :OUTPUT;
)
% solution 4 %
BEGIN
              -- define outputs with Boolean expressions
      out3 = in3 # in2 & in0 # in2 & in1;
      out2 = !in3 & in2 # in3 & !in2 & !in1
            # in3 & !in2 & !in0 # in2 & in1 & in0;
      out1 = in1 & !in0 # !in3 & in1 # in2 & !in1 & in0
            # in3 & !in2 & !in1;
      out0 = !in3 & in0 # in3 & !in0 # in3 & !in2 & !in1
            # !in3 & in2 & in1;
END;
```

See tutorial (on CD-ROM) for Example 6-2: MAXplus AHDL or Quartus AHDL

Example 6-3 (Tutorial)

Design a 4-channel data selector (multiplexer). The logic expression for this circuit is:

$$Y = (D0\ \overline{S1}\ \overline{S0} + D1\ \overline{S1}\ S0 + D2\ S1\ \overline{S0} + D3\ S1\ S0)\ EN$$

The four data inputs are D0 through D3, the data channel desired is selected with the input controls S1 and S0, and EN is an enable input. Four different design solutions will be created in AHDL files. All four will provide the same function. The 4-bit data input d[3..0] and 2-bit control input s[1..0] are declared using AHDL group notation.

In the first solution, Boolean equations will be used. The data selection combinations are set up as buried nodes with the variable section. Equations for the four possible data selection combinations and the final subdesign output are defined in the logic section.

```
SUBDESIGN multiplexer
(
    en, d[3..0], s[1..0]        :INPUT;
    y                          :OUTPUT;
)
% solution 1 %

VARIABLE
    sel[3..0]                  :NODE;        -- "buried" nodes

BEGIN

    sel0 = !s1 & !s0;          -- define 4 select combinations
    sel1 = !s1 &  s0;
    sel2 =  s1 & !s0;
    sel3 =  s1 &  s0;

    -- Boolean expression to route selected input to y
    y = (d0 & sel0 # d1 & sel1 # d2 & sel2 # d3 & sel3) & en;

END;
```

The second example solution will use an IF/THEN statement. The IF statement tests to determine the input combination for s1 and s0 if the en input is high. The notation s[ ] represents the previously defined input s[1..0]. The double equal sign is the test for equality symbol. The ELSIFs produce a prioritized set of further conditions for testing. If all other tests should fail (because en is low), the ELSE clause gives a default output result *y = GND* (logic 0).

```
SUBDESIGN multiplexer
(
      en, d[3..0], s[1..0]     :INPUT;
      y                         :OUTPUT;
)
% solution 2 %
BEGIN
              -- IFs 1st determine desired output when enabled
      IF     s[] == 0 & en   THEN   y = d0;
      ELSIF  s[] == 1 & en   THEN   y = d1;
      ELSIF  s[] == 2 & en   THEN   y = d2;
      ELSIF  s[] == 3 & en   THEN   y = d3;
      ELSE   y = GND;              -- output if disabled
      END IF;
END;
```

The third solution is similar to the second except that it uses nested IF statements. The outer condition (en is high) must be true before it is necessary to evaluate the inner IF and determine the input combination for s1 and s0.

```
SUBDESIGN multiplexer
(
      en, d[3..0], s[1..0]     :INPUT;
      y                         :OUTPUT;
)
% solution 3 %
BEGIN
                         -- uses nested IFs
      IF en THEN         -- evaluate 2nd IF when 1st one true
            IF     s[] == 0   THEN   y = d0;
            ELSIF  s[] == 1   THEN   y = d1;
            ELSIF  s[] == 2   THEN   y = d2;
            ELSE                     y = d3;
            END IF;
      ELSE   y = GND;     -- disabled output
      END IF;
END;
```

The fourth solution is a modification of the third. Nested inside the IF statement that tests the condition of en is a CASE statement. Between keywords CASE and IS will be the expression s[1..0] that is to be evaluated by the CASE statement. The alternative values for the evaluated expression are listed in the WHEN clauses. Following the WHEN clauses (after the => symbol) are the statements that are to be activated according to the value matched for the expression.

```
SUBDESIGN multiplexer
(
     en, d[3..0], s[1..0]              :INPUT;
     y                                 :OUTPUT;
)
% solution 4 %
BEGIN
                         -- CASE nested inside IF statement
     IF en THEN          -- evaluate CASE when enable is true
         CASE s[]  IS
                 WHEN  0  =>  y = d0;
                 WHEN  1  =>  y = d1;
                 WHEN  2  =>  y = d2;
                 WHEN  3  =>  y = d3;
         END CASE;
     ELSE  y = GND;      -- output when disabled
     END IF;
END;
```

See tutorial (on CD-ROM) for Example 6-3: MAXplus AHDL or Quartus AHDL

Laboratory Projects

Design PLD logic circuits for the following applications using AHDL. Compile the text file and simulate your design to verify it. Program a PLD with your design and test it in the lab.

6A.1   2-bit comparator
Test the design given in Example 6-1 (Tutorial).

6A.2   Code converter
Test the design given in Example 6-2 (Tutorial).

6A.3   Data selector
Test the design given in Example 6-3 (Tutorial).

6A.4   BCD code to 2421 code conversion
Design a logic circuit that will convert the standard (8421) BCD code into the equivalent decimal value in the 2421 code. Use Karnaugh mapping to determine the logic expressions for each of the four outputs. The codes are given in the following table.

Decimal Value	8 d	4 c	2 b	1 a	2 p	4 q	2 r	1 s
0	0	0	0	0	0	0	0	0
1	0	0	0	1	0	0	0	1
2	0	0	1	0	0	0	1	0
3	0	0	1	1	0	0	1	1
4	0	1	0	0	0	1	0	0
5	0	1	0	1	1	0	1	1
6	0	1	1	0	1	1	0	0
7	0	1	1	1	1	1	0	1
8	1	0	0	0	1	1	1	0
9	1	0	0	1	1	1	1	1
invalid	1	0	1	0	X	X	X	X
invalid	1	0	1	1	X	X	X	X
invalid	1	1	0	0	X	X	X	X
invalid	1	1	0	1	X	X	X	X
invalid	1	1	1	0	X	X	X	X
invalid	1	1	1	1	X	X	X	X

← weights (top row: 8 4 2 1 2 4 2 1)
← names (second row: d c b a p q r s)

6A.5   2-bit binary adder
Design a 2-bit binary adder using AHDL. This circuit will add the 2-bit numbers labeled A2 A1 and B2 B1 to produce the 3-bit sum S3 S2 S1. The schematic is given below.

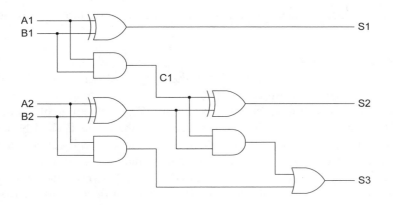

6A.6   Gray-code-to-binary conversion
Design a logic circuit that will convert a 6-bit Gray code value into its equivalent binary value. The Gray code is commonly used in shaft position encoders to decrease the possibility of errors. The Gray code is an unweighted code in which only a single bit changes from one code number to the next. For example, the Gray code value 100110 is equivalent to the binary value 111011. The Gray-to-binary code conversion algorithm is as follows:

    1.   *The most significant bit in the binary result is the same as the corresponding most significant (leftmost) Gray code bit.*

    2.   *To produce each additional binary bit, XOR the binary code bit just generated to the Gray code bit in the next adjacent position.*

    3.   *Repeat the process in step 2 to produce the binary result through the least significant bit.*

Write Boolean expressions for each of the binary outputs. Simulation hint: Use a Gray code count for the input waveform.

6A.7   BCD-to-binary converter
Design a logic circuit that will convert a 5-bit BCD input bcd[4..0] into its equivalent 4-bit binary value bin[3..0]. Since the output is only 4 bits long, the largest number that can be converted is the decimal value 15. This converter circuit should also have an output called err that will be high if the BCD input value is not in the range of 0 through 15. Use the truth table design entry technique to define only the valid input conditions and the resultant outputs (bin[3..0], err). Multiple input or output signals in a truth table are separated by commas. Use DEFAULTS to define the outputs for any invalid input combination (bin[3..0] = B"0000" and err = VCC).

6A.8   Binary-to-BCD converter
        Design a logic circuit that will convert a 5-bit binary input bin[4..0] into its equivalent
        2-digit (only 6 output bits are needed) BCD value bcd[5..0]. The converter can handle
        numbers from 0_{10} through 31_{10}. Use a truth table to define this function.

6A.9   Tens digit detector
        Design a logic circuit that will detect the equivalent tens digit value (0 through 6) for a
        6-bit input number num[5..0]. The input values will range from 0 through 63 with 6
        bits. Only one of the seven outputs (tens[6..0]) will be high at a time, indicating the
        value of the tens digit for the current input number. Use IF/THEN (and ELSIF/THEN)
        statements for your design. IF/THEN syntax automatically creates a priority of
        behavior since the first IF expression that evaluates to be true will determine the
        behavioral statement that will be applied. Any other IF clauses will be ignored after the
        first one that is true. Hint: Use the <= comparator operator in the Boolean expression
        to be evaluated by each IF statement line, and the behavioral statement following
        THEN will be the appropriate assignment for the outputs (e.g., tens[ ] = B"0000001").

6A.10   Lamp display
        Design a logic circuit that will light the number of lamps corresponding to the 3-bit
        input value that is applied (0 through 7). The inputs are named in[2..0] and the outputs
        are named out[7..1]. The following table describes the operation. Use a CASE
        statement for this design.

in2	in1	in0	out1	out2	out3	out4	out5	out6	out7
0	0	0	0	0	0	0	0	0	0
0	0	1	1	0	0	0	0	0	0
0	1	0	1	1	0	0	0	0	0
0	1	1	1	1	1	0	0	0	0
1	0	0	1	1	1	1	0	0	0
1	0	1	1	1	1	1	1	0	0
1	1	0	1	1	1	1	1	1	0
1	1	1	1	1	1	1	1	1	1

6A.11   Programmable logic unit
Design a programmable logic circuit that will perform one of four logic operations on two 4-bit inputs a[3..0] and b[3..0] when enabled by a signal named en. The desired logic function, selected by inputs s[1..0], is indicated in the following table. The 4-bit output is named f[3..0]. If the enable is low, controls s[1..0] do not matter and the outputs are all low. Each of the output bits will be a function of the corresponding a-bit and b-bit and the s1 and s0 control inputs. For example, f3 is dependent on a3, b3, s1, and s0, while f2 is dependent on a2, b2, s1, and s0. Use an IF/THEN statement to define this function. Hint: The behavioral expressions can be written just like the table.

en	s1	s0	Operation
1	0	0	f[ ] = a[ ] # b[ ]
1	0	1	f[ ] = a[ ] & b[ ]
1	1	0	f[ ] = a[ ] $ b[ ]
1	1	1	f[ ] = !a[ ]
0	X	X	f[ ] = B"0000"

6A.12   Number range detector
Design a logic circuit that, when enabled with an active-high signal named en, will detect four different ranges of values for a 5-bit input number. The inputs are labeled num4 through num0 and the outputs are labeled range1 through range4. Range1, range2, and range3 each produce active-high outputs, while range4 produces an active-low output signal. Write Boolean expressions for each of the outputs. Hint: Use the greater-than-or-equal-to (>=) and less-than-or-equal-to (<=) symbols in the Boolean expression to detect the desired range of input values for each output.

Outputs	Values detected
range1	4-12
range2	15-20
range3	18-24
range4	26-30

6A.13   Data switcher
Design a programmable logic circuit that will route two input data bits to the selected outputs as given in the function table below. The control inputs (s[1..0]) determine which of the two data inputs (in1 and in0) are to be routed to each of the two outputs (out1 and out0). The input en is an active-low enable for the data switcher. If the enable is high, we don't care what input levels are on s[1..0], and the two outputs will both be low. Use a CASE statement inside an IF/THEN statement.

en	s1	s0	out1	out0
0	0	0	in1	in0
0	0	1	in0	in0
0	1	0	in1	in1
0	1	1	in0	in1
1	X	X	0	0

COMBINATIONAL CIRCUIT DESIGN WITH VHDL

Objectives

- To implement combinational logic circuits using programmable logic devices (PLDs) with MAX+PLUS II or Quartus II development system software.
- To perform design entry of combinational logic circuits using VHDL.
- To simulate combinational logic circuits in MAX+PLUS II or Quartus II.

Suggested Part
EPM7128S or EP1C6

VHSIC Hardware Description Language (VHDL)

VHSIC (Very High Speed Integrated Circuit) Hardware Description Language (VHDL) is a text-entry, high-level language that can be used to describe complex digital circuits. VHDL files (with the filename extension .vhd) can be created to describe any portion of a project's hierarchy within MAX+PLUS II or Quartus II. The VHDL language supports various design description techniques including Boolean expressions and if/then and case statements. In VHDL, every logic circuit description consists of at least two design units, an entity declaration, and an architecture declaration. The entity declaration is used to identify the input and output ports for the design entity. The architecture declaration will describe the logical operation of the entity. Every entity of a design must be bound to a matching architecture. Architecture declarations in VHDL can contain concurrent statements and sequential statements. All concurrent statements are executed at the same time so that there is no significance to the order in which they are listed. Sequential statements, however, are executed one after another in the order that they appear in the architecture body. It is important to note that the function specified by sequential statements (referred to as a process) will be executed concurrently with other concurrent statements.

```
ENTITY simple IS
     PORT
     (
             a      :  IN BIT;
             b      :  IN BIT;
             c      :  IN BIT;
             y      :  OUT BIT
     );
END simple;

ARCHITECTURE example OF simple IS
SIGNAL       p      : BIT;
BEGIN
     p <= a AND NOT b;
     y <= p OR c;
END example;
```

Fig. 6-1 VHDL design file for a simple circuit

A simple VHDL file (simple.vhd) for a combinational logic circuit is shown in Fig. 6-1. VHDL keywords are given in capital letters. The entity declaration starts with the line *ENTITY simple IS* and continues to the line *END simple;*. The name of the entity, simple, is given in both lines. The input and output ports for the entity are listed and enclosed in parentheses. Each port for the entity is identified with a name, mode (signal direction), and a type. The port names for simple.vhd are a, b, c, and y. A colon separates the port names from the port's mode and data type. The ports' modes are defined to be in or out according to the signal directions for this entity. A port whose mode is in can be read within the architecture declaration for this entity but cannot be assigned a value. On the other hand, a port declared to be of mode out can only be assigned a value within the architecture declaration and cannot be read. Each of the signals for simple.vhd is declared to have a data type of bit, which means that they can only have two possible values: '0' or '1.' A semicolon ends each logical line. The architecture declaration starts with the line *ARCHITECTURE example OF simple IS* and continues to the line *END example.* The entity (simple) to which this architecture is bound is identified between the words OF and IS. VHDL permits multiple architecture declarations for an entity and, therefore, requires the architecture to be named (example, in this architecture). The keyword SIGNAL allows us to declare the name and type of buried node signals that only exist within the entity. The architecture body is sandwiched between keywords BEGIN and END and describes the functionality for this entity. Two signal assignment statements are given in the body of this architecture. Since these assignment statements are concurrent, it does not matter in what order they are listed. The buried node p is the input a ANDed with NOT b. The output port y is p ORed with input c.

VHDL design units (.vhd files) can be included in a project hierarchy together with other design file types (such as .gdf files). Breaking a design into smaller, more manageable blocks can be extremely helpful in creating larger systems. *A very important rule to remember when using multiple design blocks to define a system is that each design block must have a unique file name.* A built-in text editor within MAX+PLUS II and Quartus II allows the user to easily create and edit the .vhd files. The development software treats .vhd files the same as other design entry files. PLD design tasks such as syntax checking, accessing on-line help, compiling, and simulation are all available when using VHDL files. Fundamental language elements of VHDL are summarized in Figs. 6-2a and 6-2b.

VHDL LANGUAGE ELEMENTS

Reserved words

ABS	FOR	PACKAGE
ACCESS	FUNCTION	PORT
AFTER	GENERATE	PROCEDURE
ALIAS	GENERIC	PROCESS
ALL	GUARDED	RANGE
AND	IF	RECORD
ARCHITECTURE	IN	REGISTER
ARRAY	INOUT	REM
ASSERT	IS	REPORT
ATTRIBUTE	LABEL	RETURN
BEGIN	LIBRARY	SELECT
BLOCK	LINKAGE	SEVERITY
BODY	LOOP	SIGNAL
BUFFER	MAP	SUBTYPE
BUS	MOD	THEN
CASE	NAND	TO
COMPONENT	NEW	TRANSPORT
CONFIGURATION	NEXT	TYPE
CONSTANT	NOR	UNITS
DISCONNECT	NOT	UNTIL
DOWNTO	NULL	USE
ELSE	OF	VARIABLE
ELSIF	ON	WAIT
END	OPEN	WHEN
ENTITY	OR	WHILE
EXIT	OTHERS	WITH
FILE	OUT	XOR

Fig. 6-2a Summary of VHDL language elements

VHDL LANGUAGE ELEMENTS

Identifiers

- An identifier is the name of an object
- Objects are named entities that can be assigned a value and have a specific data type
- Objects include signals, variables, and constants
- Must start with an alphabet character and end with an alphabet or a numeric character
- Can contain numeric or underscore characters and cannot contain spaces
- Are not case sensitive
- May be up to 32 characters long
- Cannot contain any reserved words

Symbols

--	begins comment (to end of line)
( )	encloses port names in entity declaration; encloses highest priority operations in Boolean and arithmetic expressions
' '	encloses scalar values
" "	encloses array values
;	ends VHDL statements and declarations
,	separates objects
:	separates object identifier names from mode and data type in declarations
<=	assigns values in signal assignment statements
:=	assigns values in variable assignment statements or to constants
=>	separates signal assignment statements from WHEN clause in CASE statements
+	addition operator
−	subtraction operator
=	equality operator
/=	inequality operator
>	greater than comparator
>=	greater than or equal to comparator
<	less than comparator
<=	less than or equal to comparator
&	concatenation operator

Synthesis Data Types

BIT	object can only have single-bit values of '0' or '1'
STD_LOGIC	object with multi-value logic including '0', '1', 'X', 'Z'
INTEGER	objects with whole number (decimal) values, e.g., 54, −21
BIT_VECTOR	objects with arrays of bits such as "10010110"
STD_LOGIC_VECTOR	objects with arrays of multi-value logic, e.g., "01101XX"

Fig. 6-2b Summary of VHDL language elements

Example 6-1 (Tutorial)

Design a comparator circuit to compare the magnitudes of two 2-bit numbers (A1 A0 and B1 B0). The circuit will have three output signals: GT, LT, and EQ. GT will be high to indicate that the 2-bit A value is greater than the 2-bit B value. LT will be high if the 2-bit A value is less than the 2-bit B value. EQ will be high if the two 2-bit values are equal. The desired 3-output function is defined in the truth table shown in Table 6-1.

A1	A0	B1	B0	GT	LT	EQ
0	0	0	0	0	0	1
0	0	0	1	0	1	0
0	0	1	0	0	1	0
0	0	1	1	0	1	0
0	1	0	0	1	0	0
0	1	0	1	0	0	1
0	1	1	0	0	1	0
0	1	1	1	0	1	0
1	0	0	0	1	0	0
1	0	0	1	1	0	0
1	0	1	0	0	0	1
1	0	1	1	0	1	0
1	1	0	0	1	0	0
1	1	0	1	1	0	0
1	1	1	0	1	0	0
1	1	1	1	0	0	1

Table 6-1 Truth table for Example 6-1

Four different VHDL solutions will be given. Each one is named two_bit_compare (with a .vhd file extension) and will produce the same desired output function. The entity declaration defines the input and output ports. Two of the solutions will use the BIT_VECTOR data type for the inputs, and the other two will use INTEGER for the data type. The BIT_VECTOR data type is only an array of bits and does not have a numerical value associated with it like an INTEGER data type does. When declaring a BIT_VECTOR data type, the range of the array is also specified. The range indicates the number of bits in the array and their order (either ascending or descending). An INTEGER data type will also have a RANGE of allowable values specified. The RANGE indicates to the compiler how many bits will be necessary to represent the declared object.

For the first solution, the ports a and b are mode IN (input direction) and are two bit arrays (BIT_VECTOR data type with indexes of 1 DOWNTO 0). The bits in the array are specified to be in descending order with the word DOWNTO. The ports gt, lt, and eq are mode OUT (output direction) and are a single BIT data type. The ports for the design are enclosed in parentheses after the keyword PORT. Each of the logical lines in the entity declaration are separated by a semicolon. The last port does not have a semicolon separator, but there is one after the right-hand parenthesis to end the port declaration.

Karnaugh mapping was used to determine the Boolean equations for GT and LT in this solution (*ARCHITECTURE soln1 OF two_bit_compare IS*). The function for EQ is expressed using the XNOR function (NOT XOR in VHDL) to detect if the corresponding A and B bits are equivalent. The equations are:

$$GT = A1 \ \overline{B1} + A0 \ \overline{B1} \ \overline{B0} + A1 \ A0 \ \overline{B0}$$

$$LT = \overline{A1} \ B1 + \overline{A0} \ B1 \ B0 + \overline{A1} \ \overline{A0} \ B0$$

$$EQ = \overline{(A1 \oplus B1)} \ \overline{(A0 \oplus B0)}$$

These equations are written as concurrent signal assignment statements in the architecture declaration of the VHDL design file between the words BEGIN and END. Each of the signal assignments ends with a semicolon. Logical operators (AND and OR) in VHDL have equal precedence. Therefore, parentheses are needed to explicitly define the order of precedence for the Boolean functions. You should note that it was not necessary to simplify the logic expressions before writing the VHDL file since the compiler will simplify them for you, but it certainly saves a lot of typing!

```
ENTITY two_bit_compare IS
      PORT
      (
            a      : IN BIT_VECTOR (1 DOWNTO 0);
            b      : IN BIT_VECTOR (1 DOWNTO 0);
                   -- a & b inputs are each 2-bit arrays
            gt     : OUT BIT;
            lt     : OUT BIT;
            eq     : OUT BIT
                   -- each output is a single bit
      );
END two_bit_compare;

ARCHITECTURE soln1 OF two_bit_compare IS
BEGIN
            -- Boolean expressions for each output
      gt <= (a(1) AND NOT b(1))
            OR (a(0) AND NOT b(1) AND NOT b(0))
            OR (a(1) AND a(0) AND NOT b(0));

      lt <= (NOT a(1) AND b(1))
            OR (NOT a(0) AND b(1) AND b(0))
            OR (NOT a(1) AND NOT a(0) AND b(0));

      eq <= NOT (a(1) XOR b(1))
            AND NOT (a(0) XOR b(0));
END soln1;
```

In the second solution, the two input ports are both declared to be INTEGER data types with a RANGE of possible values from 0 TO 3. Therefore each of the two input objects a and b will require two bits in the design. The architecture declaration (*ARCHITECTURE soln2 OF two_bit_compare IS*) uses an IF/THEN statement to compare the values of the 2-bit numbers. In VHDL this is described as using a behavioral style to define an entity's architecture. The IF/THEN statement is a sequential statement and must be placed within a PROCESS. The signals given in parentheses after the word PROCESS are in the sensitivity list for the process. If any of the signals in a sensitivity list change, then the process will be invoked and the behavior will be evaluated to determine the output for the defined function. The actual process behavior is placed between another BEGIN and END PROCESS keyword set. An IF/THEN statement defines an order or priority in its evaluation. If the expression following IF is true, the behavior following the word THEN will be applied. If the first expression is false, then the expression following ELSIF is evaluated. If the second expression is true, the behavior following the second THEN will be applied. If both of the test expressions are false, then the behavior following ELSE will be applied. The order of the tests in an IF/THEN/ELSIF statement will automatically establish a priority. The first expression that is evaluated to be true will determine the resulting behavior. Any other test expressions after the first true one do not matter. The IF statement is terminated with *END IF;*.

```
ENTITY two_bit_compare IS
      PORT
      (
              a       : IN INTEGER RANGE 0 TO 3;
              b       : IN INTEGER RANGE 0 TO 3;
              -- integer inputs will have numerical values
              gt      : OUT BIT;
              lt      : OUT BIT;
              eq      : OUT BIT
      );
END two_bit_compare;

ARCHITECTURE soln2 OF two_bit_compare IS
BEGIN
      PROCESS (a, b)      -- a & b are in sensitivity list
      BEGIN
      -- 1st IF that tests true makes signal assignments
              IF (a > b) THEN
                      gt <= '1';
                      lt <= '0';
                      eq <= '0';
              ELSIF (a < b) THEN
                      gt <= '0';
                      lt <= '1';
                      eq <= '0';
              ELSE
                      gt <= '0';
                      lt <= '0';
                      eq <= '1';
              END IF;
      END PROCESS;
END soln2;
```

The third VHDL solution (*ARCHITECTURE soln3 OF two_bit_compare IS*) uses another form of sequential statement, the CASE statement. The CASE statement will select a behavior for the design unit based on the value of a given expression. A CASE statement is used within a PROCESS. When a signal in the sensitivity list changes, the PROCESS will be invoked. This solution actually has nested CASE statements. The outer CASE statement evaluates the value of the INTEGER input signal a (*CASE a IS*), and the inner CASE statement evaluates the INTEGER value of b (*CASE b IS*). It does not matter which signal is evaluated by the inner CASE or the outer CASE. It also does not matter in what order the values are checked by the WHEN clause of the CASE statement, but all possible values must be covered. Unlike the IF/THEN/ELSE statement, there is no priority for the conditions contained within the CASE statement. The desired action for each WHEN and value choice is given after the symbol =>. The CASE statement chooses one and only one of the alternative signal assignments according to the current value of the signal being evaluated. A CASE statement is terminated with *END CASE;*.

```
ENTITY two_bit_compare IS
      PORT
      (
         a  : IN INTEGER RANGE 0 TO 3;
         b  : IN INTEGER RANGE 0 TO 3;
         -- a & b will have numerical values as integers
         gt : OUT BIT;
         lt : OUT BIT;
         eq : OUT BIT
      );
END two_bit_compare;

ARCHITECTURE soln3 OF two_bit_compare IS
BEGIN
   PROCESS (a, b)      -- change on a or b invokes process
   BEGIN

      CASE a IS              -- 1st case evaluates a value

         WHEN 0   =>
             CASE b IS       -- 2nd case evaluates b value
                WHEN 0   =>
                   gt <= '0';  lt <= '0';  eq <= '1';
                WHEN 1   =>
                   gt <= '0';  lt <= '1';  eq <= '0';
                WHEN 2   =>
                   gt <= '0';  lt <= '1';  eq <= '0';
                WHEN 3   =>
                   gt <= '0';  lt <= '1';  eq <= '0';
             END CASE;

         WHEN 1   =>
             CASE b IS
                WHEN 0   =>
                   gt <= '1';  lt <= '0';  eq <= '0';
                WHEN 1   =>
                   gt <= '0';  lt <= '0';  eq <= '1';
                WHEN 2   =>
                   gt <= '0';  lt <= '1';  eq <= '0';
                WHEN 3   =>
                   gt <= '0';  lt <= '1';  eq <= '0';
             END CASE;
```

(continued)

(continued)

```
            WHEN 2   =>
                CASE b IS
                    WHEN 0   =>
                        gt <= '1';  lt <= '0';  eq <= '0';
                    WHEN 1   =>
                        gt <= '1';  lt <= '0';  eq <= '0';
                    WHEN 2   =>
                        gt <= '0';  lt <= '0';  eq <= '1';
                    WHEN 3   =>
                        gt <= '0';  lt <= '1';  eq <= '0';
                END CASE;

            WHEN 3   =>
                CASE b IS
                    WHEN 0   =>
                        gt <= '1';  lt <= '0';  eq <= '0';
                    WHEN 1   =>
                        gt <= '1';  lt <= '0';  eq <= '0';
                    WHEN 2   =>
                        gt <= '1';  lt <= '0';  eq <= '0';
                    WHEN 3   =>
                        gt <= '0';  lt <= '0';  eq <= '1';
                END CASE;
        END CASE;
    END PROCESS;
END soln3;
```

The fourth solution (*ARCHITECTURE soln4 OF two_bit_compare IS*) will use a selected signal assignment statement. This is a concurrent signal assignment statement that is used to select and assign a value to a specified signal from a list of alternatives. Since SELECT is a concurrent signal assignment statement, it is <u>not</u> placed within a process. The input ports a and b are again given the data type BIT_VECTOR since the architecture declaration does not associate a numerical value to the signals. Two buried node signals named input and output are created in the architecture declaration and are given the data type BIT_VECTOR with array sizes of 4 bits and 3 bits, respectively. The signal input is assigned to be the concatenation of the two input ports a and b. The symbol & is used to indicate that the bits for the signals should be concatenated together. This then gives us a 4-bit value to represent each of the 16 possible input signal combinations, like in a truth table. The SELECT statement starts with the phrase *WITH input SELECT*. The expression to be evaluated by the SELECT statement is placed between the keywords WITH and SELECT in that phrase. The signal assignment statement then follows the WITH … SELECT phrase, with all of the desired signal assignment values to be selected by the set of possible values for the evaluated expression given after each WHEN. You must specify <u>all</u> possible conditions for the evaluated expression. There is no priority implied by a selected signal assignment statement. The bits assigned for the signal output correspond to the individual port output bits gt, lt, and eq. The output port signals are assigned to the respective bit in the array called output.

```vhdl
ENTITY two_bit_compare IS
      PORT
      (
            a       : IN BIT_VECTOR (1 DOWNTO 0);
            b       : IN BIT_VECTOR (1 DOWNTO 0);
                    -- bit vectors do not have a value
            gt      : OUT BIT;
            lt      : OUT BIT;
            eq      : OUT BIT
      );
END two_bit_compare;

ARCHITECTURE soln4 OF two_bit_compare IS
SIGNAL        input          : BIT_VECTOR (3 DOWNTO 0);
SIGNAL        output         : BIT_VECTOR (2 DOWNTO 0);
      -- these signals are created for our convenience

BEGIN
      input <= a & b;         -- concatenates input bits

      WITH input SELECT       -- input selects output
            output        <=   "001" WHEN "0000",
                               "010" WHEN "0001",
                               "010" WHEN "0010",
                               "010" WHEN "0011",
                               "100" WHEN "0100",
                               "001" WHEN "0101",
                               "010" WHEN "0110",
                               "010" WHEN "0111",
                               "100" WHEN "1000",
                               "100" WHEN "1001",
                               "001" WHEN "1010",
                               "010" WHEN "1011",
                               "100" WHEN "1100",
                               "100" WHEN "1101",
                               "100" WHEN "1110",
                               "001" WHEN "1111";

      gt <= output(2);        -- connect array bits to ports
      lt <= output(1);
      eq <= output(0);

END soln4;
```

See tutorial (on CD-ROM) for Example 6-1: **MAXplus VHDL** or **Quartus VHDL**

Example 6-2 (Tutorial)

Design and construct a 2421-BCD-to-5421-BCD code converter. The truth table for this design is given in Table 6-2. The inputs are labeled d c b a and the outputs are p q r s. Note that in this situation, we care about only 10 of the 16 possible input combinations. The other 6 input combinations are listed at the bottom of the truth table and are labeled as "invalid." Each of the invalid input conditions should be given a default output value of 1111.

| Decimal | 2 | 4 | 2 | 1 | 5 | 4 | 2 | 1 | ← weights |
Value	d	c	b	a	p	q	r	s	← names
0	0	0	0	0	0	0	0	0	
1	0	0	0	1	0	0	0	1	
2	0	0	1	0	0	0	1	0	
3	0	0	1	1	0	0	1	1	
4	0	1	0	0	0	1	0	0	
5	1	0	1	1	1	0	0	0	
6	1	1	0	0	1	0	0	1	
7	1	1	0	1	1	0	1	0	
8	1	1	1	0	1	0	1	1	
9	1	1	1	1	1	1	0	0	
invalid	0	1	0	1	1	1	1	1	
invalid	0	1	1	0	1	1	1	1	
invalid	0	1	1	1	1	1	1	1	
invalid	1	0	0	0	1	1	1	1	
invalid	1	0	0	1	1	1	1	1	
invalid	1	0	1	0	1	1	1	1	

Table 6-2 Truth table for Example 6-2

Four VHDL solutions, each producing the same results, are given here. In each, the 4 input ports (d, c, b, a) and 4 output ports (p, q, r, s) are declared. All signals are declared to be a BIT data type.

A selected signal assignment statement is used in the first VHDL design file solution (*ARCHITECTURE solution1 OF code IS*). Two arrays (data type BIT_VECTOR) of bits named input and output are declared with SIGNAL and are, therefore, visible within the architecture for the entity named code. The signal assignment statement for input concatenates the four input bits together so that they can be treated as a unit. Each of the output port signals is assigned a specific bit in the array named output. The SELECT statement is a concurrent signal assignment statement that will select the correct value to assign to output based on the current set of bits for input. All possible values of the expression to be evaluated (input) must be covered in a SELECT statement. The phrase WHEN OTHERS is used to cover any values that are not explicitly named in the WHEN list. This will take care of any invalid bit pattern that may be applied to input. The order of the choices for the signal being evaluated does not matter because there is no priority implied in a selected signal assignment statement, but all possible values must be accounted for.

```
ENTITY code IS
      PORT
      (
             d, c, b, a  : IN BIT;
             p, q, r, s  : OUT BIT
      );
END code;

ARCHITECTURE solution1 OF code IS
SIGNAL       input       : BIT_VECTOR (3 DOWNTO 0);
SIGNAL       output      : BIT_VECTOR (3 DOWNTO 0);

BEGIN
input <= d & c & b & a;     -- concatenation of input bits

p <= output(3);             -- connect array bit to output
q <= output(2);
r <= output(1);
s <= output(0);

WITH input SELECT               -- input selects output pattern
      output    <=    "0000" WHEN "0000",
                      "0001" WHEN "0001",
                      "0010" WHEN "0010",
                      "0011" WHEN "0011",
                      "0100" WHEN "0100",
                      "1000" WHEN "1011",
                      "1001" WHEN "1100",
                      "1010" WHEN "1101",
                      "1011" WHEN "1110",
                      "1100" WHEN "1111",
                      "1111" WHEN OTHERS;
END solution1;
```

The second solution (*ARCHITECTURE solution2 OF code IS*) uses an IF/THEN statement. Like the first solution, the individual input and output port signals are grouped into arrays named **input** and **output**. Since IF/THEN is a sequential statement, it must be placed within a PROCESS. The PROCESS will be invoked whenever the BIT_VECTOR signal in its sensitivity list (**input**) changes. Each of the IF or ELSIF lines tests for a different valid **input** combination using the equal to operator. The appropriate output behavior follows the corresponding THEN. If all of the tests should fail (due to an invalid input code), then ELSE will produce the appropriate output behavior. After the PROCESS is evaluated, the signals are all concurrently updated.

```
ENTITY code IS
      PORT
      (
             d, c, b, a  : IN BIT;
             p, q, r, s  : OUT BIT
      );
END code;

ARCHITECTURE solution2 OF code IS
SIGNAL        input          : BIT_VECTOR (3 DOWNTO 0);
SIGNAL        output         : BIT_VECTOR (3 DOWNTO 0);
BEGIN
      input <= d & c & b & a;      -- concatenates inputs
      p <= output(3);              -- output array to ports
      q <= output(2);
      r <= output(1);
      s <= output(0);

      PROCESS (input)    -- change on input invokes process
      BEGIN
          IF    input = "0000"   THEN   output <= "0000";
          ELSIF input = "0001"   THEN   output <= "0001";
          ELSIF input = "0010"   THEN   output <= "0010";
          ELSIF input = "0011"   THEN   output <= "0011";
          ELSIF input = "0100"   THEN   output <= "0100";
          ELSIF input = "1011"   THEN   output <= "1000";
          ELSIF input = "1100"   THEN   output <= "1001";
          ELSIF input = "1101"   THEN   output <= "1010";
          ELSIF input = "1110"   THEN   output <= "1011";
          ELSIF input = "1111"   THEN   output <= "1100";
          ELSE                          output <= "1111";
          END IF;
      END PROCESS;
END solution2;
```

The third solution (*ARCHITECTURE solution3 OF code IS*) uses a CASE statement to define the desired function. The same two buried arrays are created, and signal assignments are made. CASE is a sequential statement and is, therefore, placed inside a PROCESS. If the array of bits named **input** changes, the PROCESS will be invoked. The signal (**input**) whose value is to be tested is sandwiched between the keywords CASE and IS. The valid input codes are listed after each WHEN choice, followed by the => symbol and the appropriate signal assignment behavior for **output**. The invalid input codes are covered by the WHEN OTHERS (for any input combination not already tested) clause. The order of the choices for the signal being evaluated does not matter, but all possible values must be accounted for.

```
ENTITY code IS
    PORT
    (
        d, c, b, a  : IN BIT;
        p, q, r, s  : OUT BIT
    );
END code;

ARCHITECTURE solution3 OF code IS
SIGNAL      input        : BIT_VECTOR (3 DOWNTO 0);
SIGNAL      output       : BIT_VECTOR (3 DOWNTO 0);
BEGIN
    input <= d & c & b & a;      -- concatenates inputs
    p <= output(3);              -- connects output ports
    q <= output(2);
    r <= output(1);
    s <= output(0);

    PROCESS (input)    -- change on input invokes process
    BEGIN
        CASE input IS
                WHEN "0000"    =>    output <= "0000";
                WHEN "0001"    =>    output <= "0001";
                WHEN "0010"    =>    output <= "0010";
                WHEN "0011"    =>    output <= "0011";
                WHEN "0100"    =>    output <= "0100";
                WHEN "1011"    =>    output <= "1000";
                WHEN "1100"    =>    output <= "1001";
                WHEN "1101"    =>    output <= "1010";
                WHEN "1110"    =>    output <= "1011";
                WHEN "1111"    =>    output <= "1100";
                WHEN OTHERS    =>    output <= "1111";
        END CASE;
    END PROCESS;
END solution3;
```

The fourth solution (*ARCHITECTURE solution4 OF code IS*) uses Boolean expressions derived with Karnaugh mapping for the output port signal assignments. Unlike the previous three solutions, we do not need to group the input and output bits into arrays. Four single-bit signals (nd, nc, nb, and na) are created within the architecture for this design. The signal assignments for these buried nodes are simply the NOTing of each of the corresponding input port signal. This makes it somewhat easier to write the signal assignment expressions for the output ports. Since signal assignment statements are concurrent statements, it does not matter what order they are listed in the architecture declaration for the design. Logical operators (AND and OR) in VHDL have equal precedence. Therefore, parentheses are needed to explicitly define the order of precedence for the Boolean functions. Notice that the circuit behavior is not obvious with this VHDL solution. Additionally, this technique requires a great deal more work by the designer!

```
ENTITY code IS
     PORT
     (
          d, c, b, a  : IN BIT;
          p, q, r, s  : OUT BIT
     );
END code;

ARCHITECTURE solution4 OF code IS
SIGNAL nd, nc, nb, na   : BIT;        -- buried nodes
BEGIN

     nd <= NOT d;
     nc <= NOT c;
     nb <= NOT b;
     na <= NOT a;

     p <= d OR (c AND a) OR (c AND b);

     q <= (nd AND c) OR (d AND nc AND nb)
          OR (d AND nc AND na) OR (c AND b AND a);

     r <= (b AND na) OR (nd AND b) OR (c AND nb AND a)
          OR (d AND nc AND nb);

     s <= (nd AND a) OR (d AND na) OR (d AND nc AND nb)
          OR (nd AND c AND b);
END solution4;
```

See tutorial (on CD-ROM) for Example 6-2: MAXplus VHDL or Quartus VHDL

Example 6-3 (Tutorial)

Design a 4-channel data selector (multiplexer). The logic expression for this circuit is:

$$Y = (D0 \ \overline{S1} \ \overline{S0} + D1 \ \overline{S1} \ S0 + D2 \ S1 \ \overline{S0} + D3 \ S1 \ S0) \ EN$$

The four data inputs are D0 through D3, the data channel desired is selected with the input controls S1 and S0, and EN is an enable input. Five different design solutions will be created in VHDL files. All solutions will use the same ENTITY declaration. The 4-bit data input d and 2-bit control input s are declared using BIT_VECTOR arrays.

In the first solution (*ARCHITECTURE boolean OF multiplexer IS*), two different variations of signal assignment statements will be used. One of the four bits for BIT_VECTOR sel will be high to indicate which of the four possible bit combinations for input port s is applied. The four data selection combinations are detected using conditional signal assignment statements (WHEN ELSE). A Boolean expression to be tested follows the keyword WHEN. If that expression is true, then the signal assignment before the WHEN will be applied. If the expression is false, then the signal assignment will be the value after the keyword ELSE. Priority is implied by the ordering of expressions in conditional signal assignments. The signal assignment for the output port y is a Boolean expression derived from the function expression above and the appropriate sel bit. Logical operators (AND and OR) in VHDL have equal precedence. Therefore, parentheses are needed to explicitly define the order of precedence for the Boolean functions.

```
ENTITY multiplexer IS
      PORT ( en    : IN BIT;
             d     : IN BIT_VECTOR (3 DOWNTO 0);
             s     : IN BIT_VECTOR (1 DOWNTO 0);
             y     : OUT BIT );
END multiplexer;

ARCHITECTURE boolean OF multiplexer IS
SIGNAL sel         : BIT_VECTOR (0 TO 3);
BEGIN
      sel(0) <= '1' WHEN (s = "00") ELSE '0';   -- conditional
      sel(1) <= '1' WHEN (s = "01") ELSE '0';   -- signal
      sel(2) <= '1' WHEN (s = "10") ELSE '0';   -- assignment
      sel(3) <= '1' WHEN (s = "11") ELSE '0';   -- statements

      y <= ((d(0) AND sel(0))        -- Boolean expression
         OR (d(1) AND sel(1))
         OR (d(2) AND sel(2))
         OR (d(3) AND sel(3))) AND en;
END boolean;
```

The second example solution (*ARCHITECTURE ifand OF multiplexer IS*) will use an IF/THEN statement. IF statements are sequential statements and are therefore contained in a PROCESS. The sensitivity list for the PROCESS must include all input signals since this is a combinational function that will be affected by any input change. The IF statement uses a compound test to determine the input combination for s if the en input is simultaneously high. The appropriate signal assignment for y is given after THEN. The ELSIFs produce a prioritized set of further conditions for testing. If all other tests should fail (because en is low), the ELSE clause gives a default output signal assignment for y.

```
ENTITY multiplexer IS
      PORT ( en    : IN BIT;
             d     : IN BIT_VECTOR (3 DOWNTO 0);
             s     : IN BIT_VECTOR (1 DOWNTO 0);
             y     : OUT BIT );
END multiplexer;

ARCHITECTURE ifand OF multiplexer IS
BEGIN
      PROCESS (en, d, s)        -- process with sensitivity list
      BEGIN
            IF    (s = "00" AND en = '1') THEN  y <= d(0);
            ELSIF (s = "01" AND en = '1') THEN  y <= d(1);
            ELSIF (s = "10" AND en = '1') THEN  y <= d(2);
            ELSIF (s = "11" AND en = '1') THEN  y <= d(3);
            ELSE            y <= '0';           -- disabled output
            END IF;
      END PROCESS;
END ifand;
```

The third solution (*ARCHITECTURE nestif OF multiplexer IS*) is similar to the second except that it uses nested IF statements. The outer condition (en is high) must be true before it is necessary to evaluate the inner IF and determine the input combination for s. Note that both the inner and outer IFs must have a corresponding END IF;.

```
ENTITY multiplexer IS
      PORT ( en    : IN BIT;
             d     : IN BIT_VECTOR (3 DOWNTO 0);
             s     : IN BIT_VECTOR (1 DOWNTO 0);
             y     : OUT BIT );
END multiplexer;

ARCHITECTURE nestif OF multiplexer IS
BEGIN
      PROCESS (en, d, s)        -- process with sensitivity list
      BEGIN
            IF (en = '1') THEN               -- nested IFs
                  IF    (s = "00") THEN   y <= d(0);
                  ELSIF (s = "01") THEN   y <= d(1);
                  ELSIF (s = "10") THEN   y <= d(2);
                  ELSE                    y <= d(3);
                  END IF;
            ELSE          y <= '0';         -- disabled output
            END IF;
      END PROCESS;
END nestif;
```

The fourth solution (*ARCHITECTURE ifcase OF multiplexer IS*) is a modification of the third. Nested inside the IF statement that tests the condition of en is a CASE statement. The signal to be evaluated by the CASE statement is s. The alternative values for s are listed after the keyword WHEN. Following the WHEN clauses (after the => symbol) are the different signal assignment statements that are to be activated according to the value for s. A PROCESS is used since IF statements and CASE statements are sequential. Each of the input signals is in the PROCESS sensitivity list since a change in any one of the inputs could cause a change in the output y.

```
ENTITY multiplexer IS
      PORT ( en    : IN BIT;
             d     : IN BIT_VECTOR (3 DOWNTO 0);
             s     : IN BIT_VECTOR (1 DOWNTO 0);
             y     : OUT BIT );
END multiplexer;

ARCHITECTURE ifcase OF multiplexer IS
BEGIN
      PROCESS (en, d, s)        -- process with sensitivity list
      BEGIN
            IF (en = '1') THEN        -- IF with nested CASE
                  CASE s IS
                        WHEN "00"    =>      y <= d(0);
                        WHEN "01"    =>      y <= d(1);
                        WHEN "10"    =>      y <= d(2);
                        WHEN "11"    =>      y <= d(3);
                  END CASE;
            ELSE          y <= '0';            -- disabled output
            END IF;
      END PROCESS;
END ifcase;
```

The fifth solution (*ARCHITECTURE assign OF multiplexer IS*) uses the WHEN ELSE of a conditional signal assignment statement to select the appropriate d input (out of four choices) for the y signal assignment statement. The Boolean expression (given after the keyword WHEN) tests for both a specific value for s and that the circuit is enabled (en = 1). According to which expression is true, the signal assignment before the appropriate WHEN will be applied. If all expressions are false (because they are disabled), then the signal assignment will be the value after the final ELSE.

```
ENTITY multiplexer IS
      PORT ( en    : IN BIT;
             d     : IN BIT_VECTOR (3 DOWNTO 0);
             s     : IN BIT_VECTOR (1 DOWNTO 0);
             y     : OUT BIT );
END multiplexer;

ARCHITECTURE assign OF multiplexer IS
BEGIN
            -- conditional signal assignment statement
      y <=  d(0)  WHEN s = "00" AND en = '1' ELSE
            d(1)  WHEN s = "01" AND en = '1' ELSE
            d(2)  WHEN s = "10" AND en = '1' ELSE
            d(3)  WHEN s = "11" AND en = '1' ELSE
            '0';           -- disabled
END assign;
```

See tutorial (on CD-ROM) for Example 6-3: MAXplus VHDL or Quartus VHDL

Laboratory Projects

Design PLD logic circuits for the following applications using VHDL. Compile the text file and simulate your design to verify it. Program a PLD with your design and test it in the lab.

6V.1   2-bit comparator
Test the design given in Example 6-1 (Tutorial).

6V.2   Code converter
Test the design given in Example 6-2 (Tutorial).

6V.3   Data selector
Test the design given in Example 6-3 (Tutorial).

6V.4   BCD code to 2421 code conversion
Design a logic circuit that will convert the standard (8421) BCD code into the equivalent decimal value in the 2421 code. Use Karnaugh mapping to determine the logic expressions for each of the four outputs. The codes are given in the following table.

| Decimal | 8 | 4 | 2 | 1 | 2 | 4 | 2 | 1 | ← weights |
Value	d	c	b	a	p	q	r	s	← names
0	0	0	0	0	0	0	0	0	
1	0	0	0	1	0	0	0	1	
2	0	0	1	0	0	0	1	0	
3	0	0	1	1	0	0	1	1	
4	0	1	0	0	0	1	0	0	
5	0	1	0	1	1	0	1	1	
6	0	1	1	0	1	1	0	0	
7	0	1	1	1	1	1	0	1	
8	1	0	0	0	1	1	1	0	
9	1	0	0	1	1	1	1	1	
invalid	1	0	1	0	X	X	X	X	
invalid	1	0	1	1	X	X	X	X	
invalid	1	1	0	0	X	X	X	X	
invalid	1	1	0	1	X	X	X	X	
invalid	1	1	1	0	X	X	X	X	
invalid	1	1	1	1	X	X	X	X	

6V.5   2-bit binary adder
Design a 2-bit binary adder using VHDL. This circuit will add the 2-bit numbers labeled A2 A1 and B2 B1 to produce the 3-bit sum S3 S2 S1. The schematic is given below.

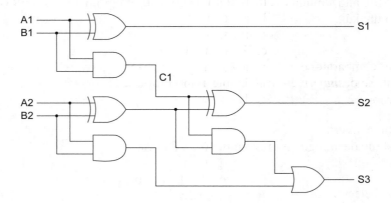

6V.6   Gray-code-to-binary conversion
Design a logic circuit that will convert a 6-bit Gray code value into its equivalent binary value. The Gray code is commonly used in shaft position encoders to decrease the possibility of errors. The Gray code is an unweighted code in which only a single bit changes from one code number to the next. For example, the Gray code value 100110 is equivalent to the binary value 111011. The Gray-to-binary code conversion algorithm is as follows:

      1.   *The most significant bit in the binary result is the same as the corresponding most significant (leftmost) Gray code bit.*
      2.   *To produce each additional binary bit, XOR the binary code bit just generated to the Gray code bit in the next adjacent position.*
      3.   *Repeat the process in step 2 to produce the binary result through the least significant bit.*

Since the output ports cannot be read to produce the next binary bit, you will need to create buried signal nodes and write the Boolean expressions for each of the binary results and then assign the buried nodes to the output port. Simulation hint: Use a Gray code count for the input waveform.

6V.7   BCD-to-binary converter
Design a logic circuit that will convert a 5-bit BCD input named bcd into its equivalent 4-bit binary value bin. Since the output is only 4 bits long, the largest number that can be converted is the decimal value 15. This converter circuit should also have an output called err that will be high if the BCD input value is not in the range of 0 through 15.

6V.8   Binary-to-BCD converter
Design a logic circuit that will convert a 5-bit binary input bin into its equivalent 2-digit (only 6 output bits are needed) BCD value bcd. The converter can handle numbers from 0_{10} through 31_{10}.

6V.9   Tens digit detector

Design a logic circuit that will detect the equivalent tens digit value (0 through 6) for a 6-bit input number num. The input values will range from 0 through 63 with 6 bits. Only one of the seven outputs (tens) will be high at a time, indicating the value of the tens digit for the current input number. Use IF/THEN (and ELSIF/THEN) statements for your design. IF/THEN syntax automatically creates a priority of behavior since the first IF expression that evaluates to be true will determine the behavioral statement that will be applied. Any other IF clauses will be ignored after the first one that is true. Hint: Use the <= comparator operator in the Boolean expression to be evaluated by each IF statement line, and the behavioral statement following THEN will be the appropriate assignment for the outputs (e.g., tens <= "0000001").

6V.10   Lamp display

Design a logic circuit that will light the number of lamps corresponding to the 3-bit input value that is applied (0 through 7). The inputs are named num and the outputs are named lites. The following table describes the operation. Use a CASE statement for this design.

num2	num1	num0	lites1	lites2	lites3	lites4	lites5	lites6	lites7
0	0	0	0	0	0	0	0	0	0
0	0	1	1	0	0	0	0	0	0
0	1	0	1	1	0	0	0	0	0
0	1	1	1	1	1	0	0	0	0
1	0	0	1	1	1	1	0	0	0
1	0	1	1	1	1	1	1	0	0
1	1	0	1	1	1	1	1	1	0
1	1	1	1	1	1	1	1	1	1

6V.11   Programmable logic unit

Design a programmable logic circuit that will perform one of four logic operations on two 4-bit input arrays named a and b when enabled by a signal named en. The desired logic function, selected by a 2-bit input array named s, is indicated in the following table. The 4-bit output array is named f. If the enable is low, the control s does not matter and the outputs are all low. Each of the output bits will be a function of the corresponding a-bit and b-bit and the s1 and s0 control inputs. For example, f3 is dependent on a3, b3, s1, and s0, while f2 is dependent on a2, b2, s1, and s0. Use an IF/THEN statement to define this function. Hint: The signal assignments can be written just like the table.

en	s1	s0	Array Logic Operation
1	0	0	f <= a OR b
1	0	1	f <= a AND b
1	1	0	f <= a XOR b
1	1	1	f <= NOT a
0	X	X	f <= "0000"

6V.12 Number range detector

Design a logic circuit that, when enabled with an active-high signal named en, will detect four different ranges of values for a 5-bit input number (see table below). The inputs are labeled num4 through num0 and the outputs are labeled values1 through values4. Values1, values2, and values3 each produce active-high outputs, while values4 produces an active-low output signal. Use IF/ELSIF to test the 5-bit input for the desired value ranges. Hint: Use the greater-than-or-equal-to (>=) and less-than-or-equal-to (<=) symbols in a Boolean expression to detect the desired range of input values for each output result.

Outputs	Values detected
values1	4–12
values2	15–20
values3	21–24
values4	26–30

6V.13 Data switcher

Design a programmable logic circuit that will route two input data bits to the selected outputs as given in the function table below. The control input, a 2-bit array named sel determines which of the two data inputs (input1 and input0) are to be routed to each of the two outputs (output1 and output0). The input en is an active-low enable for the data switcher. If the enable is high, we don't care what input levels are on sel, and the two outputs will both be low. Use a CASE statement inside an IF/THEN statement.

en	sel1	sel0	output1	output0
0	0	0	input1	input0
0	0	1	input0	input0
0	1	0	input1	input1
0	1	1	input0	input1
1	X	X	0	0

ANALYZING FLIP-FLOPS AND BASIC SEQUENTIAL CIRCUITS

Objectives

- To test the operation of SR and D latches and JK flip-flops.
- To construct a switch debouncing circuit using a simple SR latch.
- To test basic sequential circuits, including registers and counters.
- To measure the waveforms generated by counters using an oscilloscope.
- To measure the frequencies of counter signals using a frequency counter.

Suggested Parts					
7400	7404	7408	7410	74112	7474
7486	74163	SPDT switch	1-kΩ resistors		

Flip-Flops and Latches

Combinational logic circuits have outputs that are dependent only on the current inputs to the circuit. Sequential circuits, on the other hand, are dependent not only on the current inputs but also on the prior circuit conditions. Sequential circuits contain memory elements that allow them to utilize the prior circuit conditions in determining the circuit output. These memory elements consist of flip-flops and latches. There are various categories of flip-flops and latches, including SR, D, and JK types.

Several flip-flops or latches can be connected together in specific circuit configurations to construct various types of registers and counters. The 7474 and 74112 chips contain dual D and JK flip-flops, respectively. These chips also have asynchronous preset and clear inputs. The 7474 is positive-edge triggered, while the 74112 is negative-edge triggered. The 74163 contains a 4-bit binary counter. The counter will count up one in binary for each positive-edge triggering pulse received on the clock input pin. The counter chip also has four control inputs (ENT, ENP, CLR, and LOAD) that can be used to make the chip perform various other logic functions that will be investigated later.

Example 7-1

Analyze the operation of the unclocked SR latch circuit shown in Fig. 7-1 when the given input waveforms are applied.

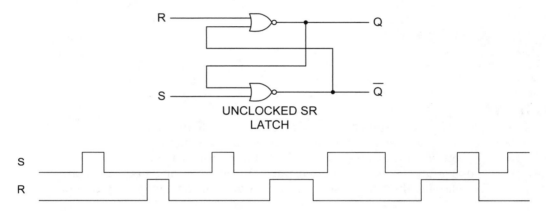

Fig. 7-1 Unclocked SR latch and input conditions

The SR latch shown in Fig. 7-1 will function as indicated in Table 7-1. The specified input waveforms will produce the results shown in Fig. 7-2. The sections of the output waveforms that are shown in a cross-hatch cannot be determined. The time period that is marked with an asterisk is the result of applying an invalid input condition (S = R = 1).

S	R	Q	$\overline{Q}$	Command
0	0	Q	$\overline{Q}$	no change
0	1	0	1	Reset
1	0	1	0	Set
1	1	0	0	*Invalid*

Table 7-1 Truth table for active-high input SR latch

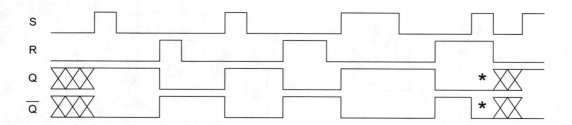

Fig. 7-2 Timing diagram results for Example 7-1

Example 7-2

Analyze the register circuit shown in Fig. 7-3 for the given input waveforms. Assume that the initial condition is **Q3 Q2 Q1 Q0** = 1 0 1 0. The results are shown in Fig. 7-4.

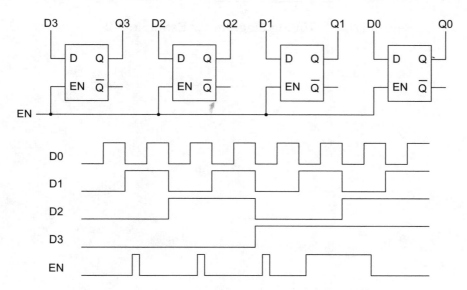

Fig. 7-3 4-bit transparent register and input conditions for Example 7-2

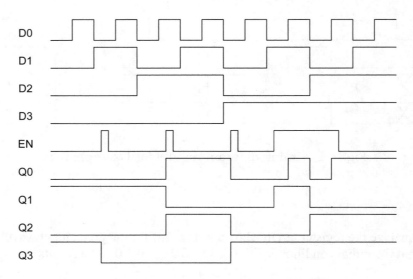

Fig. 7-4 Timing diagram for Example 7-2

Laboratory Projects

7.1   NAND SR latch
        Construct and test a NAND SR latch (see schematic below). Use two logic switches for
        the control inputs (Set and Reset) and monitor both latch outputs (Q and Qbar) with
        separate lamps. Test the latch under each of the four possible input conditions. How do
        you set the latch? What is the condition of the latch's two outputs (Q and Qbar) when
        the latch is set? How do you reset the latch? What is the condition of the latch's
        outputs when the latch is reset? How do you control the latch so that it will hold a bit of
        data? Why are the outputs named Q and Qbar? What happens to a NAND latch in the
        invalid state? Are the latch's control inputs active-high or active-low? Describe the
        operation of the latch.

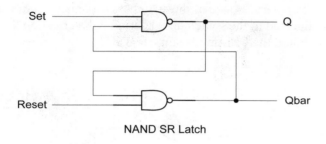

NAND SR Latch

7.2   Debouncing a logic switch

(a)   <u>Manually</u> clock a 74163 binary counter with a simple digital switch (see the following schematic). The jumper wire connects the circuit node labeled "**Simple** Digital Switch Output" to the CLK (clock) pin on the counter chip. Note that the switch circuit used for part (a) is actually a portion of the circuit to be used for part (b). Monitor the clocking signal with a logic probe as shown in the drawing. The objective is for the counter to produce a binary sequence that increments by one count each time the logic switch is flipped back and forth. Does the counter seem to count correctly? What is the counter actually doing each time the switch is cycled? What is switch bounce? How does switch bounce affect a digital circuit?

(b)   Now <u>move</u> one end of the jumper wire connected to the 74163 clock input to the output of the NAND SR latch (node labeled "**Debounced** Digital Switch Output") to eliminate the switch's contact bounce. Try clocking the counter again. Does the counter now operate correctly? What is the sequence of states for the counter's outputs? <u>Describe</u> the operation of the debouncing circuit. How does the latch eliminate the contact bounce of the switch? Disconnect (remove) the two pull-up resistors connected to the switch and determine the effect on the circuit's operation, if any. Why should the pull-up resistors be used?

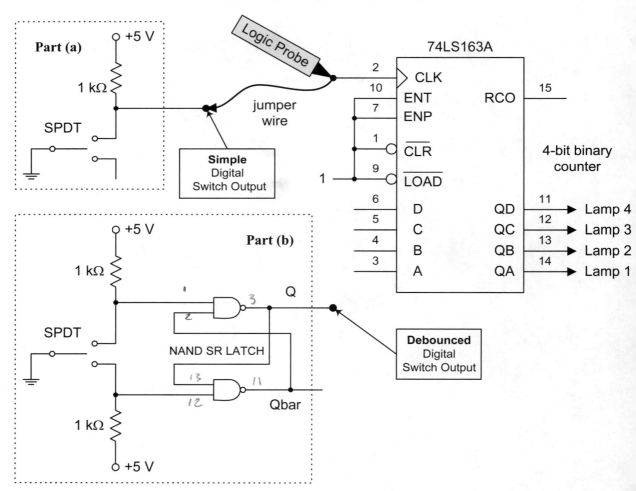

7.3 D latch

Construct and test a D latch (see schematic below). Use a logic switch for the Data input and another for the Enable. Monitor both latch outputs (**Q** and **Qbar**) with separate lamps. What does the latch do when the enable is high and the data input is changed? What does the latch do when the enable is low and the data input is changed? Is the latch's Enable active-high or active-low? How do you store data in the D latch? What part of the D latch circuit actually stores the data and which part provides the data steering (or control) of the latch? Describe the operation of the latch.

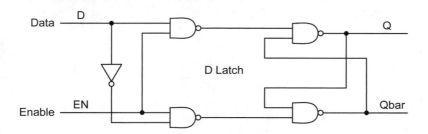

7.4 4-bit register

Construct a 4-bit register as shown below using 7474 D flip-flops. Use a <u>manual</u> clock (pushbutton) to clock the register. Connect the 4 register inputs (**D1** through **D4**) to the output of the 4-bit binary counter contained in the 74163. Connect the register's 4 inputs (**D1** through **D4**) and 4 outputs (Q1 through Q4) to separate logic lamps. Test the operation of the register by manually clocking it while the inputs are automatically changing with the clocking of the counter. Which of the register outputs is the LSB and which is the MSB? Why? What part (which level or edge?) of the manual clock signal actually triggers the register to store a new value? What does the register do between triggering signals? How would this register act differently if it were level-enabled?

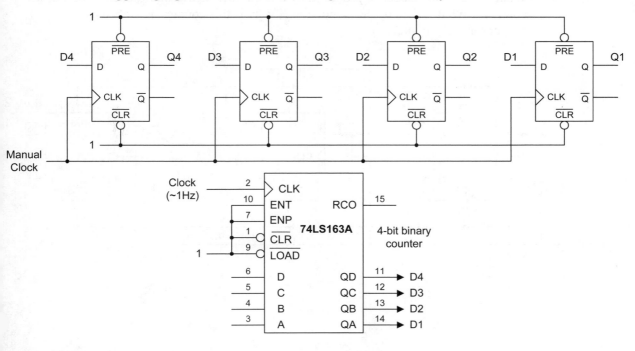

7.5   JK flip-flop

Test the operation (both synchronous and asynchronous) of one of the JK flip-flops contained in a 74112. Connect the flip-flop's J, K, PRE, and CLR control inputs to logic switches, the clock to a pushbutton, and the outputs (Q and Qbar) to lamps. Which control inputs are synchronous? Determine how to synchronously control the flip-flop to hold data, set, reset, and toggle. Which control inputs are asynchronous? Determine how to asynchronously store a zero or a one in the flip-flop. Why are the controls classified as synchronous or asynchronous? Which set of controls (synchronous or asynchronous) have priority? What is the function of the clock? Give the **truth table** for this JK flip-flop.

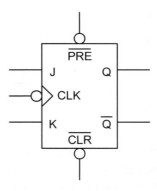

7.6   Binary counter

Construct and test the following 3-bit binary counter. Use a (debounced) pushbutton or pulser to <u>manually</u> clock the counter and observe the counter's output (QC QB QA) on 3 lamps. Assume that QC is the most significant bit and QA is the least significant bit. What is the count sequence produced by this circuit? Is this an up-counter or a down-counter? What is the counter's modulus? Why is this counter described as a "synchronous" counter?

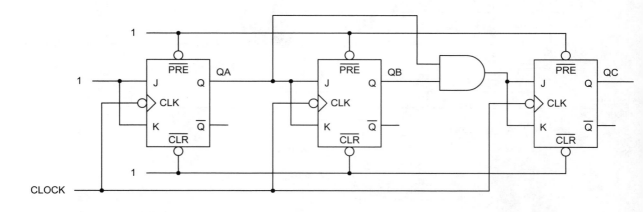

7.7   Counter timing diagram
Use an oscilloscope to observe the input and output waveforms (4 signals: CLOCK, QA, QB, QC) for the 3-bit counter in Laboratory Project 7.6. A good display on the oscilloscope will be obtained if the clock frequency is increased to at least 10 kHz. Remember that the clock signal must be TTL compatible. A 4-channel scope will provide the best display since all 4 waveforms can be viewed simultaneously, but a dual-channel scope can also be used by carefully swapping signals. Arrange the scope display in the order of decreasing signal frequency, with the highest frequency signal at the top of the screen and the lowest frequency signal at the bottom. **Trigger the oscilloscope on the lowest frequency signal.** Which signal appears to be the lowest frequency? Why? <u>Carefully</u> draw the waveforms to show the timing relationships between each of the counter outputs and the clock signal.

7.8   Frequency division
Use a frequency counter to measure the actual signal frequencies of the clock input and QA, QB, and QC outputs for the 3-bit counter in Laboratory Project 7.6. What is the frequency relationship between each of these signals?

7.9   Modifying count sequence
<u>Carefully</u> modify the 3-bit counter in Laboratory Project 7.6 as shown below. **Make sure that you disconnect the logic-high signal from the CLR inputs.** Use a low frequency (approximately 1 Hertz) TTL pulse waveform to clock the new counter circuit so that we can easily observe its output (QC QB QA) on lamps. What is the count sequence produced by the new circuit? Why is the count sequence different with the NAND gate connected to the counter? What is the new counter's modulus? What is the active-level for the CLR input? What does the CLR control do? Is the CLR control synchronous or asynchronous? What counter state actually makes the output of the NAND gate go low? Why can't we observe this state on the lamps? Why would we describe the function of the NAND gate in this circuit as a "decoder"? How would you modify the circuit again to produce a mod-6 counter? How would you modify the circuit to produce a mod-7 counter?

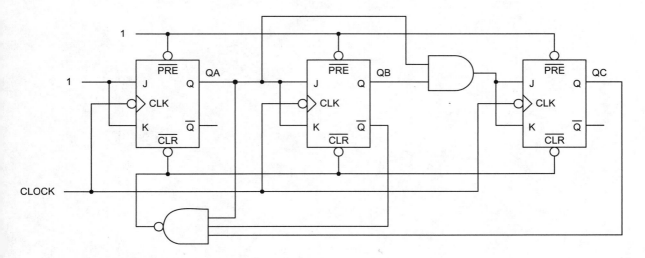

7.10   Counter using D flip-flops
D flip-flops can also be used to construct counter circuits such as the one below. As with counters constructed with JK flip-flops, the gating circuitry controls the count sequence while the flip-flops hold the current state. What is the count sequence for this circuit? What is the counter's modulus? Does the counter recycle? What makes the QA flip-flop toggle with each clock pulse? What type of logic gate causes the other D flip-flops (QB or QC) to toggle to the opposite state? Describe the operation of this counter circuit. Write the equivalent SOP logic expressions for each D input. How would you construct a 4-bit binary counter using D flip-flops?

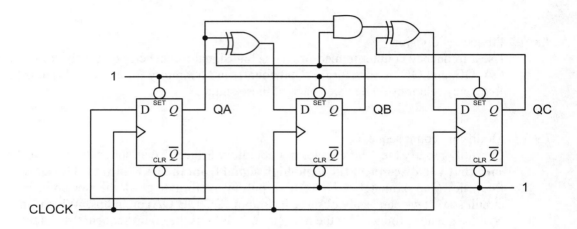

UNIT 8

TIMING AND WAVESHAPING CIRCUITS

Objectives

- To convert analog signals into logic-compatible signals using Schmitt trigger devices.
- To design and construct astable multivibrators that produce specified square waveforms.
- To design and construct monostable multivibrators that produce specified time delay patterns.

Suggested Parts			
7404	7414	74221	555
Resistors: 1.0, 1.3, 2.0, 27, 33, 47, 62, 68, 72, 82 kΩ			Capacitors: 0.001, 0.0047, 0.01, 0.1, 10 μF
Potentiometer: 10 kΩ (10-turn)			Diode: 1N4001

<u>Schmitt Triggers</u>

If a slow-changing signal is applied to the input of a logic device, the device will often produce an output signal that oscillates as the input slowly transitions between high and low logic levels. A Schmitt trigger is a waveshaping device used to convert signals in which the voltage is slowly changing (and, therefore, incompatible with logic devices) to a signal of the same frequency but is compatible with the signal transition times of logic devices. Schmitt trigger devices have an input hysteresis since they have two different specific triggering points. A positive-going threshold voltage and a negative-going threshold voltage will switch the Schmitt trigger's output between the two possible logic levels. The 7414 IC is a hex inverter chip with Schmitt trigger inputs.

One-Shots or Monostable Multivibrators

A one-shot is a timing device in which the output is triggered into a quasi-stable state and then returns to its stable state. The length of the quasi-stable state is usually controlled by an external resistor and capacitor. One-shots are typically used to produce delays in control signals for digital systems. There are two types of one-shots: retriggerable and nonretriggerable. The 74221 IC (see Fig. 8-1) contains two independent, nonretriggerable one-shots. The one-shot can be triggered by either a positive-edge on the B input or a negative-edge on the A input. The Q output will go high after the one-shot is triggered and will return to a low at the end of the delay time. The length of delay is controlled by the resistor and capacitor. The active-low CLR input will immediately terminate the delay and return the one-shot to its stable state.

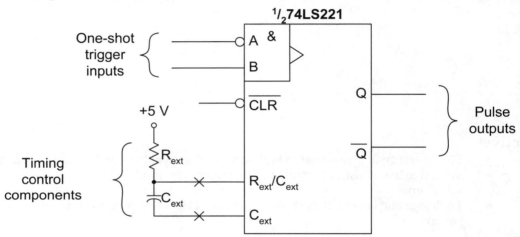

Fig. 8-1 A 74LS221 one-shot IC chip

Example 8-1

Determine the delay that will be produced when the 74LS221 one-shot shown in Fig. 8-1 is triggered if $R_{ext} = 47$ kΩ, $C_{ext} = 0.033$ μf, and the CLR input is disabled (high).

The formula for the time delay is:
$$t_w = 0.693 \ R_{ext} \ C_{ext} = 0.693 \ (47 \ k\Omega) \ (0.033 \ \mu f) = 1.075 \ ms$$

Clocks or Astable Multivibrators

An astable or free-running multivibrator has an output that continually switches back and forth between the two states, producing a square wave signal. This type of signal is often used as a clock signal to control (or trigger) synchronous circuits. The 555 IC timer is a device that can be used to produce a clock signal whose frequency and duty cycle are dependent on two external timing resistors and a timing capacitor (see Fig. 8-2).

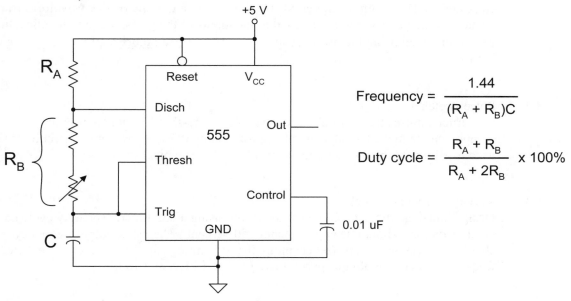

$$\text{Frequency} = \frac{1.44}{(R_A + R_B)C}$$

$$\text{Duty cycle} = \frac{R_A + R_B}{R_A + 2R_B} \times 100\%$$

Fig. 8-2 A 555 astable multivibrator with variable frequency output

Example 8-2

Determine the output frequency range that will be produced for the 555 clock circuit shown in Fig. 8-2 if $R_A = 1$ kΩ, R_B consists of a fixed 10-kΩ resistor in series with a 100-kΩ potentiometer, and $C = 0.01$ μf. Also determine the duty cycle range for the output signal.

The lowest output frequency will be obtained when R_B is at its maximum value (10 kΩ + 100 kΩ = 110 kΩ). The resultant frequency is 452.5 Hz with a duty cycle of 50.2%. The highest frequency will be obtained when the potentiometer is at its minimum value (0 Ω) so that $R_B = 10$ kΩ. This will produce an output frequency of 4762 Hz with a duty cycle of 52.4%.

Laboratory Projects

Design timing and waveshaping circuits for the following applications. Breadboard and verify your designs.

8.1   Schmitt trigger waveshaper
Use an oscilloscope to compare the output waveforms produced by a NOT gate in a 7404 and a 7414 (Schmitt trigger NOT) when either a triangle or sine waveform from a signal or function generator is applied to the inputs of the gates. Be sure to adjust the generator signal using the oscilloscope to $0 \leq V_{in} \leq +5$ V <u>before</u> applying it to the gate inputs.

8.2   Pulse stretcher
Construct a pulse stretcher circuit using a 74221 one-shot. Select appropriate components to make the pulse width approximately 0.5 s. How can this circuit also be used to eliminate the contact bounce problem of mechanical switches?

8.3   Variable frequency clock
Design and construct a clock generator circuit using a 555 timer. The duty cycle of the clock waveform should be approximately 50 percent. The clock output frequency should be variable in steps (by changing the 555 timing capacitor value). The 3 clock frequency values should be approximately 1 Hz, 1 kHz, and 10 kHz.

8.4   Waveform generator
Design and construct a waveform generator that will produce the waveforms given in the timing diagram below. Use the 555 timer to generate one of the waveforms, and then use that waveform to trigger the 2 one-shots in the 74221 to produce the other two waveforms.

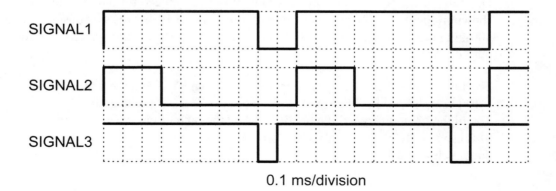

0.1 ms/division

8.5 Variable duty-cycle square wave generator

Design a variable duty-cycle square wave generator using a 555 timer. The output frequency should be 10 kHz and the duty cycle should vary from 15% to 85%. Use a 10-turn, 10-kΩ potentiometer to control the duty cycle. The diode in the modified astable multivibrator circuit below theoretically allows the R_B resistance to be shorted out during the charge cycle. The new equations for this circuit will be:

$$t_L = 0.75 \ R_B \ C$$
$$t_H = 0.75 \ R_A \ C$$

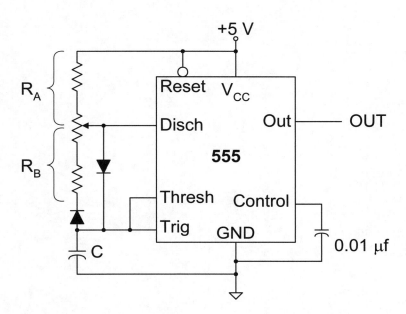

8.6 Delayed pulse

Design a timing circuit that will output a positive pulse that is 0.22 ms wide. The output pulse is delayed and does not start until 0.33 ms after being triggered by a negative-edge signal.

8.7 Clock generator using one-shots

Design a 100-Hz clock generator using the two one-shots contained in a 74221. Use a 0.1 μF timing capacitor for each one-shot. Select a timing resistor for each one-shot. Hint: Let the timeout of each one-shot trigger the other.

ARITHMETIC CIRCUITS

Objective

- To apply parallel adder circuits in arithmetic applications.

Suggested Part
    EPM7128S or EP1C6

Adder Circuit Applications

The primary building blocks in adder circuits are half adders and full adders. The basic difference between a half and a full adder is that a full adder has an additional input (3 inputs total) that allows a carry input to be handled. Both half and full adders generate a sum and a carry output. These building blocks can be implemented a number of ways using various logic gates.

Due to their versatility and usefulness, parallel adders made up of several full adder stages are available as integrated circuit devices. The 74LS283 (shown in Fig. 9-1) is an example of a 4-bit parallel binary adder chip. This MSI chip can add two 4-bit binary numbers (A4 A3 A2 A1 and B4 B3 B2 B1) together. The adder chip outputs a 5-bit sum (C4 Σ4 Σ3 Σ2 Σ1). There is also a carry input (C0) available that can be used to connect multiple 74283 chips together for larger adder applications. An 8-bit parallel adder constructed with two 74283 chips is illustrated in Fig 9-2. The inputs A8 through A1 and B8 through B1 are added together to produce the 9-bit sum labeled S9 through S1. Parallel binary adders can also be used in many arithmetic applications besides just simple addition.

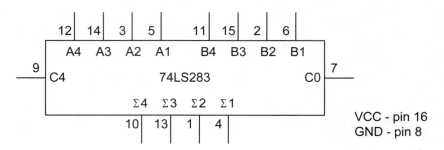

Fig. 9-1 A 74LS283 4-bit parallel binary adder chip

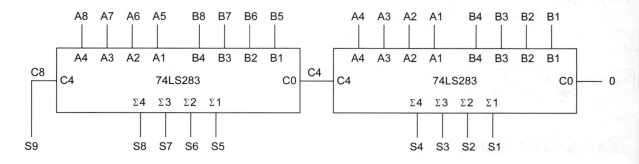

Fig. 9-2 An 8-bit parallel binary adder circuit using two 74283 chips

Example 9-1

Create an 8-bit parallel adder as shown in Fig. 9-2 using a PLD.

Our solution (see Fig. 9-3) uses the schematic capture design entry technique and employs the 74283 macrofunction (see "Schematic Capture of Macrofunctions" in MAXplus Notes or Quartus Notes in the CD-ROM Tutorials folder). The inputs and outputs are drawn as buses (see "Drawing Signal Buses" and "Manually Assigning Pin Numbers" in MAXplus Notes or Quartus Notes). Two 8-bit input ports (one for the set of A inputs and one for the set of B inputs) and one 9-bit output port (for the set of S outputs) are needed. Note that the CIN for the least significant 4-bit adder is connected to GND. The symbols for high and low logic inputs are named VCC and GND, respectively.

Sample test vectors and simulation results for this circuit are shown in Fig. 9-4.

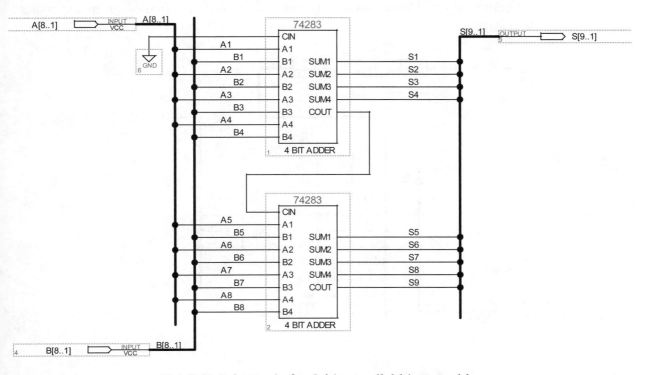

Fig. 9-3 Schematic for 8-bit parallel binary adder

		20.0ms	40.0ms	60.0ms	80.0ms
A[8..1]	-	00110110	00000010	10101010	11111111	11111000
B[8..1]	-	00011101	00000010	01010101	00000001	00001111
S[9..1]	-	001010011	000000100	011111111	100000000	100000111

Fig. 9-4 Simulation results for 8-bit parallel adder

Example 9-2

Design a logic circuit that will add one, subtract one, or produce no change in a 4-bit input value i[3..0] as shown in the following table. The 4-bit output is f[3..0] and m[1..0] are the control inputs.

m1	m0	Operation
0	X	No change
1	0	Add one
1	1	Subtract one

A 2-level, hierarchical design is created for Example 9-2. The top-level design file (shown in Fig. 9-5) uses schematic capture. It contains a 74283 macrofunction and the symbol created for the lower-level control block. The inputs and outputs are both represented in a bus style for the default symbol since they were defined as groups in the **control** block. Notice that signal names may be different than the given port names on a symbol.

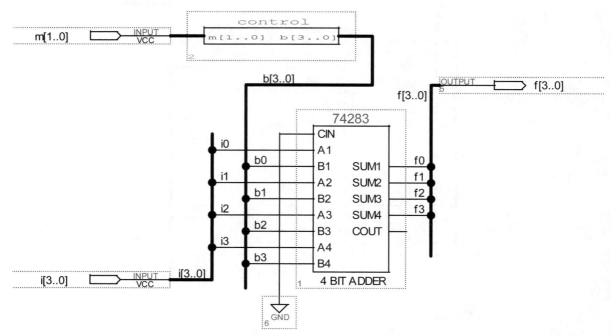

Fig. 9-5 Top-level schematic for Example 9-2

```
CONSTANT    addone = B"0001";
CONSTANT    subone = B"1111";
CONSTANT    zero = B"0000";
            -- create names for 3 constant values

SUBDESIGN   control
(
     m[1..0]              :INPUT;
     b[3..0]              :OUTPUT;
)

BEGIN
     CASE   m[]  IS              -- choose function
          WHEN   2        =>  b[] = addone;
          WHEN   3        =>  b[] = subone;
          WHEN OTHERS  =>  b[] = zero;
     END CASE;
END;
```

Fig. 9-6 Lower-level AHDL file for Example 9-2

The lower level file, named **control**, can easily be implemented in either AHDL (see Fig. 9-6) or VHDL (see Fig. 9-7). The control block provides the necessary value (0, +1, or –1) that will be added using 2's-complement arithmetic to the 4-bit input number at the top level. These three values are defined as CONSTANTs (named **addone**, **subone**, and **zero**) in this file. In AHDL, the CONSTANT statements are declared outside the other design sections, while in VHDL, constant declarations are placed within the architecture or process that requires it or globally within design units called packages. A Case statement is used to select the desired constant that will be output from this control block according to the control inputs **m**[1..0]. The "when others" choice will take care of any undefined combination of **m**.

```
ENTITY   control IS
PORT (
      m              :  IN BIT_VECTOR (1 DOWNTO 0);
      b              :  OUT BIT_VECTOR (3 DOWNTO 0) );
END control;

ARCHITECTURE create_constants OF control IS
CONSTANT   addone  :  BIT_VECTOR (3 DOWNTO 0)      := "0001";
CONSTANT   subone  :  BIT_VECTOR (3 DOWNTO 0)      := "1111";
CONSTANT   zero    :  BIT_VECTOR (3 DOWNTO 0)      := "0000";
                -- create names for 3 constant values
BEGIN
      PROCESS (m)
      BEGIN
            CASE   m  IS         -- choose function
                  WHEN  "10"  =>    b <= addone;
                  WHEN  "11"  =>    b <= subone;
                  WHEN OTHERS =>    b <= zero;
            END CASE;
      END PROCESS;
END create_constants;
```

Fig. 9-7 Lower-level VHDL file for Example 9-2

The design is compiled from the top-level schematic file with the desired AHDL or VHDL lower-level file for **control** in the same project folder. Results of simulating the top-level design for Example 9-2 are shown in Fig. 9-8.

		20.0ms	40.0ms	60.0ms	80.0ms	100.0ms	120.0ms	140.0ms	160.0ms	180.0ms	200.0
m[1..0]	B 00	00 X 01 X 10 X 11	00 X 01 X 10 X 11	00 X 01 X 10 X 11	00 X 01 X 10 X 11	00 X 01 X 10 X 11
i[3..0]	B 0100	0100	1010	1111	0000	0111
f[3..0]	B 0100	0100 X0101 X0011 X	1010 X1011 X1001 X	1111 X0000 X1110 X	0000 X0001 X1111 X	0111 X1000 X0110 X

Fig. 9-8 Simulation results for Example 9-2

Laboratory Projects

Design arithmetic circuits for the following applications. Breadboard and verify your designs.

9.1   Eight-bit adder
        Demonstrate the operation of the design given in Example 9-1.

9.2   Incrementer/decrementer circuit
        Demonstrate the operation of the design given in Example 9-2.

9.3   BCD to binary converter
        Design a 2-digit BCD-to-binary converter to be implemented with an EPM7128. Use a schematic for the design entry. The inputs are the BCD tens digit (t[3..0]) and ones digit (u[3..0]). The output is the equivalent 7-bit binary value (b[6..0]). Note: Insert a buffer named "wire" (primitive component in the library) between the u0 input and the b0 output shown in the schematic below. This will allow you to name each end of the wire with the respective input and output signal names. Otherwise, you will not be able to label the single wire with both names.

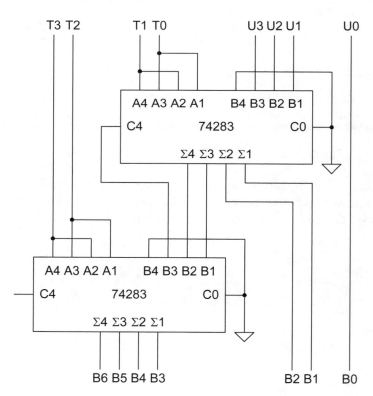

9.4   Four-bit adder/subtractor

Design a 4-bit adder/subtractor to be implemented with an EPM7128. Create a hierarchical design consisting of the top level and two lower level blocks (the controlled complement block and the overflow block). The adder/subtractor circuit can handle signed numbers (using 2's-complement arithmetic techniques). F is a control input to the circuit that determines if the circuit will add $(A + B)$ or subtract $(A - B)$ the 4-bit data inputs. The overflow detector circuit will output a high signal at V if the adder/subtractor produces an incorrect result due to an overflow condition. Overflow occurs when like-signed numbers are added together but the sign of the result is not the same sign. Hints: Perform subtraction by forming the 1's-complement of the B input (the subtrahend) and adding 1 (with the carry input) plus the A input (the minuend). Remember that the B input should not be complemented for addition $(F = 0)$. To design the overflow circuit, define in a truth table when an overflow exists by monitoring each of the 3 sign bits (2 operands and answer).

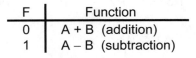

F	Function
0	A + B (addition)
1	A − B (subtraction)

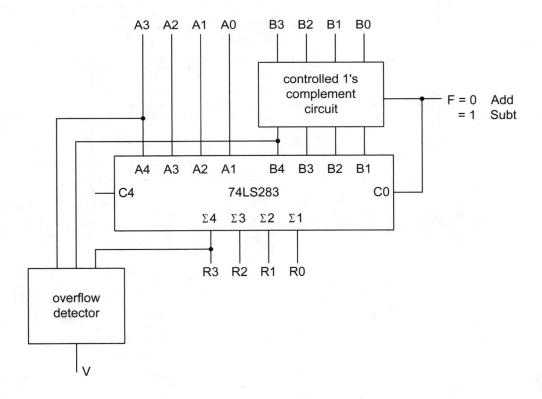

9.5   Binary multiplier

Design an unsigned binary multiplier to be implemented with an EPM7128. The multiplier circuit should handle 4-bit multiplicands (A3 A2 A1 A0) and 2-bit multipliers (B1 B0) to produce 6-bit products (P5 P4 P3 P2 P1 P0). The partial products are created by ANDing the appropriate <u>pair</u> of input bits. Note: Insert a buffer named "wire" (primitive component in the library) between the A0•B0 output and the P0 output shown in the schematic below. This will allow you to name each end of the wire with the respective signal names. Otherwise, you will not be able to label the single wire with both names.

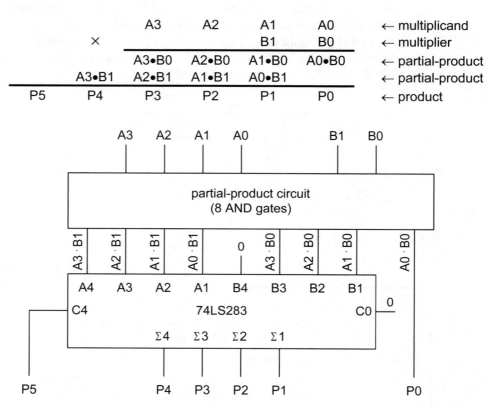

9.6   BCD adder

Design a 4-bit BCD adder to be implemented with an EPM7128. The two BCD inputs are P3 P2 P1 P0 and Q3 Q2 Q1 Q0. Cin is the carry input for the BCD adder stage. The BCD digit sum is S3 S2 S1 S0, and Cout is the BCD carry output. The first parallel adder performs an initial binary addition of the 4-bit numbers. The "greater than 9 detector" block determines if the 5-bit intermediate sum produced by the first adder (C4 Z4 Z3 Z2 Z1) is greater than 9. If so, the binary sum will be corrected by adding six (0110_2) with the second parallel adder and Cout will be high. If the intermediate sum is less than or equal to 9, Cout is zero and no correction is necessary (i.e., add 0000). Hint: An IF statement to check c4 and z[4..1] in an HDL file is an easy design solution for the "greater than 9 detector" block.

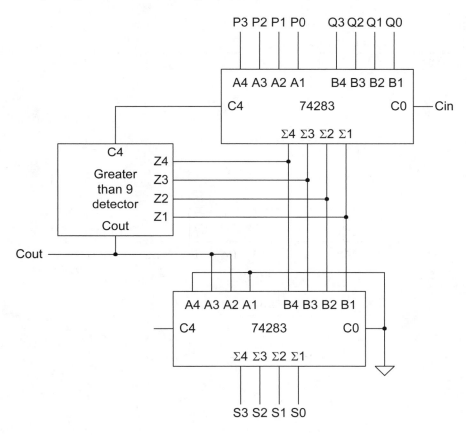

ANALYZING AND TESTING SYNCHRONOUS COUNTERS

Objectives

- To analyze synchronous counter circuits and thus predict their theoretical operation.
- To construct and test the operation of synchronous counter circuits using standard logic devices.
- Use schematic capture to construct and test the operation of synchronous counter circuits with programmable logic devices (PLDs).
- To simulate synchronous counter circuits with MAX+PLUS II or Quartus II.

Suggested Parts					
7400	7408	7411	7420	7432	7474
7486	74112	EPM7128S or EP1C6			

Synchronous Counters

Synchronous or parallel counters are triggered by a common clocking signal applied to each flip-flop. Because of this clocking arrangement, all flip-flops react to their individual synchronous control inputs at the same time. The count sequence depends on the control signals input to each flip-flop. Additionally, the flip-flop asynchronous control inputs, preset and clear, may be used to modify the count sequence.

Example 10-1

Analyze the synchronous counter circuit given in Fig. 10-1. Draw the state transition diagram (include <u>all</u> 8 possible states) for the counter. Also draw the counter's timing diagram. Determine the modulus for the counter.

To analyze the counter, the circuit excitation (or present state/next state) table given in Table 10-1 is produced. The counter is assumed to start at state 000. The analysis indicates that the counter is a mod-5 counter (see Fig. 10-2).

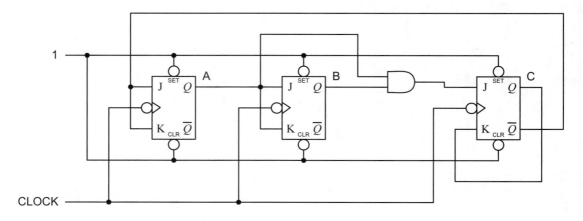

Fig. 10-1 Synchronous counter schematic for Example 10-1

CLOCK	Present State C B A	J_C K_C	J_B K_B	J_A K_A	Next State C B A
0	0 0 0	0 0	0 0	1 1	0 0 1
1	0 0 1	0 0	1 1	1 1	0 1 0
2	0 1 0	0 0	0 0	1 1	0 1 1
3	0 1 1	1 0	1 1	1 1	1 0 0
4	1 0 0	0 1	0 0	0 0	0 0 0
	1 0 1	0 1	1 1	0 0	0 1 1
	1 1 0	0 1	0 0	0 0	0 1 0
	1 1 1	1 1	1 1	0 0	0 0 1

Table 10-1 Complete present state/next state table for Example 10-1

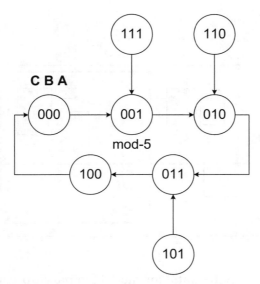

Fig. 10-2 State transition diagram for synchronous counter in Example 10-1

Sequential Circuits in PLDs

Sequential circuits can be easily implemented in PLDs using schematic capture techniques in MAX+PLUS II and Quartus II. The primitives library contains DFF, JKFF, SRFF, and TFF flip-flops and latches. See "Implementing Sequential Circuits" and "Manually Assigning Pin Numbers" in MAXplus Notes or Quartus Notes in the CD-ROM Tutorials folder.

Example 10-2

Create a mod-16 binary up-counter using an Altera PLD. Apply an external CMOS-compatible clock input to an available global clock pin.

The schematic for the mod-16 counter is shown in Fig. 10-3. The counter outputs are named QD QC QB QA (with QD = MSB). The flip-flops are JKFF primitives. The asynchronous preset and clear inputs on the JKs will default to a high condition if left unconnected. The clock input is connected to a global primitive to tell the compiler that we desire this input to be placed on a dedicated global input pin. The design is compiled after assigning the clock input to an unused global clock pin. The simulation results are shown in Fig. 10-4.

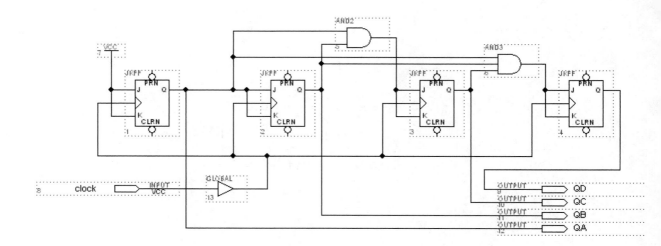

Fig. 10-3 Schematic for mod-16 binary up-counter

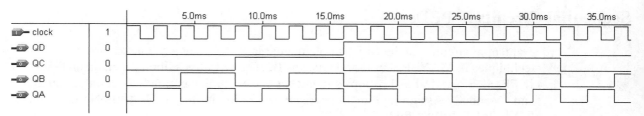

Fig. 10-4 Mod-16 binary up-counter simulation results

Laboratory Projects

Analyze the following recycling, synchronous counter circuits. For each counter, determine the count sequence, determine the counter's modulus, and sketch its timing diagram (show the clock input and the flip-flops' Q outputs). Construct and test the operation of the counter circuits using either standard logic devices or a PLD (using schematic capture). Your instructor may designate a specific circuit method for implementation. Use an oscilloscope to compare the output waveforms for each of the counters with your theoretical prediction. Simulate each circuit that is constructed with a PLD. Note: The JK flip-flops in a 74112 are negative-edge triggered, while all flip-flop primitives in MAX+PLUS II or Quartus II are positive-edge triggered.

10.1   Counter 1

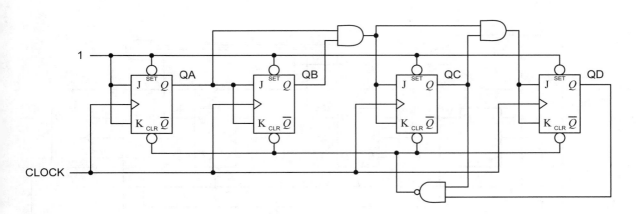

10.2   Counter 2

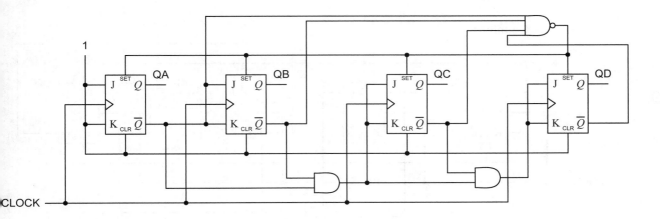

10.3   Counter 3

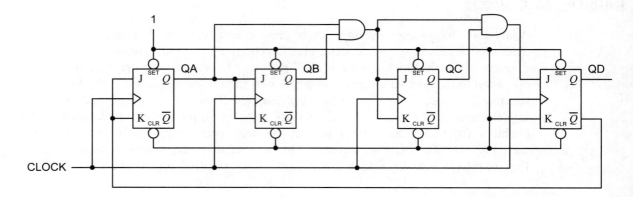

10.4   Counter 4

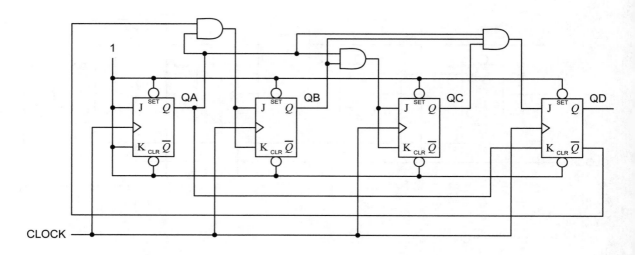

10.5   Counter 5

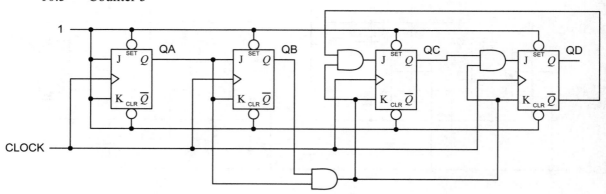

10.6   Counter 6

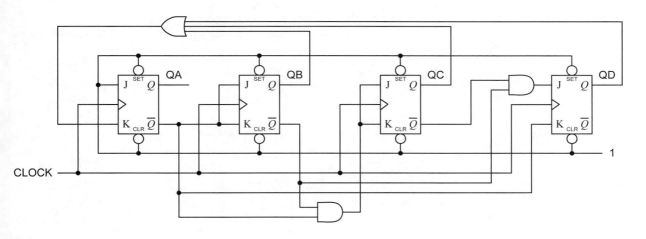

10.7   Counter 7

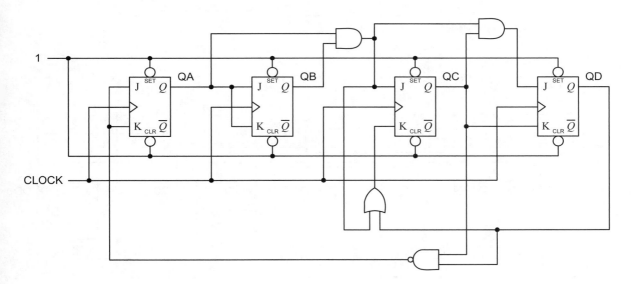

10.8   Counter 8

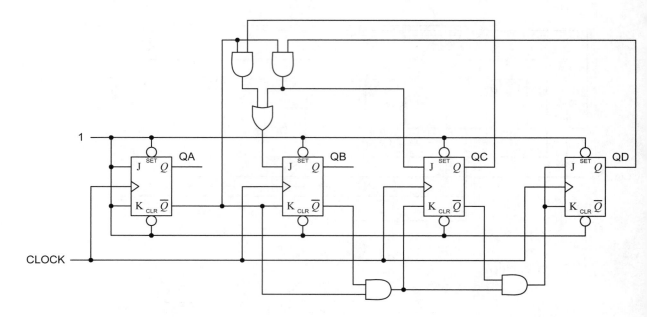

10.9   Counter 9

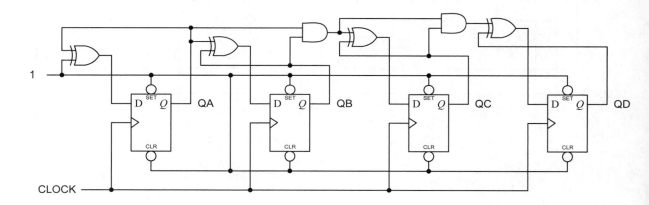

10.10   Counter 10

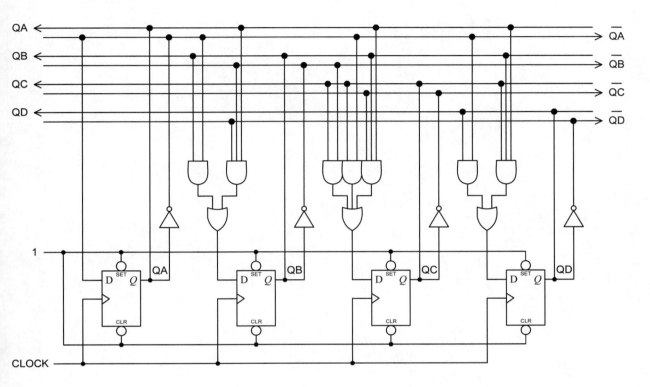

TESTING REGISTER AND COUNTER FUNCTIONS

Objectives

- To test the operation of standard register and counter functions.
- To perform design entry of sequential logic circuits using schematic capture in
- MAX+PLUS II or Quartus II.
- To simulate sequential logic circuits in MAX+PLUS II or Quartus II.

.

Suggested Parts					
7400	7404	74160	74163	74175	74190
74375	EPM7128S or EP1C6				

Sequential Circuit Operation with Standard MSI Chips and Macrofunctions

Various register and counter designs have been integrated into chips to make circuit applications more convenient for the logic designer. Some variations include the number of flip-flops contained in the chip, the counter modulus, synchronous or asynchronous flip-flop triggering, synchronous or asynchronous counter resetting, synchronous or asynchronous counter loading, up/down count control, and various counter cascading implementations. Different feature combinations are found in different chip part numbers. Mod-16 and mod-10 IC counters are commonly available. A mod-10 counter is also referred to as a decade or BCD counter.

The macrofunction library in MAX+PLUS II or Quartus II contains many standard types of register and counter functions that can be used to easily and quickly design more complex logic circuits. Most of the macrofunctions are named by a 74XXX number and are equivalent in functionality to the standard part with the same part number. Schematic capture of macrofunctions with Altera software is done the same way as it is done for logic circuits made from primitive devices such as gates and flip-flops. See "Schematic Capture of Macrofunctions," "Implementing Sequential Circuits," and "Manually Assigning Pin Numbers" in MAXplus Notes or Quartus Notes in the CD-ROM Tutorials folder.

Example 11-1

Create a mod-16 binary up-counter using a 74163 macrofunction in an Altera PLD. Apply an external CMOS-compatible clock input to an available global clock pin.

The schematic for the mod-16 counter is shown in Fig. 11-1. The counter outputs are named QD QC QB QA (with QD = MSB). All control inputs (ENT, ENP, LDN, and CLRN) are connected to a high logic level. This condition will enable the counter to count and disable the parallel load and counter clear functions. The parallel data inputs D C B A are arbitrarily connected to a high logic level also, but the data inputs actually do not matter since the parallel load control is disabled. The clock input is connected to a global primitive to tell the compiler that we desire this input to be placed on a dedicated global input pin. The design is compiled after assigning the clock input to an unused global clock pin. The simulation results are shown in Fig. 11-2.

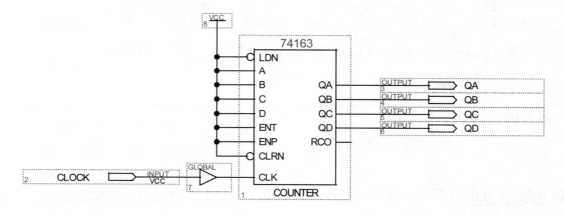

Fig. 11-1 Schematic for mod-16 binary up-counter using 74163 macrofunction

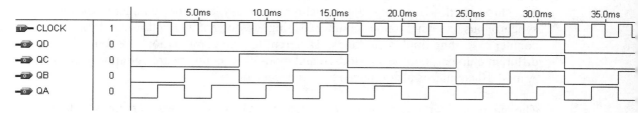

Fig. 11-2 Mod-16 binary up-counter simulation results

Laboratory Projects

Construct and test each of the following logic circuits using either standard 74-series parts or a PLD with the macrofunctions programmed using schematic entry. Simulate the circuits that are implemented on a PLD.

11.1   Latch and register operation

Compare the operation of a 74175 register with a 74375 latch using a 74163 binary counter for a data source. Apply a low-frequency clock signal (~1Hz) to cntr_clk and use a logic switch (or pulser) for the store input. Connect outputs qd qc qb qa and reg4 reg3 reg2 reg1 to lamps. Which of the 74163 outputs is the LSB? Which is the MSB? What is the count sequence produced by the 74163? Test the operation of the register by changing the store input. What specific part (rising/falling edge or high/low level?) of the store signal will store a new data value? Which of the 74175 outputs should be considered the MSB? Why? Next monitor outputs qd qc qb qa and latch4 latch3 latch2 latch1 with lamps. Test the operation of the latch by changing the store input. What specific part (rising/falling edge or high/low level?) of the store signal will store a new data value? Why is the latch called a "transparent" latch? Which of the 74375 outputs should be considered the MSB? Why? Describe the differences in operation between the 74175 register and the 74375 latch.

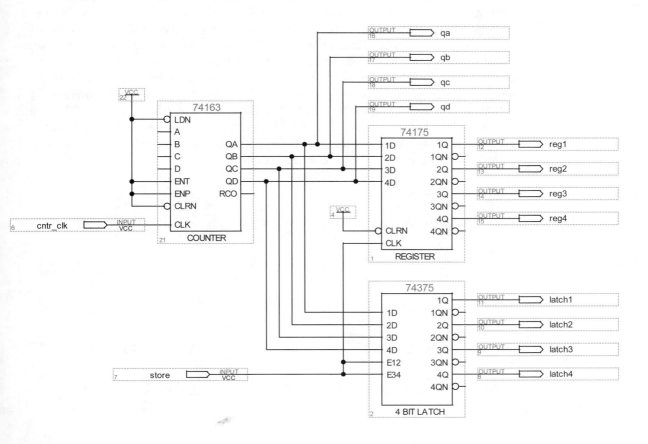

11.2   Binary counter signal frequencies
Apply a TTL-compatible clock signal with a frequency of approximately 64 kHz to the binary counter in a 74163 while ENT, ENP, LOAD, and CLR are all high. Use a frequency counter to measure the actual signal frequencies of the clock input, the four counter outputs (QA, QB, QC, and QD), and the output labeled RCO. What is the frequency relationship between each of these signals?

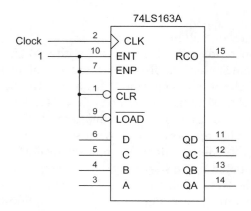

11.3   Modifying the count sequence
Construct the "original circuit" shown below. Use a low-frequency TTL pulse waveform (~1 Hz) to clock the counter and observe its output (QD QC QB QA) on lamps. What is the count sequence produced by the original circuit? What is the counter's modulus? Next change the counter circuit by connecting a NAND gate to the CLR input as shown in the "modified circuit." What is the new count sequence produced by the modified circuit? What is the counter's new modulus? What is the name for a counter with this count sequence? Why is the count sequence different with the NAND gate connected to the counter? What is the active-level for the CLR input? What does the CLR control do? Is the CLR control synchronous or asynchronous? How do you know? How would you modify the circuit again to produce a mod-13 counter? What count sequence would be produced?

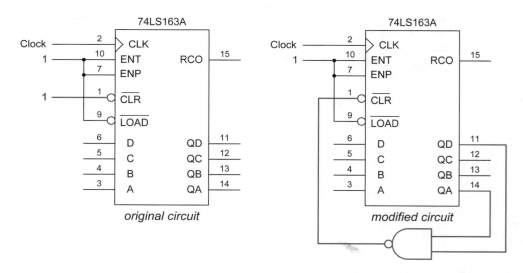

11.4   Decade counter timing diagram
Use an oscilloscope to observe the input and output waveforms (5 signals: clock, QA, QB, QC, QD) for the "modified circuit" in Laboratory Project 11.3. Increase the TTL-compatible clock frequency to approximately 10 kHz. With a 4-channel scope you will only be able to view four waveforms at a time, so it will be necessary to swap the signals applied to the scope. **Always trigger the oscilloscope on the lowest frequency signal.** <u>Carefully</u> draw the waveforms to show the timing relationships between each of the counter outputs and the clock signal. Measure the clock input frequency and the QD output frequency. What is the relationship between the two signal frequencies? How does that compare to the counter's modulus?

11.5   Decade counter operation
Test the operation of a 74160 decade counter chip. Connect the control inputs (ENT, ENP, CLR, and LOAD) and the data inputs (D, C, B, and A) to logic switches. Use a (debounced) pulser for the clock. Connect the outputs (QD, QC, QB, QA, and RCO) to lamps. Start your investigation with highs on each of the 4 control inputs and manually clock the counter until it recycles. Describe the operation of the counter. What is the function of the RCO output? Clock the counter while changing the ENT and ENP controls. What is the function of ENT and ENP? Are the ENT and ENP controls active-high or active-low? Return the ENT and ENP controls to a high signal and investigate the CLR control. What does CLR do? Is the CLR control active-high or active-low? Is the CLR control synchronous or asynchronous? Which function has priority, the count operation or the clear? How do you know? Disable the clear function, apply a low to the LOAD, and clock the chip with various BCD values on the D C B A inputs. Describe the function of the LOAD control. Is the LOAD control active-high or active-low? Is the LOAD control synchronous or asynchronous? Which has priority, the count operation or the load? How do you know? Which function (count, clear, or load) has the highest priority?

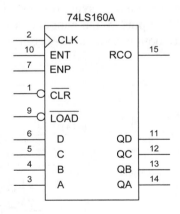

11.6   Self-stopping counter
Construct and test the operation of the following decade counter circuit. Use a low-frequency clock to trigger the counter and connect the CLR input to a "normally high" pulser switch. What happens to the counter's output when the pulser applies a low signal to CLR? Describe the operation of the circuit when the pulser is released (high signal to CLR). Why is this circuit called a "self-stopping" counter? What makes it stop counting? How do you "restart" the counter?

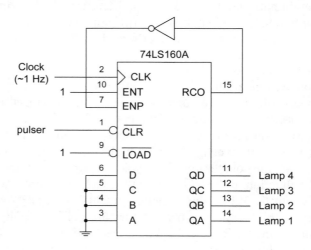

11.7   Mod-9 counters
Compare the operation of the following counter circuits using a low frequency (~1 Hz) clock to trigger the 74160. Test "circuit 1." What is the count sequence? When does RCO output a high? Is the LOAD function synchronous or asynchronous? How do you know? Modify the circuit to test "circuit 2." What is the new count sequence? Is the CLR function synchronous or asynchronous? How do you know? What is happening to the RCO output? What happened to state 9? What is the name for this type of state? Why are both circuits mod-9 counters?

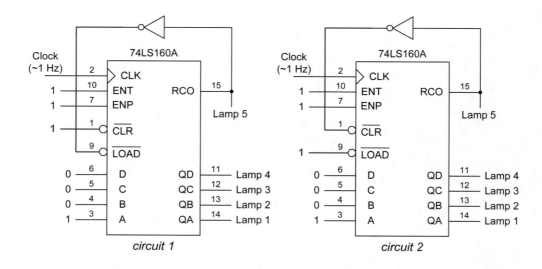

11.8   Up/down counter operation

Test the operation of a 74190 decade counter chip. Connect the control inputs (CTEN, D/U, and LOAD) and the data inputs (D, C, B, and A) to logic switches. Use a (debounced) pulser for the clock. Connect the outputs (QD, QC, QB, QA, and Max/Min) to lamps. Start your investigation with CTEN = 0, D/U = 0, and LOAD = 1 and manually clock the counter until it recycles. Again clock the counter while CTEN = 1. What is the function of CTEN? Is CTEN active-high or active-low? Enable the counter and clock it repeatedly while D/U = 1. What is the count sequence when D/U = 0 and when D/U = 1? What is the function of D/U? Describe the operation of the Max/Min output for the two input conditions of D/U. Apply a low to the LOAD with various BCD values on the D C B A inputs. Describe the function of the LOAD control. Is the LOAD control active-high or active-low? Is the LOAD control synchronous or asynchronous? Which function has priority, the count operation or the load? How do you know?

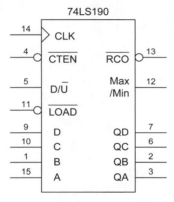

11.9   Mod-N counter

Construct and test the operation of the following counter circuit. Set the switches to a BCD value and clock the counter with a low frequency (~1 Hz) signal until it recycles. Change the switches to a new BCD value and again clock the counter until it recycles. What is the relationship between the switch value and the modulus of this counter? Why do we not want to set the switch value to 0000 or 0001?

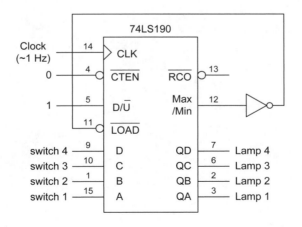

COUNTER APPLICATIONS USING MACROFUNCTIONS

Objectives

- To control the operation of standard counters.
- To produce specified count sequences using standard counters.
- To produce specified signal frequencies using frequency divider circuits.
- To apply standard counters in design applications requiring the cascading of counters together.

Suggested Parts					
7400	7404	7410	7447	74160	74163
74190	MAN72	330-Ω resistors	EPM7128S or EP1C6		

Applications of Standard Counters

Counters have a number of common applications, including the counting of items or objects, keeping track of time, frequency division, and controlling a sequence of activities. In frequency division, the input (applied to the clock) signal frequency is divided by a specified factor to produce the resultant lower output frequency of the divider. These circuits may be implemented using standard MSI counter chips or equivalent macrofunctions in MAX+PLUS II or Quartus II. See MAXplus Notes or Quartus Notes in the CD-ROM Tutorials folder.

Example 12-1

Design a mod-8 counter that counts the sequence of 1 through 8 and then recycles. Use either standard 74162 or 74190 decade counters.

Both solutions using standard IC chips are shown in Fig. 12-1. Since the counter needs to recycle back to 1 after 8, it will be necessary to load the binary number 0001 into the counter at the proper time. The load function on the 74162 is synchronous; therefore the counter state 8 must be detected to control the LOAD on the next clock pulse. This can be done simply with an inverter since the only time that QD goes high in the specified count sequence is at state 8. On the other hand, the load function on the 74190 is asynchronous, and the transient state 9 must be detected to control LOAD. State 9 (for which QD and QA are simultaneously high) can be decoded in this count sequence using a NAND gate. Each solution uses a decoding gate that has an active-low output to match the active-low input for the LOAD control. Both counters have count enables that must be appropriately tied to a logic level (ENT = ENP = 1 or CTEN = 0). The 74160 has an active-low clear (CLR) that needs to be tied high to be disabled. The 74190 is an up/down counter that requires D/U to be tied low to count up.

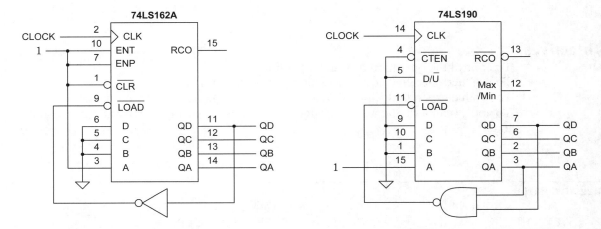

Fig. 12-1 Two standard IC chip solutions to Example 12-1

The desired solution can be easily implemented with MAX+PLUS II or Quartus II. The design using the 74162 macrofunction is shown in Fig. 12-2. The unused control inputs ENT, ENP, and CLR on the 74162 macrofunction are connected to a fixed high (VCC) or low (GND) input as shown in Fig. 12-1. The counter outputs are merged into a bus labeled q[3..0]. The individual signals going into the bus must be labeled and are, therefore, appropriately named q0, q1, etc.

The simulation results are shown in Fig. 12-3. The count sequence automatically starts at 0000_2 due to the power-on reset for all flip-flops in the PLD. The count-up sequence recycles to 1 (due to the load) after state 1000_2 (8) so that the desired count sequence of 1 through 8 is produced.

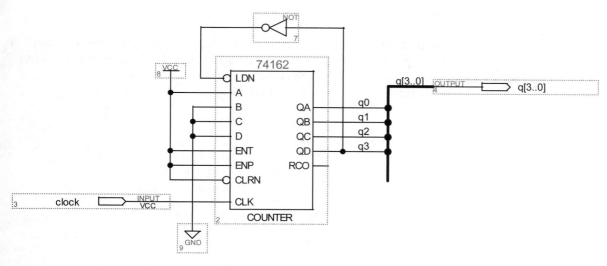

Fig. 12-2 Altera solution using the 74162 macrofunction

Fig. 12-3 Simulation results for Example 12-1 design

Example 12-2

Design a frequency divider circuit using the 74162 (decade counter) and 74163 (binary counter) macrofunctions in MAX+PLUS II or Quartus II that will produce three different frequencies: 180 kHz, 20 kHz, and 12 kHz. A 1.8-MHz clock signal is available.

A solution is shown in Fig. 12-4. The 1.8-MHz input signal must be divided by 10 to obtain 180 kHz, which can be done using a mod-10 counter (74LS162). The 180-kHz output (out0) is taken from the RCO (Ripple Carry Out) pin. The function of the RCO is to detect the final (terminal) counter state, which would be 1001_2 (9) for a decade counter. Therefore, we will have one pulse out on the RCO for every 10 pulses in on clk_in. The unused input controls on the macrofunctions are all high, which will automatically enable the counters (ENT and ENP) and disable the unused load (LDN) and clear (CLRN) functions. The data inputs are arbitrarily tied high also.

The 180-kHz signal must be divided by 9 to obtain the desired 20-kHz signal. This is done with a second 74162 macrofunction configured as a mod-9 counter. The active-low clear (CLRN) is synchronous in a 74162. Therefore, we will detect the counter state 1000_2 (8) with the inverter to clear on the next clock pulse. The resulting 0 through 8 count sequence will be a mod-8. The 20-kHz output (out1) is taken at the

QD pin, which will produce a single high pulse for every 9 input pulses on the CLK pin.

The 180-kHz signal must also be divided by 15 to obtain the final desired frequency of 12 kHz (out2). A mod-15 counter can be obtained with a 74163 macrofunction. By detecting a final state of 1110_2 (14), the counter will be synchronously cleared on the next clock pulse, producing a 0 through 14 count sequence for a mod-15.

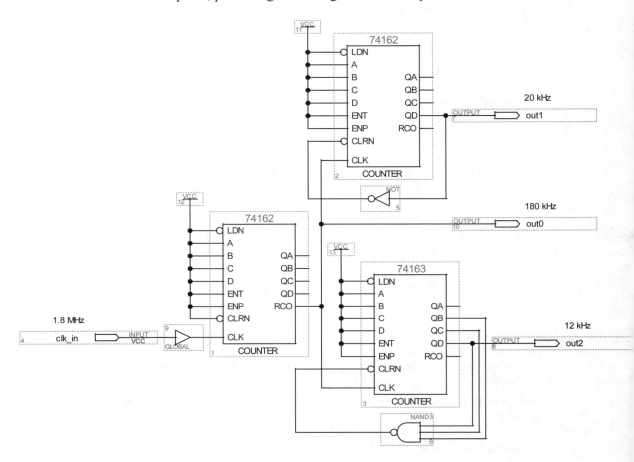

Fig. 12-4 Solution for Example 12-2

Example 12-3

Design a mod-100 down-counter circuit using the 74191 mod-16 binary counter macrofunction. The binary count sequence should be 100 down to 1 and recycle.

A solution is shown in Fig. 12-5. Two 74191 macrofunctions are cascaded together by parallel (synchronously) clocking both chips and connecting the RCO output of one chip to the GN enable of the other. This means that the 74191 on the left in the schematic will contain the 4 least significant bits for the counter. Only the first 3 bits of the 74191 on the right will be needed since decimal value 100 equals 1100100_2

(requiring only 7 bits total). The MSB for the mod-100 counter is **QG**. Both counter chips will count down if the **DNUP** control is high. When each counter chip reaches 0000, its **MXMN** (Max/Min) output will go high. We need to detect when both counter chips reach zero simultaneously, which can be accomplished with the NAND gate, whose output then controls <u>both</u> active-low load enable pins. The binary number 01100100 is loaded asynchronously (making the state 00000000_2 a transient state) so that the count sequence is then 100 down to 1.

The Max/Min is controlled by the count direction pin **DNUP**. This output on the 74191 (and its BCD counterpart, the 74190) will decode the final count state in the up-count (**DNUP** = 0) <u>or</u> down-count (**DNUP** = 1) sequence. If either the 74191 or the 74190 is configured to count down, the final state will be 0000. But if the counter is counting up, the final count state will be 1111_2 (15) for the 74191 and 1001_2 (9) for the 74190. Likewise, the **RCO** output (which is active-low) will detect the final count state as determined by the **DNUP** control. The **RCO**, however, is a bit more complex. It is also controlled by the active-low count enable **GN** and the clock input signal. The **RCO** output will "track" the clock signal at the final counter state when the counter is enabled. That is, **RCO** goes low at the final state only when **GN** = 0 and the clock input is zero.

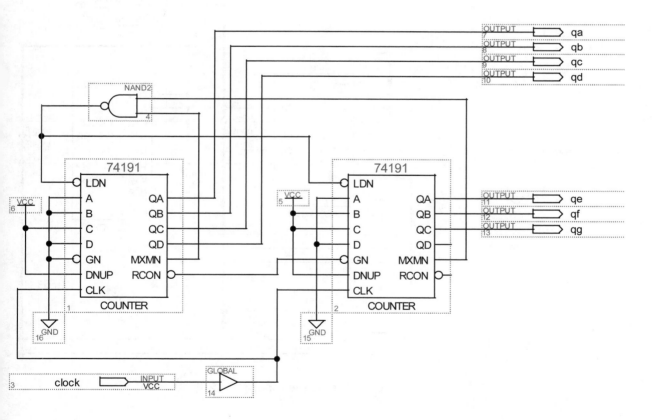

Fig. 12-5 Solution for Example 12-3

Example 12-4

Design a self-stopping BCD counter circuit using the 74160 decade counter macrofunction. The count sequence should be 0 to 36, and then the counter should stop. The counter can be asynchronously reset with an active-low signal named resetn. The counter also needs to have an active-low count enable named enn.

A solution is shown in Fig. 12-6. Two 74160 BCD counter macrofunctions are cascaded together by synchronously clocking both chips and connecting the RCO output of one 74160 to the ENT enable of the other. The 74160 on the left is the one's digit, and the one on the right is the ten's digit for the two-digit counter. Since the RCO output is a function of the chip's ENT input, both 74160s can be enabled/disabled by controlling the ENT pin on the least significant digit. The count enables are active-high, so an inverter is needed for the enn control signal. The asynchronous clear pin for each chip is connected to the resetn control signal. The active-low load function is disabled with a logic high input. The final count state 36 (in BCD) is detected (decoded) by the NAND gate output going low, which then is used to disable both 74160s through the ENP count enable control. The two output digits are each on buses.

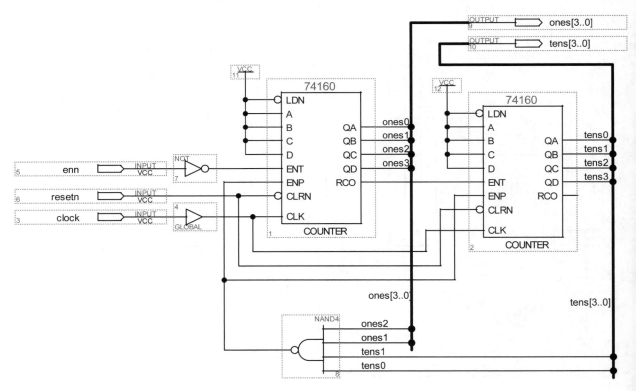

Fig. 12-6 Solution for Example 12-4

Example 12-5

Design a mod-4096 binary counter circuit using the 74163 mod-16 counter macrofunction. The counter can be synchronously loaded with an active-low signal named ldn. The counter also needs to have an active-high count enable named en. Decode the maximum count value (decimal 4095).

A solution is shown in Fig. 12-7. A 12-bit binary counter is needed to produce a mod-4096 count sequence, which will require three 74163 macrofunctions to be cascaded together. The least significant bit in the mod-4096 counter is labeled q0 and the most significant bit is q11. Synchronous clocking must be used since the counter is to be synchronously loaded. All three load control pins must be connected to ldn. The 12-bit input for the parallel data is labeled d[11..0]. The RCO output for each 74163 will go high when the count reaches 1111_2 if the chip's ENT count enable input is high. The counters are cascaded together by connecting the RCO output of the least significant counter (U1) to the ENT of the next counter (U2) and then, finally, the RCO from U2 to the ENT of the most significant counter (U3). Controlling the ENT on U1 will enable or disable the entire 12-bit counter. If ENT is low, the counter is disabled, and RCO will also be low. Therefore, the output signal labeled max will detect (decode) the maximum count value ($1111\ 1111\ 1111_2$) <u>only</u> when the counter is enabled. The data input and counter output signals are each grouped in buses. Note that the en input and max output are connected by labeling the respective signal lines.

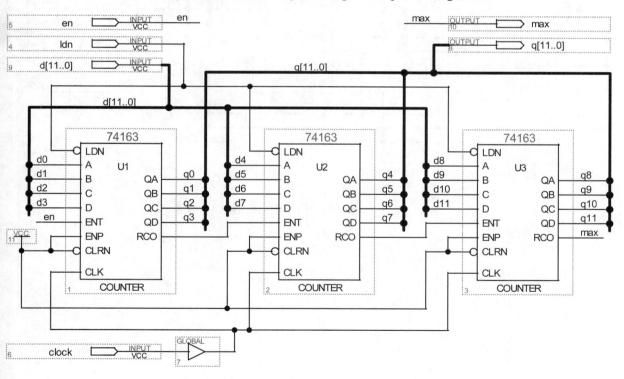

Fig. 12-7 Solution 1 for Example 12-5

Note that the problem statement did not specify that the decoder output should also be controlled by en, as it will be in Fig. 12-7. If that solution is undesirable, the design can be modified slightly (see Fig. 12-8). The ENT count enable on U1 is permanently enabled with the high input, and the RCO to ENT cascading is done as in the previous solution. This will now also permanently enable the decoder output max. The count enable function instead can be controlled with the ENP enable on all three chips. The two count enables ENT and ENP on the 74160 to 74163 series of counter macrofunctions are slightly different. ENT also enables the RCO output, which decodes the maximum count value on the counter chip, but ENP does not control the RCO output.

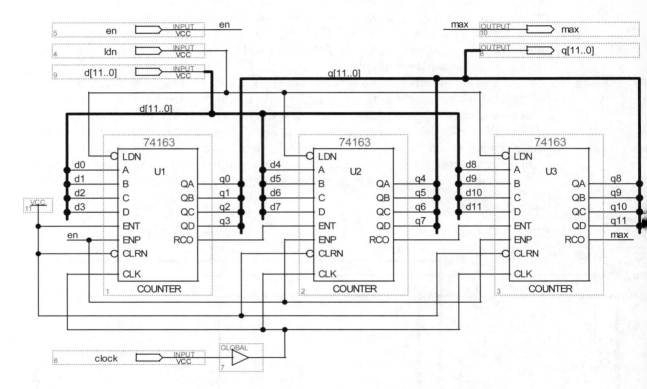

Fig. 12-8 Solution 2 for Example 12-5

Laboratory Projects Using a PLD

12.1   Counter circuit upgrade

The following counter circuit has been designed with standard logic devices (counters and JK flip-flop). Use schematic capture in MAX+PLUS II or Quartus II to implement this design in a PLD. Group each of the counter outputs and the parallel input data into separate buses. Simulate and test your chip.

Circuit operation procedure:

1. *Apply the desired BCD value to* cycles[3..0].
2. *Pulse* start *low momentarily.*
3. Clock *the binary counter (74191) through the mod-16 sequence, and the counter will then automatically reverse the count direction.*
4. *The binary counter will continue cycling through the count sequence (up and down), while BCD* count[3..0] *(74190) decrements each time the binary counter completes a mod-16 sequence until the BCD counter reaches zero and stops.*

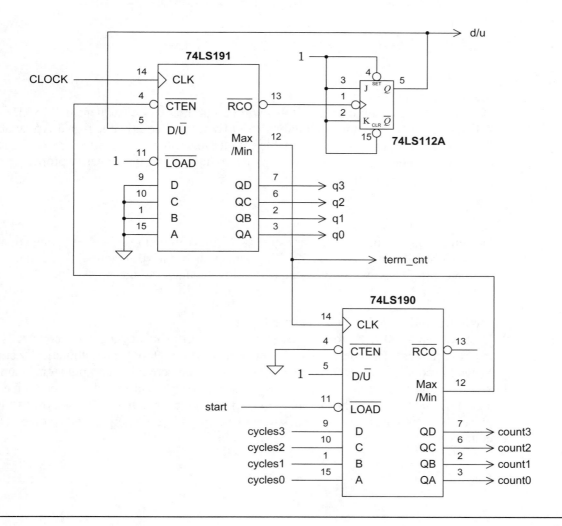

12.2   Mod-13 count sequence
        Design a mod-13 counter using a 74161 macrofunction that produces the count
        sequence specified in the following state transition diagram. The counter should have
        an active-low enable (en). Note: Transient states (which <u>may</u> be present) are not
        shown in the diagram. Simulate, construct, and test the counter circuit. What causes a
        "spike" in one of the output waveforms?

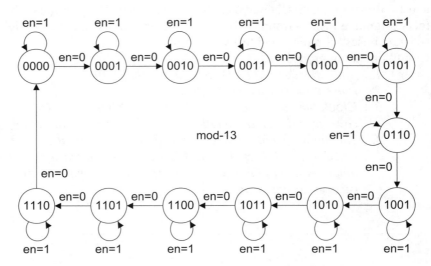

12.3   Frequency divider
        Design a frequency divider circuit that will output three pulse frequencies: 25 kHz, 10
        kHz, and 2.5 kHz. Assume that only a 150-kHz CMOS-compatible signal is available
        for the divider input. Use any available counter macrofunctions. Simulate, construct,
        and test the frequency divider circuit. Use a frequency counter to verify proper
        operation of your circuit design.

12.4   Mod-200 binary counter
        Design a mod-200 binary counter using 74163 macrofunctions. The recycling count
        sequence should be from 1 to 200. The counter should have an active-high count
        enable control. Simulate, construct, and test the counter circuit.

12.5   Mod-100, self-stopping BCD down-counter
        Design a mod-100, self-stopping BCD down-counter using any available counter
        macrofunctions. The counter should count down from 99 to 0 and automatically stop.
        When the counter has reached the end of its count, an active-high output signal named
        stop should be asserted. The count sequence will be asynchronously started with a
        signal named restart. The counter will start counting down from 99 when restart is
        pulsed high (reloading 99) and back low again. Simulate, construct, and test the
        counter circuit.

12.6   Mod-1000 BCD counter
Design a mod-1000 BCD counter using macrofunctions. The counter should have an active-low count enable named cntn. The counter should also have an active-high synchronous data load control named ld and an active-low synchronous clear control named clrn. Simulate, construct, and test the counter circuit.

12.7   On-board clock divider and switchable counter circuit
Design a frequency divider circuit that will produce a 10-kHz signal from the on-board crystal oscillator that is connected to pin 83 on the EPM7128SLC84. The 10-kHz signal will be used to clock a counter. The counter modulus can be switched with an input control named count to be either mod-10 (count = 0) or mod-16 (count = 1). Use macrofunctions and hierarchical design entry. Simulate, construct, and test the frequency divider and counter circuit. Use the simulator's cursors to measure the internal 10-kHz clock frequency. Use an oscilloscope and frequency counter to verify the counter output signals and the internal clock. The internal clock signal may not be exactly 10 kHz. Why not?

12.8   Programmable frequency divider
Design a programmable frequency divider circuit using a 74191 macrofunction. The input signal frequency can be divided by a 4-bit variable F ($2 \leq F \leq 15$) that will be input via logic switches. To avoid using a transient signal for the output signal, detect the counter state 0001_2 with appropriate gates to produce one output pulse each time the "programmable" counter cycles through its designated count sequence. Simulate, construct, and test the frequency divider circuit. Use a frequency counter to verify proper operation of your circuit design. Hint: Count down from F and asynchronously reload F when the counter reaches 0000_2.

12.9   Cascaded frequency divider
Design a frequency divider circuit that will produce a 500-Hz signal when it is enabled by an active-high signal named div. Use a 60-kHz clock signal for the frequency divider input. Synchronously cascade together a 74160 and a 74161 macrofunction for the frequency divider circuit. Do not use a transient spike for the output signal. Simulate, construct, and test the frequency divider circuit. Use a frequency counter to verify proper operation of your circuit design.

Laboratory Projects Using Standard IC Counter Chips

12.10   Mod-7 count sequence
Design a mod-7 counter using a 74160 that produces the following count sequence. Note: Transient states (which <u>may</u> be present) are not shown in the diagram. Construct and test your counter circuit.

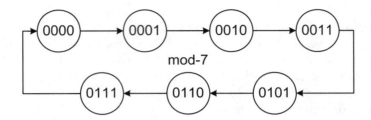

12.11   Mod-100 BCD counter and display
Design a mod-100 counter by cascading 74190 and 7S160 decade counter chips together. Display the count sequence on a 2-digit, 7-segment display, if available. Construct and test the counter circuit.

12.12   Waveform generator circuits
Design frequency divider circuits that will produce each of the 4 output signals labeled B through F shown in the following timing diagram. The TTL-compatible input signal A has a frequency of 100 kHz. Use only 74160 and 74163 counter chips and any necessary gates. Determine the frequency division factor and duty cycle of each output signal. How do the frequencies of B through F compare? Construct and test the frequency divider circuits. Use an oscilloscope to verify the input and output signals.

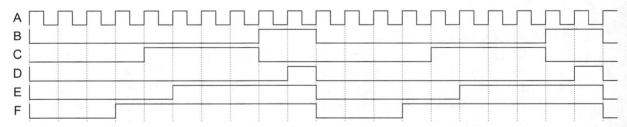

12.13   Frequency divider circuit
Design a logic circuit using 74160 and 74163 binary counter chips to produce output frequencies of 7.5 kHz and 4 kHz. The input signal is a TTL-compatible signal with a frequency of 60 kHz. Construct and test the complete circuit. Use a frequency counter to verify proper operation of your circuit design.

SYNCHRONOUS COUNTER DESIGN WITH FLIP-FLOPS

Objectives

- To design synchronous JK and D flip-flop counters with specified sequences using Karnaugh mapping.
- To verify synchronous counter designs using logic simulation and circuit testing.

Suggested Parts				
7408	7411	7432	7474	74112
EPM7128S or EP1C6				

<u>Synchronous Counter Design</u>

Synchronous sequential circuits may be designed by developing a transition table from the desired state sequence. A transition table is used to identify the synchronous inputs that must be applied to each flip-flop to produce the specified count sequence. The Boolean expression for each flip-flop input can be derived by Karnaugh mapping the transition table information. The set of logic equations describes the necessary input circuitry for each flip-flop. This procedure can be applied to any type of flip-flop and any desired count sequence (as long as the logic simplification is manageable with Karnaugh mapping).

Example 13-1

Use flip-flops to design a synchronous, mod-7 counter with the sequence of states given in the state transition diagram of Fig. 13-1. Create two design solutions, one using JK flip-flops and the other using D flip-flops.

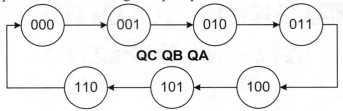

Fig. 13-1 Mod-7 counter state transition diagram for Example 13-1

First, complete a present state/next state table, as illustrated in Table 13-1, to describe the desired sequence from the given state diagram.

Present State			Next State		
QC_n	QB_n	QA_n	QC_{n+1}	QB_{n+1}	QA_{n+1}
0	0	0	0	0	1
0	0	1	0	1	0
0	1	0	0	1	1
0	1	1	1	0	0
1	0	0	1	0	1
1	0	1	1	1	0
1	1	0	0	0	0
1	1	1	X	X	X

Table 13-1 Present state/next state table for Example 13-1

Next, for the JK design, list the state transitions for each flip-flop so that the desired sequence is created, and determine the required flip-flop inputs that will produce this sequence. This information is recorded in an excitation table (see Table 13-2).

Present States			State Transitions			Flip-flop Inputs					
QC_n	QB_n	QA_n	$QC_n{\to}QC_{n+1}$	$QB_n{\to}QB_{n+1}$	$QA_n{\to}QA_{n+1}$	JC	KC	JB	KB	JA	KA
0	0	0	$0 \to 0$	$0 \to 0$	$0 \to 1$	0	X	0	X	1	X
0	0	1	$0 \to 0$	$0 \to 1$	$1 \to 0$	0	X	1	X	X	1
0	1	0	$0 \to 0$	$1 \to 1$	$0 \to 1$	0	X	X	0	1	X
0	1	1	$0 \to 1$	$1 \to 0$	$1 \to 0$	1	X	X	1	X	1
1	0	0	$1 \to 1$	$0 \to 0$	$0 \to 1$	X	0	0	X	1	X
1	0	1	$1 \to 1$	$0 \to 1$	$1 \to 0$	X	0	1	X	X	1
1	1	0	$1 \to 0$	$1 \to 0$	$0 \to 0$	X	1	X	1	0	X
1	1	1	$1 \to X$	$1 \to X$	$1 \to X$	X	X	X	X	X	X

Table 13-2 Excitation table for Example 13-1

Record the information for each flip-flop J and K input in separate K maps (see Fig. 13-2) and determine the appropriate, simplified Boolean expressions. Note that "don't care" output conditions (Xs in the K maps) may be defined as either 0s or 1s and may be used to simplify the expressions. The schematic for the synchronous circuit design (see Fig. 13-3) can now be drawn from the J and K flip-flop input equations determined by K mapping.

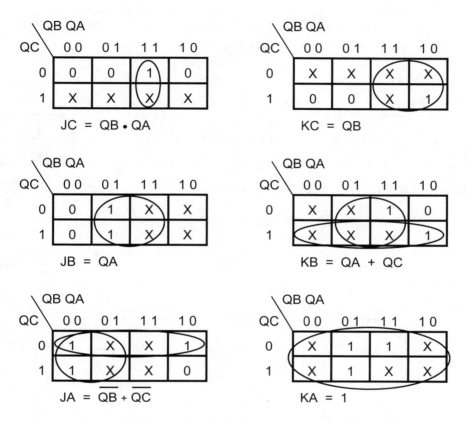

Fig. 13-2 Karnaugh mapping of J and K inputs for Example 13-1

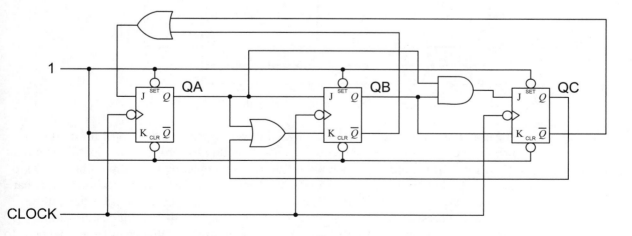

Fig. 13-3 Schematic for synchronous JK flip-flop design in Example 13-1

For the D flip-flop design, we only need to consult the present state/next state table shown in Table 13-1. The D inputs needed to produce the specified next state for each present state are the same as the next state bits. Thus a combinational circuit that produces the necessary corresponding next bit for each state must be designed for each flip-flop's D input. Record this information for each flip-flop in a separate K map (see Fig. 13-4) and determine the appropriate, simplified Boolean expression. The schematic for the synchronous circuit design (see Fig. 13-5) can now be drawn from the D flip-flop input equations determined by K mapping.

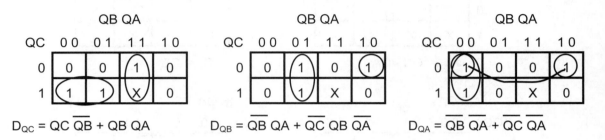

$D_{QC} = QC\ \overline{QB} + QB\ QA$

$D_{QB} = \overline{QB}\ QA + \overline{QC}\ QB\ \overline{QA}$

$D_{QA} = \overline{QB}\ \overline{QA} + \overline{QC}\ \overline{QA}$

Fig. 13-4 Karnaugh mapping of D inputs for Example 13-1

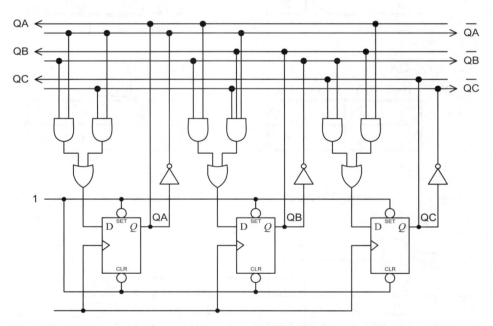

Fig. 13-5 Schematic for synchronous D flip-flop design in Example 13-1

The circuit design should then be analyzed to verify proper circuit operation. It may also be necessary for the counter to be self-correcting for proper operation in the circuit application. If so, the circuit should be analyzed completely (for all possible states) to determine whether the circuit design is self-correcting. The self-correction feature can also be "designed in" by initially specifying the desired circuit action for the unused states in the present state/next state table. Analyzing the two circuit designs for Example 13-1 verifies not only correct circuit operation but that each circuit happens to be self-correcting since the unused state 111 returns into the count sequence loop.

Laboratory Projects

Design each of the following synchronous counters using either a PLD or standard (JK or D) flip-flops and gate chips. Do not use the asynchronous flip-flop inputs (PRE or CLR) in the circuit designs. Construct and test each circuit design. Use an oscilloscope to display the timing diagram for each counter.

13.1 Mod-6 synchronous counter design

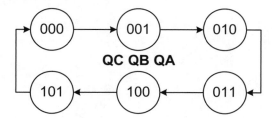

13.2 Mod-5 synchronous, down counter design

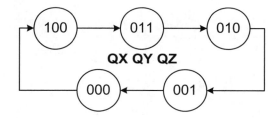

13.3 Synchronous 8421 BCD counter design

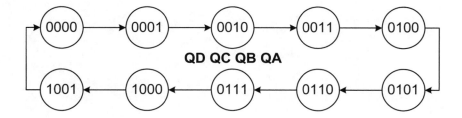

13.4   Synchronous 8421 BCD down-counter design
Design a synchronous 8421 BCD down-counter. The outputs are QD QC QB QA. QA
is the LSB.

13.5   Synchronous mod-11 counter
Design a recycling, synchronous mod-11 counter. The count sequence should be 0000
through 1010. The outputs are QD QC QB QA (QA = LSB).

SEQUENTIAL CIRCUIT DESIGN WITH ALTERA HARDWARE DESCRIPTION LANGUAGE

Objective

- To design sequential logic circuits implemented with programmable logic devices (PLDs) using Altera Hardware Description Language (AHDL).

Suggested Part
EPM7128S or EP1C6

Sequential Circuits Using AHDL

The design and implementation of sequential circuits using the Altera Hardware Description Language is carried out in much the same fashion as for combinational circuits. The flip-flops contained in the Altera PLDs can be treated as SR, JK, D, or T-type flip-flops in which the control inputs are produced by the programmable AND/OR gate structure in the PLD. Due to ease of use, D flip-flops are most commonly utilized in hardware description languages. AHDL is a high-level language that provides many options for defining sequential circuits, including IF/THEN and CASE statements and TABLEs.

Fig. 14-1 shows an AHDL design description that creates a single D flip-flop. The SUBDESIGN section declares the input and output ports for d_ff.tdf. A single D flip-flop (the primitive name is DFF in MAX+PLUS II or Quartus II) is declared in the VARIABLE section. This is called a register declaration in AHDL. The flip-flop, whose instance name is q_out, will be connected to the subdesign output port since this name was also declared to be an output port in the SUBDESIGN section. All primitives have input ports and output ports. The connections to the primitives necessary for your design will be described in the Logic section (between the BEGIN and END) of the AHDL file. DFF primitives have clock and d inputs and a q output. These ports are named .clk, .d, and .q, respectively. These port names are appended to the instance name (q_out) given in the register declaration. Since all primitives have only one output, you can also use just the instance name without the .q added onto the instance name. Flip-flop primitives have optional active-low preset (.prn) and clear (.clrn) input ports. If they are not needed in a design, they are simply omitted from the Logic section. In this case, the primitive's input ports .clk, .prn, .clrn, and .d are connected to the subdesign's input ports named clock, preset, clear, and data, respectively. This is simply a wiring list for the desired flip-flop. Results for the simulation of d_ff.tdf are given in Fig. 14-2.

```
SUBDESIGN d_ff
(
data, clock, preset, clear          :INPUT;
q_out                               :OUTPUT;
)

VARIABLE
q_out         :DFF;
       -- create single D flip-flop named q_out
BEGIN
q_out.clk = clock;        -- connect clock port
q_out.prn = preset;       -- active-low preset port
q_out.clrn = clear;       -- active-low clear port
q_out.d = data;           -- D input port
END;
```

Fig. 14-1 AHDL description creating a single D flip-flop

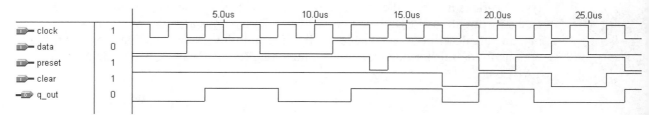

Fig. 14-2 Simulation results for the AHDL D flip-flop

Example 14-1

Design a mod-16, binary up/down counter using AHDL. The count direction is controlled by dir (dir = 1 for count up).

An AHDL text file solution named updncntr.tdf is shown in Fig. 14-3. Four flip-flops will be needed for a mod-16 counter. Accordingly, four D flip-flops (DFF) named count[3..0] are declared in the VARIABLE section. The D flip-flops form essentially a "buried" register inside the updncntr block. A register was created since it is very easy to produce the desired binary count sequence by either incrementing or decrementing the current state contained in the register by one. The Logic section (after the keyword BEGIN) describes the functionality of this block. The first statement *count[ ].clk = clock* identifies the name of the signal (clock) that is connected to the clock port (.clk) on the set of flip-flops (named count[ ]). The IF/THEN statement tests the input dir. If dir is true (or high), then the inputs (.d port) to the set of D flip-flops (count[ ]) will be one more than the current output (.q port) from the register. Otherwise (dir = 0), the new input should be one less than the current output from the register. The result of incrementing or decrementing the register's contents, of course, is a count-up or a count-down sequence, respectively. The register is buried, which means that it is not connected directly to the SUBDESIGN's output port. The statement, *q[ ] = count[ ]*, will connect the register's outputs (the .q port is understood) to the output port for updncntr. The results of simulating the AHDL design file are shown in Fig. 14-4.

```
SUBDESIGN  updncntr
(
      clock, dir         : INPUT;
      q[3..0]            : OUTPUT;
)
VARIABLE
      count[3..0]        : DFF;     -- create 4-bit register
BEGIN
      count[].clk = clock;    -- connect clock to register

      IF   dir   THEN          -- dir=1 to count up
           count[].d = count[].q + 1;
      ELSE                     -- dir=0 to count down
           count[].d = count[].q - 1;
      END IF;

      q[] = count[].q;        -- connects buried reg to port
END;
```

Fig. 14-3 AHDL file for the binary up/down counter design for Example 14-1

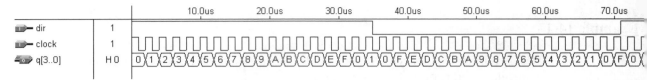

Fig. 14-4 Simulation of the AHDL file for Example 14-1

Pin numbers can be assigned as necessary for a top-level design file. See "Manually Assigning Pin Numbers" in MAXplus Notes or Quartus Notes in the CD-ROM Tutorials folder.

Example 14-2

Design a decade counter using AHDL. The mod-10 counter has a count enable, parallel load, and asynchronous clear controls as shown in Table 14-1. The counter should also produce a ripple carry output signal (rco) that goes high during the last state in the count sequence when the counter is enabled.

clear	load	enable	clock	function
1	X	X	X	CLEAR
0	0	0	↓	HOLD
0	1	X	↓	LOAD
0	0	1	↓	COUNT UP

Table 14-1 Example 14-2 functions

An AHDL text file solution named mod10.tdf is shown in Fig. 14-5. Four flip-flops will be needed for the decade counter. Accordingly, four D flip-flops (DFF) named counter[3..0] are declared in the VARIABLE section. In this example, the outputs from the D flip-flops are also connected to the output port for the block. The register is not "buried" in this example. In the Logic section, the output rco is declared to be normally low with the DEFAULTS statement. The clock port for the set of D flip-flops (named counter[ ]) is declared with the *counter[ ].clk = !clock* statement. The NOT symbol (!) preceding the signal name is due to the need for a negative-edge-triggered counter (see Table 14-1) when the internal flip-flops are always positive-edge-triggered. All flip-flops have an optional asynchronous clear capability. The statement *counter[ ].clrn = !clear* is used to declare that the clear port (which is always active-low) on the set of D flip-flops should be controlled by the NOT clear signal since Table 14-1 indicates an active-high clear control is desired for the decade counter.

The IF/THEN statement is actually a nested IF/THEN in this example. IF statements automatically establish a priority of action by the order in which they are written. The first tested condition that evaluates to being true (high) will determine the outcome of the IF/THEN statement. The outer IF statement first tests to determine if load is active. If so, then the statement *counter[ ].d = d[ ]* will be applied. This statement will parallel load the 4-bit input d[3..0] into the register when clocked. If load is not true, then the next priority is to test enable. If enable is true, then a secondary test will be made with the nested IF. The register **counter[ ]** is tested to see if the contents equals 9. If so, then the value to be input at the next clock should be 0000_2. This will recycle the counter back to zero after reaching the terminal count of 9 for our decade counter. Also, the **rco** output should go high at this state. If the count has not yet reached 9, then the counter should be incremented on the next clock (*counter[ ].d = counter[ ].q + 1*). Finally, if both **load** and **enable** tests should fail, then the counter should perform the remaining function of holding the current count. For a D flip-flop to hold the same data when it is clocked, the output must be fed back into the input, which can be accomplished with the statement, *counter[ ].d = counter[ ].q*.

Simulation of the design is shown in Fig. 14-6. Assign a target device and appropriate pin numbers for the AHDL file. Then recompile and program the PLD.

```
SUBDESIGN  mod10
(
     clock, load, enable, clear, d[3..0]      :INPUT;
     counter[3..0], rco                        :OUTPUT;
)
VARIABLE
     counter[3..0]                             :DFF;
BEGIN
     DEFAULTS
          rco = GND;           -- rco is normally low output
     END DEFAULTS;

     counter[].clk  = !clock;       -- clock on NGT
     counter[].clrn = !clear;       -- active-high clear

     IF  load  THEN     -- synchronous load highest priority
          counter[].d = d[];        -- parallel data inputs
     ELSIF  enable  THEN            -- test for count enable
          IF counter[].q == 9   THEN      -- at max count?
               counter[].d = B"0000";  -- then recycle &
               rco = VCC;              -- assert rco
          ELSE                     -- count up
               counter[].d = counter[].q + 1;
          END IF;
     ELSE                              -- hold count if disabled
          counter[].d = counter[].q;
     END IF;
END;
```

Fig. 14-5 AHDL design file for the decade counter of Example 14-2

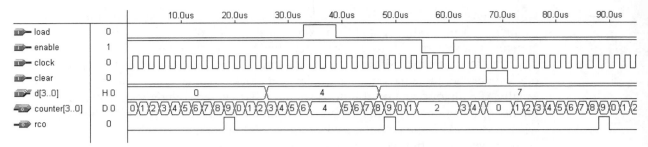

Fig. 14-6 Simulation results for Example 14-2

Example 14-3

Design a counter using AHDL that produces the 4-bit, irregular, recycling count sequence given in the timing diagram of Fig. 14-7. Also include an asynchronous reset to zero control for this counter and a count enable.

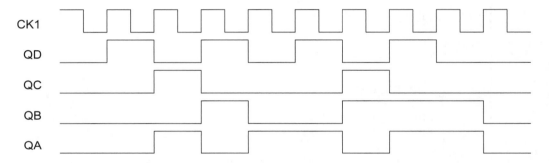

Fig. 14-7 Timing diagram for the sequential design of Example 14-3

An AHDL solution is shown in Fig. 14-8. The VARIABLE section has a state machine named seq defined with the keyword MACHINE. A state machine is basically a sequential circuit. In the definition of a state machine, the phrase "OF BITS" is optional. This phrase is used if it is necessary to name the individual output bits of the sequential circuit. In this example, the outputs are named qd, qc, qb, qa to match the names given in the timing diagram above. The phrase "WITH STATES" must be given for a state machine. This phrase identifies how many states are present in the sequential circuit and the names used to represent those states. In this example, the states have been named arbitrarily s0, s1, s2, …, s8. Since there are nine states in this list and we have defined a 4-bit state machine, which could have 16 combinations, there are evidently some bit combinations that we are not concerned with. Another option in defining state machines is the specific bit pattern associated with each state. Some applications may not care what the states look like, just that the states occur in a specified order. In this example, the timing diagram gave us the specific pattern for each state in the sequence so that information is given for each state named by the WITH STATES phrase. Note the punctuation used in defining the state machine.

```
SUBDESIGN  irreg_cnt
(
     ck1, reset, count              :INPUT;
     qa, qb, qc, qd                 :OUTPUT;
)
VARIABLE
     seq            :MACHINE OF BITS (qd, qc, qb, qa)
                    WITH STATES (
                          s0 = B"0000",
                          s1 = B"1000",
                          s2 = B"0101",
                          s3 = B"1010",
                          s4 = B"0001",
                          s5 = B"1001",
                          s6 = B"0110",
                          s7 = B"1011",
                          s8 = B"0011");
%
state machine seq has 4 output bits that are connected
to output ports, bit patterns are defined for each state

counter modulus is defined by sequence of state names
defined in logic section below
%

BEGIN
     seq.clk = ck1;           -- PGT on ck1 to clock seq
     seq.reset = reset;       -- asynchronous reset port
     seq.ena = count;         -- active-high enable port

     TABLE
     % present-state              next-state %
          seq            =>           seq;
          s0             =>           s1;
          s1             =>           s2;
          s2             =>           s3;
          s3             =>           s4;
          s4             =>           s5;
          s5             =>           s6;
          s6             =>           s7;
          s7             =>           s8;
          s8             =>           s0;
     END TABLE;
END;
```

Fig. 14-8 AHDL file for the irregular counter in Example 14-3

In the Logic section, we again see the clock port for the state machine assigned. A state machine has an optional, active-high, asynchronous reset port available. The reset port name for a state machine is .**reset**. This example specified an asynchronous reset control that is accomplished with the statement *seq.reset = reset*. A state machine also has an optional active-high enable port available. The design specification for a count enable is achieved with the statement *seq.ena = count*.

A TABLE is used to define the sequence for this state machine. It gives the "present state/next state" pattern for the state machine as defined in the timing diagram of Fig. 14-7. For any present state listed on the left side of the table, the next state to be produced after being clocked is given on the right side. The state machine recycles with the line *s8 => s0*. It is important to note that AHDL is a "concurrent language" and, as such, the line-by-line order in the TABLE does not matter; only the next state in each individual line matters.

Simulation results are shown in Fig. 14-9. The desired recycling, irregular count sequence is produced by this state machine. The simulation also verifies the asynchronous reset and count enable.

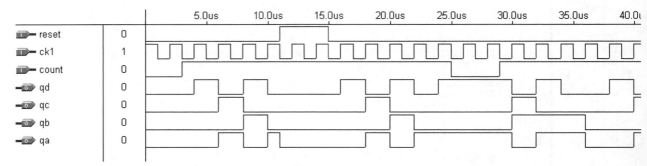

Fig. 14-9 Simulation results for Example 14-3

An alternate AHDL solution for Example 14-3 is shown in Fig. 14-10. A CASE statement is used in the Logic section to produce the desired irregular sequence for this design. Each state is identified with a WHEN clause. The present state will then determine the appropriate behavioral assignment for the state machine to produce the required next state.

```
SUBDESIGN   irreg_cnt2
(
     ck1, reset, count              :INPUT;
     qa, qb, qc, qd                 :OUTPUT;
)
VARIABLE
     seq             :MACHINE OF BITS (qd, qc, qb, qa)
                     WITH STATES (
                           s0 = B"0000",
                           s1 = B"1000",
                           s2 = B"0101",
                           s3 = B"1010",
                           s4 = B"0001",
                           s5 = B"1001",
                           s6 = B"0110",
                           s7 = B"1011",
                           s8 = B"0011");
%
state machine seq has 4 output bits that are connected
to output ports, bit patterns are defined for each state

counter modulus is defined by sequence of state names
defined in logic section below
%

BEGIN
     seq.clk = ck1;          -- PGT on ck1 to clock seq
     seq.reset = reset;      -- asynchronous reset port
     seq.ena = count;        -- active-high enable port

     -- desired sequence defined by CASE statement
     CASE   seq   IS
          WHEN   s0   =>   seq = s1;
          WHEN   s1   =>   seq = s2;
          WHEN   s2   =>   seq = s3;
          WHEN   s3   =>   seq = s4;
          WHEN   s4   =>   seq = s5;
          WHEN   s5   =>   seq = s6;
          WHEN   s6   =>   seq = s7;
          WHEN   s7   =>   seq = s8;
          WHEN   s8   =>   seq = s0;
     END CASE;
END;
```

Fig. 14-10 Alternate AHDL file for the irregular counter in Example 14-3

Example 14-4

Design a bidirectional, full-step controller for a stepper motor using AHDL. The controller will produce a clockwise sequence pattern when cw = 1 and a counterclockwise sequence pattern when cw = 0. The stepper motor sequence is shown in Fig. 14-11.

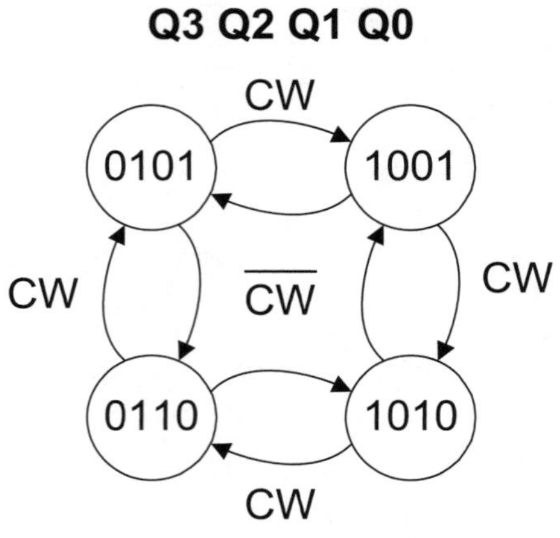

Q3 Q2 Q1 Q0

Fig. 14-11 State transition diagram for the stepper controller of Example 14-4

An example solution using AHDL is shown in Fig. 14-12. The SUBDESIGN name is given in single quotes because it includes the nonalphanumeric hyphen character. The application's bit combinations are specified in the state machine that is defined in the VARIABLE section. The state 0000_2 (initial) is included since the chip will automatically reset all flip-flops at power-up, and it will be necessary to define how to get out of that state and into the specified sequence to drive the stepper motor. The state machine's sequence is defined in the Logic section using a TABLE. The table includes the input control variable cw along with the present state for the machine called **stepper** on the input side of the table. The present state and the logic level for cw will determine the correct next state that should be produced by the state machine, except for the **initial** state produced at power-up. At power-up, we do not care what the next state is, just that the machine gets into the specified count sequence. The next state 1010_2 was chosen arbitrarily from the list of valid states for the stepper motor controller.

Simulation results for this design are shown in Fig. 14-13. The count sequence for each direction is correct for the recycling state machine.

```
SUBDESIGN 'full-step'  -- single-quotes due to hyphen
(
    step, cw    :INPUT;
    q[3..0]     :OUTPUT;
)
VARIABLE
    stepper      :MACHINE OF BITS (q[3..0])
                  WITH STATES (
                        initial = B"0000",
                        s1 = B"1010",
                        s2 = B"0110",
                        s3 = B"0101",
                        s4 = B"1001");
    -- power-on state (0000) defined to start up stepper
BEGIN
    stepper.clk = step;            -- clock input

    -- present-state next-state table defines sequence
    TABLE
        stepper,  cw   =>     stepper;
        initial,  X    =>     s1;
        s1,       1    =>     s2;
        s1,       0    =>     s4;
        s2,       1    =>     s3;
        s2,       0    =>     s1;
        s3,       1    =>     s4;
        s3,       0    =>     s2;
        s4,       1    =>     s1;
        s4,       0    =>     s3;
    END TABLE;
END;
```

Fig. 14-12 AHDL file for the stepper motor controller

An alternative AHDL design for Example 14-4 is shown in Fig. 14-14. A CASE statement is used to test for each defined state of the state machine with the WHEN clauses. The power-up state (initial) will always be followed by s1 after a ↑-edge on the clock input (step). Each of the other next state assignments is dependent on the direction control (cw). The state assignment will produce the clockwise count sequence if cw = 1, and the state assignment after ELSE will produce the counterclockwise sequence if cw = 0.

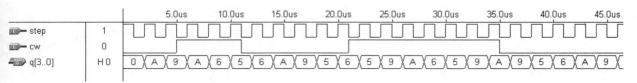

Fig. 14-13 Simulation results for Example 14-4

```
SUBDESIGN  'full-step2'     -- single-quotes due to hyphen
(
      step, cw    :INPUT;
      q[3..0]     :OUTPUT;
)
VARIABLE
      stepper      :MACHINE OF BITS (q[3..0])
                    WITH STATES (
                          initial = B"0000",
                          s1 = B"1010",
                          s2 = B"0110",
                          s3 = B"0101",
                          s4 = B"1001");
      -- power-on state (0000) defined to start up stepper
BEGIN
      stepper.clk = step;              -- clock input

      -- stepper sequence controlled with CASE & IF
      CASE   stepper  IS    -- CASE determines present-state
            WHEN  initial  =>   stepper = s1;
            WHEN  s1   =>
                  IF  cw   THEN  stepper = s2;    -- go CW
                  ELSE  stepper = s4;            -- go CCW
                  END IF;
            WHEN  s2   =>
                  IF  cw   THEN  stepper = s3;
                  ELSE  stepper = s1;
                  END IF;
            WHEN  s3   =>
                  IF  cw   THEN  stepper = s4;
                  ELSE  stepper = s2;
                  END IF;
            WHEN  s4   =>
                  IF  cw   THEN  stepper = s1;
                  ELSE  stepper = s3;
                  END IF;
      END CASE;
END;
```

Fig. 14-14 Alternate AHDL file for the stepper motor controller

Example 14-5

Design a sequential circuit that will wait in an idle state for a trigger input (start) to occur and then output a single pulse four clock cycles later. The sequential circuit will then wait for another trigger signal. The state transition diagram for this delay circuit is shown in Fig. 14-15. The state machine should also be self-correcting.

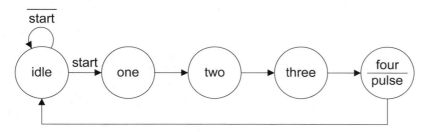

Fig. 14-15 State transition diagram for Example 14-5

An AHDL solution is shown in Fig. 14-16. A 3-bit state machine named mach is defined in the VARIABLE section. With 3 bits, there are 8 possible combinations, of which only 5 will be used. The remaining 3 states are given "dummy" names. The bit patterns have not been defined for this state machine since we do not really care what they look like. The compiler will assign bit patterns for each state. We can identify the compiler-assigned bit patterns by looking in the report file after compilation. This state machine will not be connected to output ports on the SUBDESIGN. The state machine will be "buried." A CASE statement is used to define the sequence of states for our state machine. When the state machine is in the idle state, it will be waiting for the start signal to go high (and the ↑ clock) in order to proceed to the next state (one). After starting the sequence, the state machine will step through each state on each ↑ clock. The WHEN OTHERS clause will take care of any state (including the 3 "extra" states) that is not otherwise defined within the CASE statement. With the 3 unused states taken care of, the state machine will be self-correcting. Upon reaching state four, the pulse expression will be true until the next ↑ clock, when the state machine returns to idle. Notice that the only output needed is the signal named pulse.

The results of the simulation for Example 14-5 are shown in Fig. 14-17. The buried state machine (notice its "buried handle") has been included in the simulation to verify its correct operation. Only the state names are given by the simulator since the bit values were not user-defined. The second start signal did not initiate the machine sequence since it occurred after the ↑ clock.

```
SUBDESIGN  delay
(
      clock       : INPUT;
      start       : INPUT;
      pulse       : OUTPUT;
)
VARIABLE
      mach          : MACHINE         -- "buried" machine
                      WITH STATES (
                                    idle,
                                    one,
                                    two,
                                    three,
                                    four,
                                    extra1,     -- dummy state
                                    extra2,     -- dummy state
                                    extra3);    -- dummy state
BEGIN
      mach.clk = clock;

      CASE   mach   IS
            WHEN idle =>          -- mach waits here
                  IF start THEN  mach = one;     -- go
                  ELSE           mach = idle;   -- wait
                  END IF;
            WHEN one =>           -- advances when clocked
                  mach = two;
            WHEN two =>           -- advances when clocked
                  mach = three;
            WHEN three =>         -- advances when clocked
                  mach = four;
            WHEN OTHERS =>        -- all other states to idle
                  mach = idle;
      END CASE;

      pulse = mach == four;   -- detect when at state four
END;
```

Fig. 14-16 AHDL file for Example 14-5

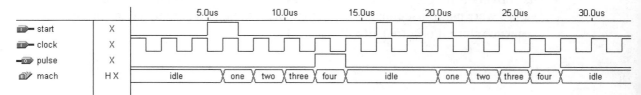

Fig. 14-17 Simulation results for Example 14-5

Example 14-6

Design the state machine (using AHDL) that is defined by the state transition diagram given in Fig. 14-18. The state machine has three inputs (trig and delay[1..0]) that control the sequence of states. The logic circuit will produce the three output signals named outs[3..1] according to the current state for the machine. The states are named, but the bit patterns for each state are not defined in this design.

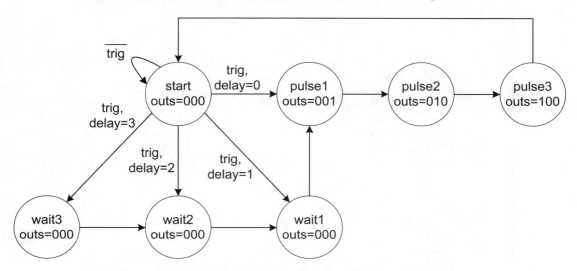

Fig. 14-18 State transition diagram for Example 14-6

An example AHDL solution named state_machine is shown in Fig. 14-19. The state machine (sm) is buried since its outputs are not connected to the output ports for the SUBDESIGN. Eight states are defined for the state machine sm by name only (start, wait1, wait2, wait3, pulse1, pulse2, pulse3, dummy). The optional bit patterns for the MACHINE definition were left for the compiler to determine since we do not care what they actually look like. A minimum of three flip-flops (bits) will be required to produce the eight states for sm. Assigning bit names is also optional in AHDL. By checking the report file, we can see that the compiler created the bit names sm~1, sm~2, and sm~3 for this state machine. A TABLE is used in the Logic section to describe the operation of the state machine and the outputs named outs[3..1]. The input side of the table lists the current states and input conditions that will determine the next state for the state machine. If an input signal has no effect on a particular state, it has an X, which indicates that we "don't care" about that variable. The output side of the table lists the resulting next states for each present state/input combination. The right side of the table also gives the outputs to be produced for each present state. Be careful! These are combinational outputs (outs[3..1]) that match up with the appropriate present state, not the next state!

Simulation results for Example 14-6 are shown in Figs. 14-20a and 14-20b. The buried state machine sm has been included in the simulation to make it easier to verify the circuit's operation.

```
SUBDESIGN  state_machine
(
      clock, trig, delay[1..0]        :INPUT;
      outs[3..1]                      :OUTPUT;
)
VARIABLE
      sm    :MACHINE           -- buried state machine sm
            WITH STATES (start, wait1, wait2, wait3,
                        pulse1, pulse2, pulse3, dummy);
BEGIN
      sm.clk = clock;

%  present-state (with control inputs) next-state table
   to produce current outputs for each state  %
      TABLE
      sm,        trig,    delay[]    =>    sm,        outs[];
      start,     0,       X          =>    start,     B"000";
      start,     1,       0          =>    pulse1,    B"000";
      start,     1,       1          =>    wait1,     B"000";
      start,     1,       2          =>    wait2,     B"000";
      start,     1,       3          =>    wait3,     B"000";
      pulse1,    X,       X          =>    pulse2,    B"001";
      pulse2,    X,       X          =>    pulse3,    B"010";
      pulse3,    X,       X          =>    start,     B"100";
      wait1,     X,       X          =>    pulse1,    B"000";
      wait2,     X,       X          =>    wait1,     B"000";
      wait3,     X,       X          =>    wait2,     B"000";
      dummy,     X,       X          =>    start,     B"000";
      END TABLE;
END;
```

Fig. 14-19 AHDL file for Example 14-6

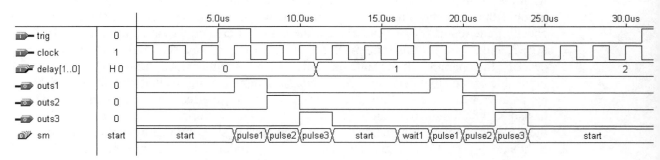

Fig. 14-20a Simulation of Example 14-6

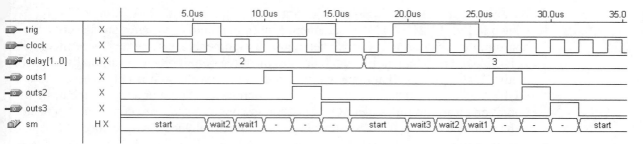

Fig. 14-20b Simulation of Example 14-6

```
SUBDESIGN   state_machine2
(
     clock, trig, delay[1..0]      :INPUT;
     outs[3..1]                    :OUTPUT;
)
VARIABLE
     sm    :MACHINE           -- buried state machine sm
           WITH STATES (start, wait1, wait2, wait3,
                      pulse1, pulse2, pulse3, dummy);
BEGIN
     DEFAULTS
           outs[] = B"000";        -- outs default to 0
     END DEFAULTS;

     sm.clk = clock;

     CASE   sm   IS                -- identify sm states
       WHEN   start  =>
           IF trig       THEN      -- trig exits start
              CASE delay[] IS      -- determines next state
                   WHEN 0   =>   sm = pulse1;
                   WHEN 1   =>   sm = wait1;
                   WHEN 2   =>   sm = wait2;
                   WHEN 3   =>   sm = wait3;
              END CASE;
           ELSE                    sm = start;
           END IF;
       WHEN wait1 =>     sm = pulse1;
       WHEN wait2 =>     sm = wait1;
       WHEN wait3 =>     sm = wait2;
       WHEN pulse1 =>    sm = pulse2;    outs[] = B"001";
       WHEN pulse2 =>    sm = pulse3;    outs[] = B"010";
       WHEN pulse3 =>    sm = start;     outs[] = B"100";
       WHEN OTHERS =>    sm = start;  -- returns to start
     END CASE;
END;
```

Fig. 14-21 Alternate AHDL file for Example 14-6

169

An alternative AHDL technique for defining the state machine for Example 14-6 is shown in Fig. 14-21. A CASE statement is used to identify the states and describe the appropriate behavior(s). Multiple behavioral assignments are separated by semicolons. A DEFAULTS statement is used to declare the three output bits to be normally low. Active-high signals will automatically default to low levels, so it is not necessary to use a DEFAULTS statement like we did in this example solution, but it makes the design's operation clearer to the reader. Only the output conditions that are different then need to be assigned. Next state assignments are also given for each CASE clause. Most state transitions are unconditional in this design, requiring only a ↑ clock. To get out of the state named start, however, will also require that the input signal trig be active (high). The next state after start is also dependent upon the input control named delay[1..0], which is determined by the CASE statement testing for the appropriate input value and assigning the correct state machine behavior.

Example 14-7

Design a mod-1000, recycling BCD counter using the mod10.tdf design in Example 14-2. The counter will have the functions given in Table 14-2. The AHDL file for the mod10 counter is repeated in Fig. 14-22.

clear	load	enable	clock	function
1	X	X	X	CLEAR
0	0	0	↓	HOLD
0	1	X	↓	LOAD
0	0	1	↓	COUNT UP

Table 14-2 Example 14-7 functions

A top-level schematic/block diagram file (Fig. 14-23) can be created using the default symbol for the mod10.tdf design. Three copies of the mod10 symbol will be needed, one for the ones digit, one for the tens digit, and one for the hundreds digit. The three mod10 stages are cascaded together by connecting the rco output (which detects the terminal state 9 when the counter is enabled) to the next digit's enable control. The enable input on the ones digit will control all of the mod10 counters. The enable input on the tens digit will be high only if the ones digit is a 9 and the mod-1000 counter is enabled. Likewise, the hundreds digit will be enabled only if the tens digit and the ones digit are both 9 (and the counter is enabled). The load and clear controls are connected to all three counter stages.

Sample simulation results for the mod-1000 counter are shown in Fig. 14-24.

```
SUBDESIGN   mod10
(     clock, load, enable, clear, d[3..0]          :INPUT;
      counter[3..0], rco                           :OUTPUT;        )
VARIABLE
      counter[3..0]                                :DFF;
BEGIN
      DEFAULTS
            rco = GND;          -- rco is normally low output
      END DEFAULTS;
      counter[].clk  = !clock;        -- clock on NGT
      counter[].clrn = !clear;        -- active-high clear
      IF   load   THEN      -- synchronous load highest priority
            counter[].d = d[];        -- parallel data inputs
      ELSIF   enable   THEN           -- test for count enable
            IF counter[].q == 9   THEN      -- at max count?
                  counter[].d = B"0000";  -- then recycle &
                  rco = VCC;              -- assert rco
            ELSE                          -- count up
                  counter[].d = counter[].q + 1;
            END IF;
      ELSE                              -- hold count if disabled
            counter[].d = counter[].q;
      END IF;
END;
```

Fig. 14-22 AHDL design file for the decade counter from Example 14-2

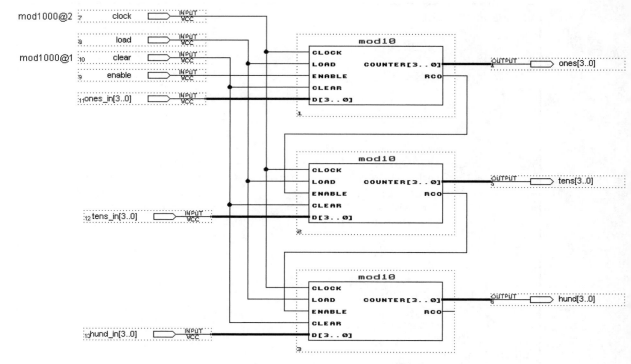

Fig. 14-23 Top-level design file for Example 14-7

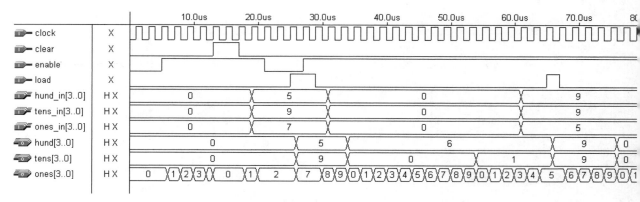

Fig. 14-24 Sample simulation results for Example 14-7

Example 14-8

A digital design is given in Fig. 14-25. Examine this case-study design to determine its operation. It is a hierarchical design consisting of several sequential and combinational logic blocks. The circuit will count a preselected number of sets of units and then output a stop signal. Each unit to be counted will clock a counter (named unit_counter) that can be switched between two different mod numbers (24 or 36) controlled by the logic input size. Each set then will be either 24 or 36 units. The number of sets desired (you can choose from 1 through 9 sets) will be applied to count[3..0] and the active-low startn signal will be pulsed.

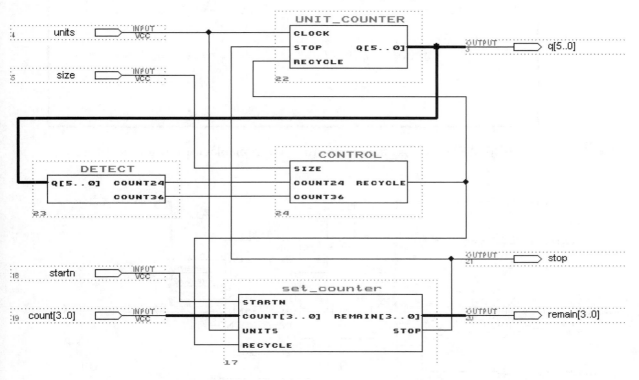

Fig. 14-25 Top-level design file (vary_count.gdf) for Example 14-8

The unit_counter block (see Fig. 14-26) is a sequential circuit that is defined using AHDL. It is simply a 6-bit binary counter that can be synchronously recycled to 000001_2 and asynchronously cleared. Stop will go high when the down counter contained in the set_counter block reaches zero, which will hold the unit_counter at zero with the asynchronous clear. The recycle signal is produced by the control block.

The set_counter block shown in Fig. 14-27 contains a 74190 macrofunction used as a down counter to keep track of the number of sets of units that still remain to be counted. The down counter is triggered on the falling edge of the clocking signal named units when unit_counter is recycled at the end of either a 24- or 36-unit set. The asynchronous startn signal will load in the desired number of sets. When startn is asserted, the output signal stop will go low and the counter will be enabled. When the count on the 74190 reaches zero, stop will go high and the counter will be disabled.

```
SUBDESIGN  unit_counter
(
      clock, stop, recycle     :INPUT;
      q[5..0]                   :OUTPUT;
)

VARIABLE
      q[5..0]                   :DFF;        -- 6-bit register

BEGIN
      q[].clk = clock;
      q[].clrn = !stop;         -- active-high asynch. clear

      IF   recycle  THEN
           q[].d = B"000001";         -- recycles back to 1
      ELSE
           q[].d = q[].q + 1;         -- increment count
      END IF;
END;
```

Fig. 14-26 AHDL design file for the unit_counter block in Example 14-8

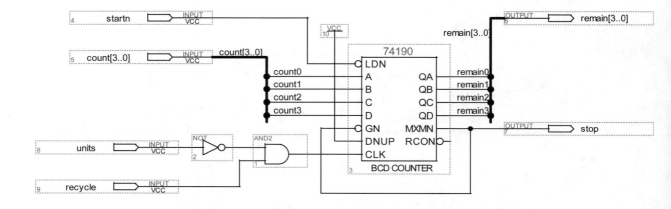

Fig. 14-27 Design file for set_counter block in Example 14-8

The **detect** block (see Fig. 14-28) is an AHDL-defined combinational circuit. This circuit monitors the output of **unit_counter** to determine when the count reaches the values 24 and 36. The output signals **count24** and **count36** are fed to the **control** block.

The **control** block (see Fig. 14-29) is also a combinational circuit defined with AHDL. This circuit determines when the **unit_counter** should be recycled. The number of units in a set (either 24 or 36 units) is selected with **size**. A buried node named **done** defines the logic necessary to tell the **unit_counter** to recycle.

```
CONSTANT   state24 = 24;
CONSTANT   state36 = 36;

SUBDESIGN   detect
(
     q[5..0]                    :INPUT;
     count24, count36           :OUTPUT;
)

BEGIN
             -- detects when counter input = 24
     IF   q[] == state24 THEN   count24 = VCC;
     ELSE   count24 = GND;
     END IF;
             -- detects when counter input = 36
     IF   q[] == state36 THEN   count36 = VCC;
     ELSE   count36 = GND;
     END IF;
END;
```

Fig. 14-28 AHDL design file for the detect block in Example 14-8

```
SUBDESIGN   control
(
     size                       :INPUT;
     count24, count36           :INPUT;
     recycle                    :OUTPUT;
)

VARIABLE
     done                       :NODE;        -- buried node

BEGIN
             -- size selects which count value is used
     done  =  !size & count24  #  size & count36;

             -- when done is active, then time to recycle
     IF  done  THEN  recycle = VCC;
     ELSE  recycle = GND;
     END IF;
END;
```

Fig. 14-29 AHDL design file for the control block in Example 14-8

A sample of the simulation results for Example 14-8 is shown in Fig. 14-30. The top half shows screen dumps with size low and count = 4. This input combination will produce 4 sets of 24 units. The bottom half of the figure illustrates the simulation results when size is high and count = 3. The circuit produced count sequences for 3 sets of 36 units before stop goes high and the counters are disabled.

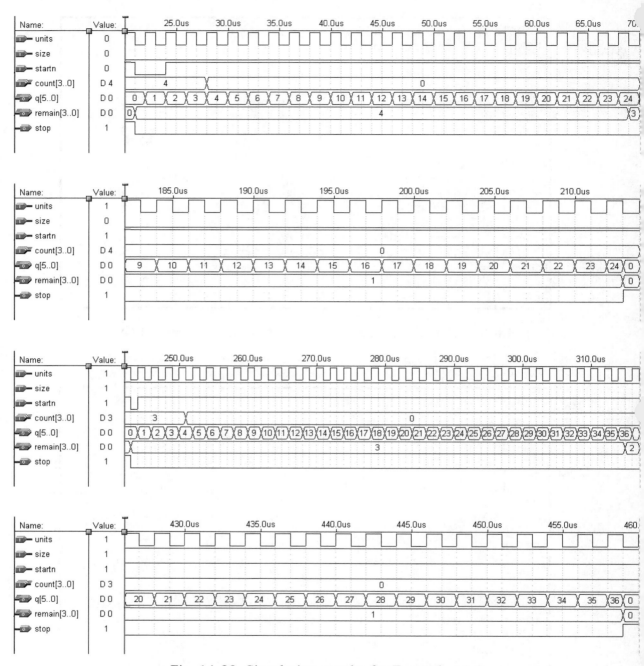

Fig. 14-30 Simulation results for Example 14-8

Laboratory Projects

14A.1   Gray code counter

Design a 4-bit, up/down, recycling Gray code counter using AHDL. The count
direction is controlled by a signal called dir, as indicated in the following function table.
Label the counter outputs q[3..0]. The circuit also should produce an output signal
called index, which goes low whenever the counter state is 0000.

dir	operation
0	Count Up
1	Count Down

Gray code sequence

	q3	q2	q1	q0	
count up sequence	0	0	0	0	
	0	0	0	1	
	0	0	1	1	
	0	0	1	0	
	0	1	1	0	
	0	1	1	1	
	0	1	0	1	
	0	1	0	0	
	1	1	0	0	
	1	1	0	1	
	1	1	1	1	
	1	1	1	0	
	1	0	1	0	
	1	0	1	1	count down sequence
	1	0	0	1	
	1	0	0	0	

14A.2   Up/down BCD counter

Design a mod-10, recycling, BCD up/down counter using AHDL. The counter's
function table is given below. Inputs c[1..0] control the counter's function. The
counter should also produce an active-low ripple carry output signal called carryn. The
carry output signal should only be asserted at 9 when counting up or at 0 when counting
down.

c1	c0	operation
0	0	Reset
0	1	Count Down
1	0	Count Up
1	1	Hold Count

14A.3   Mod-60 BCD counter

Design a mod-60, recycling BCD counter using AHDL. The counter should have an active-low, synchronous reset (resn) signal. The count sequence will be 0 through 59_{10} in BCD. Create a hierarchical design with separate TDF files for the tens digit and the ones digit. Use a GDF file for the top-level file (interconnects the two TDF files).

14A.4   Mod-100 binary counter

Design a mod-100, recycling binary counter using AHDL. The counter is triggered with $\downarrow$ clocks and should have an active-high count enable called enable. The counter will also output a single active-high pulse (called pulse) during each mod-100 count sequence. The pulse occurs at the end of the count sequence. The pulse width will be controlled by an input signal called w, as shown in the table below. Essentially, w changes the duty cycle of the divide-by-100 output signal.

W	PULSE width
0	5 clock periods
1	10 clock periods

14A.5   Stepper motor sequence controller

Design a half-step sequencer to control a stepper motor using AHDL. The sequencer should produce the appropriate sequence of states to drive the motor either clockwise (CW) or counterclockwise (CCW) without using a binary counter (i.e., produce the half-step count sequence directly). The stepper direction is controlled by an input signal named cw. The stepper enable is called go. The function table is given below. Make sure the sequencer is self-starting. Hint: The enable input to a state machine is the .ena port.

GO	CW	function
0	X	HALT
1	0	CCW
1	1	CW

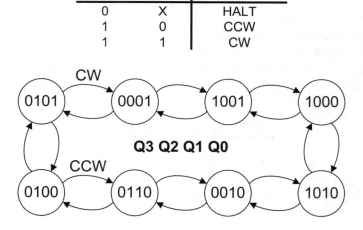

Half-step sequence for stepper motor control

14A.6   Variable frequency divider

Design a variable frequency divider using AHDL. The frequency divider should divide the input frequency by one of four different factors. The divide-by factor is controlled by two mode controls, as described by the following function table. The mode controls are used to change the modulus of the counter used for the frequency division. The output waveform will be high for two clock cycles starting at state zero. Hint: Define buried combinational circuit nodes (in the VARIABLE section) that can then define (in the Logic section with Boolean expressions) the four different conditions that can exist when the counter should be recycled.

M1	M0	divide by:
0	0	5
0	1	10
1	0	12
1	1	15

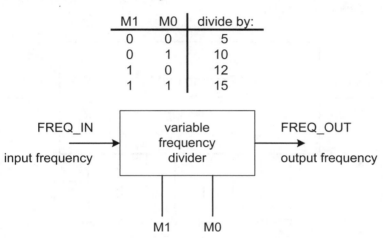

14A.7   Digital lock

Design a digital lock circuit using AHDL. The lock will have a 4-bit data input and an **enter** signal. **The enter signal is a manual clock signal for the counter.** Use a mod-5 binary counter to keep track of the sequencing through the combination. A sequence of four 4-bit numbers will make up the lock combination (that you will input for your design). Each 4-bit input number will be applied (via switches), and then the manual **enter** signal ($\uparrow$clock) will be pulsed. The machine states must be sequenced in the proper order to unlock the lock. The START state is followed by the intermediate states STATE1, then STATE2, then STATE3, and then finally DONE, which "unlocks" the lock. If an incorrect input combination is "entered" during any counter state, the counter will return to START. The state transition diagram for the digital lock is shown below.

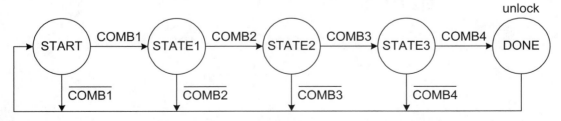

Returns to START if incorrect combination is applied

14A.8 Programmable frequency divider

Design an 8-bit programmable frequency divider using AHDL. The input signal frequency (freq_in) will be divided by a variable 8-bit binary input value (B7 through B0). The output signal (freq_out) that is produced should be a single pulse each time the divider circuit counts through the modulus represented by B7..0. Hint: Detect the counter state 00000001_2 for the output frequency signal, synchronously load in the frequency division factor (b[7..0]) when the counter reaches this state (00000001_2), count down, and repeat.

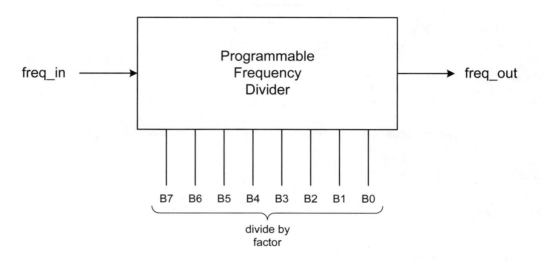

14A.9 State machine

Design the following state machine using AHDL. Make the design self-correcting by forcing any other state to go to 001_2 on the next ↑ clock.

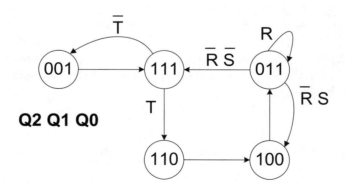

SEQUENTIAL CIRCUIT DESIGN WITH VHDL

Objective

- To design sequential logic circuits implemented with programmable logic devices (PLDs) using VHDL.

Suggested Part
     EPM7128S or EP1C6

Sequential Circuits Using VHDL

The design and implementation of sequential circuits using VHDL is carried out in much the same fashion as for combinational circuits. The flip-flops contained in the MAX7000S family can be treated as SR, JK, D, or T-type flip-flops in which the control inputs are produced by the programmable AND/OR gate structure in the PLD. Due to ease of use, D flip-flops are most commonly utilized in hardware description languages. The high-level language, VHDL, provides many options for defining sequential circuits, including IF/THEN and CASE statements.

Shown in Fig. 14-1 is a VHDL design description that creates a single D flip-flop. The ENTITY design unit declares the input and output ports for d_ff.vhd to be a BIT data type. The behavioral description for a single D flip-flop is described in the ARCHITECTURE design unit. This is accomplished within a PROCESS in VHDL since the behavior of a flip-flop is sequential. Sequential behavior can only be defined in a PROCESS. It is important to remember that the PROCESS statement itself is concurrent; just the statements inside the PROCESS are sequential. The sensitivity list for this PROCESS includes the signals clock, preset, and clear. If any of these signals should change, then the PROCESS will be invoked to determine the resultant output (q_out). The asynchronous inputs clear and preset are active-low and have priority in the D flip-flop's operation. They are, therefore, tested first in the IF statement, and the corresponding signal assignment behavior is described after each THEN. If neither of the asynchronous inputs invoked the PROCESS, then it must have been the clock signal that changed. The given Boolean expression (*clock'EVENT AND clock = '1'*) tests for a positive edge on the clock signal. The 'EVENT portion of the expression is a predefined property called an attribute for a named signal. The 'EVENT attribute is used to test if a transition has occurred on the associated signal, clock in this example. There are two possible transitions that may occur on any signal, positive-going and negative-going. We, of course, must define which of these is the clock edge that triggers our flip-flop. The other portion of the Boolean expression (*AND clock = '1'*) defines the desired edge. The *clock = '1'* will select the positive edge. If we had instead used the expression *(clock'EVENT AND clock = '0')*, then the flip-flop would be triggered on the negative edge. So, if the flip-flop receives the correct clock edge and the asynchronous inputs clear and preset are both inactive (high), then the flip-flop will have the input called data stored. It is important to note that in using a behavioral description for a flip-flop or latch in VHDL, the actual device is implied by an incomplete description within the PROCESS. The memory characteristic for these devices is implied because the IF statement does not explicitly describe how this device should act if none of the tested Boolean expressions is true. There is no final ELSE with the corresponding signal assignment. Results for the simulation of d_ff.vhd are given in Fig. 14-2.

VHDL

```
ENTITY d_ff IS
PORT (
data, clock, preset, clear          : IN BIT;
q_out                               : OUT BIT
);
END d_ff;

ARCHITECTURE simple OF d_ff IS
BEGIN
     PROCESS (clock, preset, clear)
          -- invoke process if any listed signal changes
     BEGIN
               -- priority order: clear, preset, clock
          IF    (clear = '0')     THEN  q_out <= '0';
          ELSIF (preset = '0')    THEN  q_out <= '1';
          ELSIF (clock'EVENT AND clock = '1')
                                   THEN  q_out <= data;
          END IF;
               -- memory is implied, no ELSE is listed
     END PROCESS;
END simple;
```

Fig. 14-1 VHDL description creating a single D flip-flop

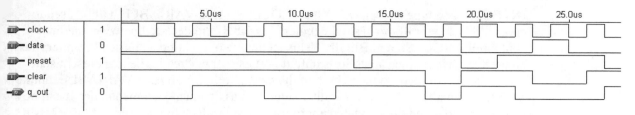

Fig. 14-2 Simulation results for the VHDL D flip-flop

Example 14-1

Design a mod-16, binary up/down counter using VHDL. The count direction is controlled by dir (dir = 1 for count up).

```
ENTITY updncntr IS
PORT (
        clock, dir          : IN BIT;
        q                   : OUT INTEGER RANGE 0 TO 15
                            -- output q will need 4 bits
);
END updncntr;

ARCHITECTURE a OF updncntr IS
BEGIN
        PROCESS (clock)          -- look for clock change
        VARIABLE count    : INTEGER RANGE 0 TO 15;
              -- create a variable for counter value

        BEGIN
              IF (clock'EVENT AND clock = '1')      THEN
                    IF  (dir = '1')   THEN   -- count up
                          count := count + 1;
                    ELSE                        -- count down
                          count := count - 1;
                    END IF;
              END IF;      -- count holds with no clock
        q <= count;        -- count value to output port
        END PROCESS;
END a;
```

Fig. 14-3 VHDL file for the binary up/down counter design for Example 14-1

A VHDL text file solution named updncntr.vhd is shown in Fig. 14-3. In order to allow the output port named q to be treated as a numerical value that can be incremented or decremented, it is assigned an INTEGER data type in the ENTITY declaration. By declaring a RANGE of 0 to 15 for this output port, the compiler will determine that four flip-flops will be needed. The actual count sequence and, therefore, the counter's modulus still must be defined in the PROCESS statement that is contained in the ARCHITECTURE design unit. An internal VARIABLE named count with an

INTEGER data type is declared in the PROCESS. This VARIABLE will be used to create the behavior of the desired counter. Variables are declared between the lines containing PROCESS and BEGIN. This technique of creating a "buried" counter must be used in VHDL since an entity's output port cannot be "read" (i.e., its present state cannot be determined) to then count to the next state. In VHDL, a VARIABLE, unlike an output signal, can be used on either side of an assignment statement since it can be read as an input and then updated appropriately to produce the desired output. Only a change in the clock signal (contained in the sensitivity list) will invoke the PROCESS and, thereby, produce the next state. The first IF statement tests for a logic level change, with the 'EVENT attribute AND also a high for the clock signal. This notation in VHDL is used to describe a positive-going edge for the named signal. If clock instead has a negative-going transition (NGT), the IF statement fails the test and the counter will hold its current state. If the signal clock experienced a positive-going transition (PGT), then the following nested IF statement will be evaluated to determine the condition of the input signal dir. If dir is high, then the VARIABLE count will be incremented by adding 1 to its present state in the variable assignment statement *count := count + 1*. Otherwise (i.e., dir = 0), the VARIABLE count will be decremented with the variable assignment statement *count := count − 1*. The result of incrementing or decrementing the register's contents is a count-up or a count-down sequence, respectively. The 4-bit VARIABLE count will automatically recycle on the next ↑ clock when it has reached the terminal state. The signal assignment statement, *q <= count*, will connect the VARIABLE count to the output port for updncntr. This signal assignment statement must be placed within the PROCESS since variables are only defined locally. The results of simulating the VHDL design file are shown in Fig. 14-4.

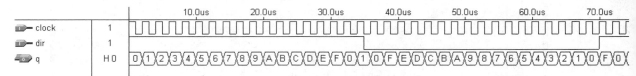

Fig. 14-4 Simulation of the VHDL file for Example 14-1

Pin numbers can be assigned as necessary for a top-level design file. See "Manually Assigning Pin Numbers" in MAXplus Notes or Quartus Notes in the CD-ROM Tutorials folder.

Example 14-2

Design a decade counter using VHDL. The mod-10 counter has a count enable, parallel load, and asynchronous clear controls as shown in Table 14-1. The counter should also produce a ripple carry output (rco) signal that goes high during the last state in the count sequence when the counter is enabled.

clear	load	enable	clock	Function
1	X	X	X	CLEAR
0	0	0	↓	HOLD
0	1	X	↓	LOAD
0	0	1	↓	COUNT UP

Table 14-1 Example 14-2 functions

A VHDL solution named mod10.vhd is shown in Fig. 14-5. The ENTITY declaration includes the output signal q specified as an INTEGER data type whose values will range from 0 to 15. The compiler uses this information to determine that four bits will be needed for the output port. Actually, we will only have values up to 9 for this BCD counter design but four bits will still be necessary. The range of values declared in the ENTITY is just used to determine the number of bits that will be necessary. The count sequence and therefore the counter's modulus are determined by the description contained in the ARCHITECTURE design unit. A VHDL PROCESS statement contains the sequential statements that describe the behavior of the mod-10 counter. The sensitivity list only needs to include the clock, asynchronous clear, and enable signals. A VARIABLE named counter with a data type of INTEGER is declared within the PROCESS. Variables can exist in a PROCESS (or PROCEDURE or FUNCTION). The VARIABLE counter is used to keep track of and update the value in the counter. In VHDL, the output ports cannot be "read"; they can only be "written (output) to." So we would not know what the current count value is. A variable, on the other hand, can be "read" and updated to the next state. When the PROCESS is invoked, the entity's output will be updated with the signal assignment statement $q <= counter$. Variables are declared between PROCESS and BEGIN. The first IF statement within the PROCESS will test the counter to determine if it is at the terminal state 9 when the counter is enabled. If this condition is true, rco will output a high; otherwise rco will be low. The nested IF statements are used to define the behavior of the mod-10 counter. According to the function table (Table 14-1), the asynchronous clear should have priority over the other counter functions, so it is evaluated first. Notice that the assignment statement for variables uses a different symbol (:=) than is used for signals. If the test for clear (active-high input) fails, then the ELSIF will next test for a negative edge (*clock'EVENT AND clock = '0'*) on clock. IF statements automatically establish a priority of action by the order in which they are written. The first tested condition that evaluates to being true (high) will determine the outcome of the IF/THEN statement. If a negative edge occurred on clock, then the next level of IF statements will test to see if the counter is to be loaded; in which case, counter should get the value of d (*counter*

:= d). Note that the load function has priority (since it is tested first) over the count function. If the counter is enabled but load is low and a negative edge is applied to clock, then the count value should be incremented (*counter := counter + 1*), unless we have already reached the terminal state of 9 in our decade counter. The innermost IF statement will cause the counter to recycle to 0 after reaching 9. If the counter is clocked but disabled, then the count should stay the same. In VHDL, this behavior of not changing the state is implied by not describing any other action. The actual memory characteristic of a register or counter is implied, so you do not need to describe it with the phrase *ELSE counter := counter* in the second-level IF statement.

VHDL

```
ENTITY mod10 IS
PORT (
      clock                    : IN BIT;
      load, enable, clear      : IN BIT;
      d                        : IN INTEGER RANGE 0 TO 15;
      q                        : OUT INTEGER RANGE 0 TO 15;
      rco                      : OUT BIT
);
END mod10;

ARCHITECTURE bcd OF mod10 IS
BEGIN
      PROCESS (clock, clear, enable)
                  -- invoke process if clock or clear changes
            VARIABLE   counter          : INTEGER RANGE 0 TO 15;
      BEGIN
                  -- rco detects terminal count when enabled
            IF ((counter = 9) AND (enable = '1')) THEN
                        rco <= '1';
            ELSE        rco <= '0';
            END IF;

            IF (clear = '1') THEN   counter := 0;
                  -- asynchronous clear has priority
            ELSIF (clock'EVENT AND clock = '0') THEN
                  IF (load = '1')  THEN   counter := d;
                        -- synchronous load
                  ELSIF  (enable = '1')  THEN
                        IF (counter = 9)  THEN  -- recycle
                                    counter := 0;
                        ELSE        counter := counter + 1;
                        END IF;
                  -- hold count behavior is implied
                  END IF;
            END IF;

            q <= counter;       -- output counter to ports
      END PROCESS;
END bcd;
```

Fig. 14-5 VHDL design file for the decade counter of Example 14-2

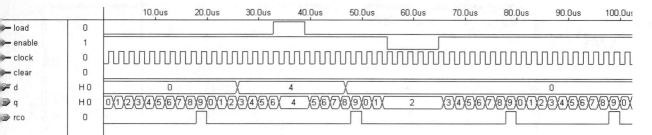

Fig. 14-6 Simulation results for Example 14-2

Simulation of the design is shown in Fig. 14-6. Assign a target device and appropriate pin numbers for the VHDL file. Then recompile and program the PLD.

Example 14-3

Design a counter using VHDL that produces the 4-bit, irregular, recycling count sequence given in the timing diagram of Fig. 14-7. Also include an asynchronous reset to zero control for this counter and a count enable.

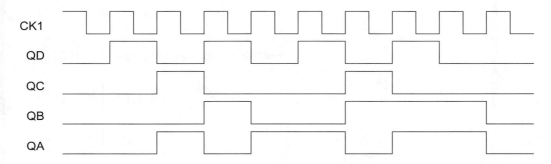

Fig. 14-7 Timing diagram for the sequential design of Example 14-3

```
ENTITY irreg_cnt IS
PORT (
      ck1, reset, count              : IN BIT;
      qa, qb, qc, qd                 : OUT BIT
);
END irreg_cnt;

ARCHITECTURE soln1 OF irreg_cnt IS
BEGIN
      PROCESS (ck1, reset)     -- process sensitivity list
          VARIABLE seq       : BIT_VECTOR (3 DOWNTO 0);
      BEGIN
          IF (reset = '1')          THEN  seq := "0000";
          ELSIF (count = '0')       THEN  seq := seq;
          ELSIF (ck1'EVENT AND ck1 = '1')      THEN
                CASE seq IS         -- define sequence
                      WHEN "0000" =>    seq := "1000";
                      WHEN "1000" =>    seq := "0101";
                      WHEN "0101" =>    seq := "1010";
                      WHEN "1010" =>    seq := "0001";
                      WHEN "0001" =>    seq := "1001";
                      WHEN "1001" =>    seq := "0110";
                      WHEN "0110" =>    seq := "1011";
                      WHEN "1011" =>    seq := "0011";
                      WHEN "0011" =>    seq := "0000";
                      WHEN OTHERS =>    seq := "0000";
                END CASE;
          END IF;
          qa <= seq(0);              -- output each bit
          qb <= seq(1);
          qc <= seq(2);
          qd <= seq(3);
      END PROCESS;
END soln1;
```

Fig. 14-8 VHDL file for the irregular counter of Example 14-3

A VHDL solution is shown in Fig. 14-8. The sensitivity list for this PROCESS contains the signals ck1 and reset. The VARIABLE seq, a BIT_VECTOR defined within the PROCESS, is used to define the irregular count sequence for this 4-bit counter. The reset signal is asynchronous and therefore has priority over the counting function, so it must be tested in the IF statement first. If the counter is being reset, then the variable assignment statement will make seq = 0000. If the test for the reset function fails, we will then test to see if the counter is disabled (*count = '0'*), which will keep the counter at the same state (*seq := seq*). Finally, if the counter is not being reset but it is enabled, then we will need to check to see if the correct positive-going clock edge has been applied (*ck1'EVENT AND ck1 = '1'*). A CASE statement is used to define the irregular count sequence for this counter. Each of the used states for this counter is identified with a WHEN clause, and the appropriate next state is assigned to the variable seq. All possible combinations of the expression to be evaluated (seq) must be covered in the WHEN statements. The WHEN OTHERS choice will take care of the unused states for this counter. The appropriate bit in the VARIABLE seq is assigned to the corresponding output port by the set of signal assignment statements.

Simulation results are shown in Fig. 14-9. The desired recycling, irregular count sequence is produced by this state machine. The asynchronous reset and count enable are also verified by the simulation.

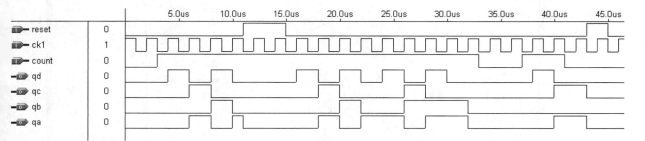

Fig. 14-9 Simulation results for Example 14-3

An alternate VHDL solution for Example 14-3 is shown in Fig. 14-10. In this solution, a SIGNAL named output is created as a BIT_VECTOR. Like the first solution, a VARIABLE named seq is also created. But this time, seq is given the data type INTEGER. As an INTEGER, seq can then be incremented to produce a mod-9 counter. The CASE statement determines the state of the dummy counter seq, which will then select the appropriate bit pattern for output. Each of the nine used states is identified with a WHEN clause. This is essentially creating a code converter so that the proper state sequence is produced.

```
ENTITY irreg_cnt IS
PORT (
      ck1, reset, count        : IN BIT;
      qa, qb, qc, qd           : OUT BIT
);
END irreg_cnt;

ARCHITECTURE soln2 OF irreg_cnt IS
      SIGNAL output              : BIT_VECTOR (3 DOWNTO 0);
BEGIN
      PROCESS (ck1, reset)     -- process sensitivity list
          VARIABLE seq         : INTEGER RANGE 0 TO 15;
      BEGIN
            IF (reset = '1')          THEN  seq := 0;
            ELSIF (count = '0')       THEN  seq := seq;
            ELSIF (ck1'EVENT AND ck1 = '1')      THEN
                  IF (seq = 8)        THEN  seq := 0;
                  ELSE                      seq := seq + 1;
                  END IF;
            END IF;
            CASE seq IS
                  WHEN 0 =>            output <= "0000";
                  WHEN 1 =>            output <= "1000";
                  WHEN 2 =>            output <= "0101";
                  WHEN 3 =>            output <= "1010";
                  WHEN 4 =>            output <= "0001";
                  WHEN 5 =>            output <= "1001";
                  WHEN 6 =>            output <= "0110";
                  WHEN 7 =>            output <= "1011";
                  WHEN 8 =>            output <= "0011";
                  WHEN OTHERS =>       output <= "0000";
            END CASE;
            qa <= output(0);          -- output each bit
            qb <= output(1);
            qc <= output(2);
            qd <= output(3);
      END PROCESS;
END soln2;
```

Fig. 14-10 Alternate VHDL file for the irregular counter of Example 14-3

Example 14-4

Design a bidirectional, full-step controller for a stepper motor using VHDL. The controller will produce a clockwise sequence pattern when $cw = 1$ and a counterclockwise sequence pattern when $cw = 0$. The stepper motor sequence is shown in Fig. 14-11.

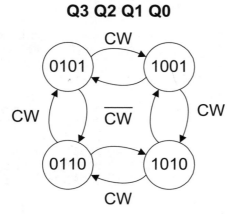

Fig. 14-11 State transition diagram for the stepper controller of Example 14-4

An example solution using VHDL is shown in Fig. 14-12. The input BIT named **step** is the clock input to the stepper controller. A VARIABLE named **stepper** is declared to be a 4-bit BIT_VECTOR data type in the PROCESS statement. The present state and the logic level for **cw** will determine the correct next state that should be produced by the state machine. The IF/ELSE statement is used to test **cw** and determine the count direction for the stepper controller. Each of the two count directions is specified with a separate CASE statement. For each value of **cw**, the correct variable assignment is determined based on the current value of **stepper**. The chip will automatically reset all flip-flops at power-up and it will be necessary to define how to get out of that state and into the specified sequence to drive the stepper motor. At power-up, we do not care what the next state is, just that the counter gets into the specified count sequence. The next state 1010_2 was chosen arbitrarily from the list of valid states for the stepper motor controller. The WHEN OTHERS in the CASE statement will automatically take care of state 0000_2, as well as any other undefined state. The value for **stepper** is assigned to the output port q. Simulation results for this design are shown in Fig. 14-13. The count sequence for each direction is correct for the recycling state machine.

```
ENTITY full_step IS
PORT (
      step, cw             : IN BIT;
      q                    : OUT BIT_VECTOR (3 DOWNTO 0)
);
END full_step;

ARCHITECTURE solution1 OF full_step IS
BEGIN
     PROCESS (step)               -- step is clock input
         VARIABLE   stepper   : BIT_VECTOR (3 DOWNTO 0);
     BEGIN
        IF (step'EVENT AND step = '1') THEN
            IF (cw = '1')    THEN
                CASE stepper IS        -- CW sequence
                     WHEN "1010" =>  stepper := "0110" ;
                     WHEN "0110" =>  stepper := "0101" ;
                     WHEN "0101" =>  stepper := "1001" ;
                     WHEN "1001" =>  stepper := "1010" ;
                     WHEN OTHERS =>  stepper := "1010" ;
                END CASE;
            ELSE
                CASE stepper IS        -- CCW sequence
                     WHEN "1010" =>  stepper := "1001" ;
                     WHEN "1001" =>  stepper := "0101" ;
                     WHEN "0101" =>  stepper := "0110" ;
                     WHEN "0110" =>  stepper := "1010" ;
                     WHEN OTHERS =>  stepper := "1010" ;
                END CASE;
            END IF;
        END IF;
     q <= stepper;        -- output to port
     END PROCESS;
END solution1;
```

Fig. 14-12 VHDL file for the stepper motor controller

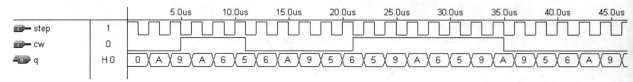

Fig. 14-13 Simulation results for Example 14-4

An alternative VHDL design for Example 14-4 is shown in Fig. 14-14. A VARIABLE named **stepper** is declared in the PROCESS statement to be an INTEGER with a 0 to 3 RANGE of values. The value of **cw**, tested with an IF/ELSE statement, will control whether **stepper** is to be incremented or decremented. The VARIABLE **stepper** was given the INTEGER data type so that it could be manipulated mathematically by adding 1 to it or subtracting 1 from it. The CASE statement is used to assign the correct bit pattern to the output port **q**.

VHDL

```
ENTITY full_step IS
PORT (
      step, cw            : IN BIT;
      q                   : OUT BIT_VECTOR (3 DOWNTO 0)
);
END full_step;

ARCHITECTURE solution2 OF full_step IS
BEGIN
      PROCESS (step)            -- step is clock input
      VARIABLE     stepper    : INTEGER RANGE 0 TO 3;
                  -- integer data type has numerical value
      BEGIN
            IF (step'EVENT AND step = '1') THEN
                  IF (cw = '1')      THEN
                                     stepper := stepper + 1;
                  ELSE             stepper := stepper - 1;
                  END IF;
            END IF;

            CASE stepper IS   -- assign bit patterns
                  WHEN 0 =>   q <= "1010" ;
                  WHEN 1 =>   q <= "0110" ;
                  WHEN 2 =>   q <= "0101" ;
                  WHEN 3 =>   q <= "1001" ;
            END CASE;
      END PROCESS;
END solution2;
```

Fig. 14-14 Alternate VHDL file for the stepper motor controller

Example 14-5

Design a sequential circuit that will wait in an idle state for a trigger input (**start**) to occur and then output a single pulse four clock cycles later. The sequential circuit will then wait for another trigger signal. The state transition diagram for this delay circuit is shown in Fig. 14-15. The state machine should also be self-correcting.

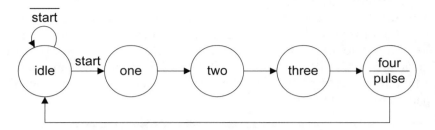

Fig. 14-15 State transition diagram for Example 14-5

A VHDL solution is shown in Fig. 14-16. This example illustrates the use of a new VHDL data type called enumerated. An enumerated data type named count_state is created with the *TYPE count_state IS* statement. The enumerated data type allows us to refer to states by name only (idle, one, two, three, four, extra1, extra2, extra3). Since there are 8 state names, the compiler determines that 3 bits will be needed to distinguish the states from one another. With 3 bits, there are 8 possible combinations, of which only 5 will be actually used in this design. The remaining 3 states are given the "dummy" names of extra1, extra2, and extra3. An internal VARIABLE named mach is declared to be this user-defined data type called count_state. The bit patterns have not been defined for this VARIABLE since we do not really care what they look like. The compiler will assign bit patterns for each state. We can identify the compiler-assigned bit patterns by looking at the simulation after compilation. The VARIABLE mach will be used to create a "buried" state machine, one that is not connected to the entity's output ports. In the PROCESS, a CASE statement is used to define the sequence of states for our state machine. When the state machine is in the idle state, it will be waiting for the start signal to go high (and the ↑ clock) in order to proceed to the next state (one). After starting the sequence, the state machine will step through each state on each ↑ clock. The WHEN OTHERS clause will take care of any state (including the 3 "extra" states) that is not otherwise defined within the CASE statement. With the 3 unused states taken care of, the state machine will be self-correcting. Upon reaching state four (i.e., *mach = four* is true), the output port pulse will be assigned a 1; otherwise pulse will be a 0. Notice that the only output needed is the signal named pulse.

The results of the simulation for Example 14-5 are shown in Fig. 14-17. The buried state machine (notice its "buried handle") has been included in the simulation to verify its correct operation. Notice that the simulator result gives the bit values that were assigned by the compiler for the enumerated state names of mach. The second start signal did not initiate the machine sequence since it occurred after the ↑ clock.

```
ENTITY delay IS
PORT (
      clock        : IN BIT;
      start        : IN BIT;
      pulse        : OUT BIT
);
END delay;

ARCHITECTURE vhdl OF delay IS
BEGIN
      PROCESS (clock)
      TYPE count_state IS (idle, one, two, three, four,
                                extra1, extra2, extra3);
            -- enumerated data type called count_state
      VARIABLE mach       : count_state;
      BEGIN
         IF (clock'EVENT AND clock = '1') THEN
            CASE  mach  IS   -- describe mach sequence
               WHEN idle =>
                     IF (start = '1') THEN
                                       mach := one;
                     ELSE              mach := idle;
                     END IF;
               WHEN one =>       mach := two;
               WHEN two =>       mach := three;
               WHEN three =>     mach := four;
               WHEN OTHERS =>    mach := idle;
            END CASE;
         END IF;
               -- detect state to assert pulse
         IF (mach = four)      THEN  pulse <= '1';
         ELSE                        pulse <= '0';
         END IF;
      END PROCESS;
END vhdl;
```

Fig. 14-16 VHDL file for Example 14-5

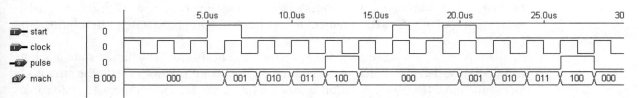

Fig. 14-17 Simulation results for Example 14-5

Example 14-6

Design the state machine (using VHDL) that is defined by the state transition diagram given in Fig. 14-18. The state machine has three inputs—trig, delay(1), and delay(0)—that control the sequence of states. The logic circuit will produce a 3-bit array output named outs that is dependent upon the current state for the machine. The states are named, but the bit patterns for each state are not defined in this design.

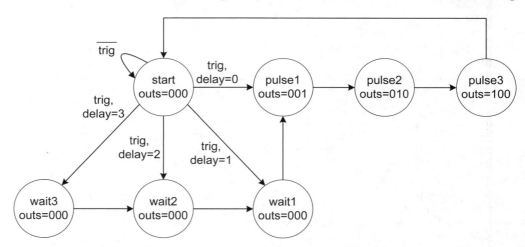

Fig. 14-18 State transition diagram for Example 14-6

An example VHDL solution named state_machine is shown in Fig. 14-19. Seven states are defined for the internal SIGNAL named machine. The states are listed by name only (start, wait1, wait2, wait3, pulse1, pulse2, pulse3) using an enumerated data type called states. The SIGNAL machine is used to create a buried state machine (its outputs are not connected to the output ports for the ENTITY). The bit patterns for machine were left for the compiler to determine since we do not care what they actually look like. A minimum of three flip-flops (bits) will be required to produce the seven states for machine. By checking the report file, we can see that the compiler created the bit names machine~1, machine~2, and machine~3 for this state machine. We can also see in the report what bit pattern was created for each of the seven states. Two CASE statements and an IF/ELSE statement are used to describe the operation of machine. The 3-bit output port (outs) values are assigned using a conditional signal assignment (WHEN/ELSE) statement to test for the appropriate state of machine.

Simulation results for Example 14-6 are shown in Fig. 14-20. The buried state machine (machine) has been included in the simulation to make it easier to verify the circuit's operation. Note that the simulation shows the bit values for the enumerated state names for machine.

```
ENTITY state_machine IS
PORT (
     clock, trig        : IN BIT;
     delay              : IN INTEGER RANGE 0 TO 3;
     outs               : OUT BIT_vector (1 TO 3)
);
END state_machine;

ARCHITECTURE enumerated OF state_machine IS
TYPE states IS
     (start, wait1, wait2, wait3, pulse1, pulse2, pulse3);
SIGNAL machine          : states;    -- enumerated data type

BEGIN
     outs <=      "100" WHEN (machine = pulse1) ELSE
                  "010" WHEN (machine = pulse2) ELSE
                  "001" WHEN (machine = pulse3) ELSE
                  "000";
          -- conditional signal assignment

PROCESS (clock)
BEGIN
   IF (clock'EVENT AND clock = '1') THEN
      CASE machine IS           -- define machine sequence
         WHEN   start  =>
            IF (trig = '1')   THEN  -- wait for trig
               CASE delay IS  -- determine delay
                  WHEN 0     =>     machine <= pulse1;
                  WHEN 1     =>     machine <= wait1;
                  WHEN 2     =>     machine <= wait2;
                  WHEN 3     =>     machine <= wait3;
               END CASE;
            ELSE                    machine <= start;
            END IF;
         WHEN wait1     =>          machine <= pulse1;
         WHEN wait2     =>          machine <= wait1;
         WHEN wait3     =>          machine <= wait2;
         WHEN pulse1    =>          machine <= pulse2;
         WHEN pulse2    =>          machine <= pulse3;
         WHEN pulse3    =>          machine <= start;
         WHEN OTHERS    =>          machine <= start;
      END CASE;
   END IF;
END PROCESS;
END enumerated;
```

Fig. 14-19 VHDL file for Example 14-6

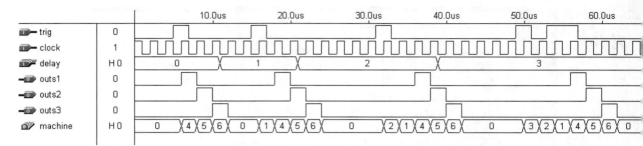

Fig. 14-20 Simulation for Example 14-6

Example 14-7

Design a mod-1000, recycling BCD counter using the mod10.vhd design in Example 14-2. The counter will have the functions given in Table 14-2. The VHDL file for the mod10 counter is repeated in Fig. 14-21.

clear	load	enable	clock	function
1	X	X	X	CLEAR
0	0	0	↓	HOLD
0	1	X	↓	LOAD
0	0	1	↓	COUNT UP

Table 14-2 Example 14-7 functions

A top-level design file (Fig. 14-22) can be created using the symbol for the mod10.vhd design. Three copies of the mod10 symbol will be needed, one for the ones digit, one for the tens digit, and one for the hundreds digit. The three mod10 stages are cascaded together by connecting the rco output (which detects the terminal state 9 when the counter is enabled) to the next digit's enable control. The enable input on the ones digit will control all of the mod10 counters. The enable input on the tens digit will only be high if the ones digit is a 9 and the mod-1000 counter is enabled. Likewise, the hundreds digit will only be enabled if the tens digit and the ones digit are both 9 (and the counter is enabled). The load and clear controls are connected to all three counter stages.

```
ENTITY mod10 IS
PORT (
      clock                    : IN BIT;
      load, enable, clear      : IN BIT;
      d                        : IN INTEGER RANGE 0 TO 15;
      q                        : OUT INTEGER RANGE 0 TO 15;
      rco                      : OUT BIT
);
END mod10;

ARCHITECTURE bcd OF mod10 IS
BEGIN
      PROCESS (clock, clear, enable)
                  -- invoke process if clock or clear changes
            VARIABLE  counter        : INTEGER RANGE 0 TO 15;
      BEGIN
                  -- rco detects terminal count when enabled
            IF ((counter = 9) AND (enable = '1')) THEN
                      rco <= '1';
            ELSE          rco <= '0';
            END IF;

            IF (clear = '1') THEN   counter := 0;
                  -- asynchronous clear has priority
            ELSIF (clock'EVENT AND clock = '0') THEN
                IF (load = '1')  THEN   counter := d;
                      -- synchronous load
                ELSIF  (enable = '1')  THEN
                      IF (counter = 9)  THEN  -- recycle
                                  counter := 0;
                      ELSE          counter := counter + 1;
                      END IF;
                END IF;
            END IF;

            q <= counter;        -- output counter to ports
      END PROCESS;
END bcd;
```

Fig. 14-21 VHDL design file for the decade counter from Example 14-2

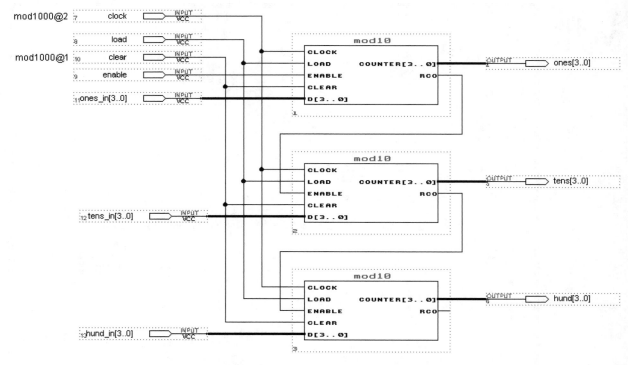

Fig. 14-22 Top-level design file for Example 14-7

An alternate solution is shown in Fig. 14-23. This technique uses a VHDL design file to describe the interconnections between the mod-10 counters for the top-level description. This design method is said to use a structural style. The mod10.vhd file is declared to be a COMPONENT in the top-level file. The ports for the mod10 entity are given within the COMPONENT declaration. Two additional single-bit signals (riplcary1 and riplcary10) are also declared to make the connections between the ones and tens digit counters and between the tens and hundreds digit counters (see Fig. 14-22). The mod10 counter module is instantiated three times in the top-level file. Each time the counter module is used, it is given a unique label (ones_digit, tens_digit, hund_digit), and the appropriate wiring connection for each port is given in the PORT MAP using named associations. The list of named associations has the COMPONENT port name on the left of the => symbol and the top-level port name on the right. Notice how riplcary1 is used as a "wire" that connects the rco output from the ones_digit to the enable input on the tens_digit. Another "wire" (riplcary10) connects the tens_digit to the hund_digit. The final rco output, produced by the hund_digit module, is not used in our application so it is "connected" (it must be given a named association) in the PORT MAP to OPEN, a keyword that means exactly what it says.

Sample simulation results for either design solution of the mod-1000 counter are shown in Fig. 14-24.

```
ENTITY mod1000v IS
PORT ( clock, load, clear, enable    : IN BIT;
        ones_in, tens_in, hund_in    : IN INTEGER RANGE 0 TO 15;
        ones, tens, hund             : OUT INTEGER RANGE 0 TO 15
    );
END mod1000v;


ARCHITECTURE structure OF mod1000v IS
SIGNAL riplcary1, riplcary10         : BIT;
COMPONENT mod10
    PORT (       clock               : IN BIT;
                 load, clear, enable : IN BIT;
                 d                   : IN INTEGER RANGE 0 TO 15;
                 q                   : OUT INTEGER RANGE 0 TO 15;
                 rco                 : OUT BIT   );
END COMPONENT;
BEGIN
    ones_digit  :       mod10
        PORT MAP (clock => clock, load => load, clear => clear,
        enable => enable, d => ones_in, q => ones,
        rco => riplcary1);
    tens_digit  :       mod10
        PORT MAP (clock => clock, load => load, clear => clear,
        enable => riplcary1, d => tens_in, q => tens,
        rco => riplcary10);
    hund_digit  :       mod10
        PORT MAP (clock => clock, load => load, clear => clear,
        enable => riplcary10, d => hund_in, q => hund,
        rco => OPEN);
END structure;
```

Fig. 14-23 Alternate VHDL top-level solution for Example 14-7

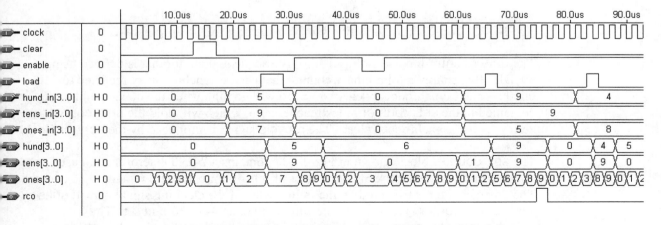

Fig. 14-24 Sample simulation results for Example 14-7

Example 14-8

A digital design is given in Fig. 14-25. Examine this case-study design to determine its operation. It is a hierarchical design consisting of several sequential and combinational logic blocks. The circuit will count a preselected number of sets of units and then output a stop signal. Each unit to be counted will clock a counter (named unit_counter) that can be switched between two different mod numbers (24 or 36) controlled by the logic input size. Each set then will be either 24 or 36 units. The number of sets desired (you can choose from 1 through 9 sets) will be applied to count[3..0] and the active-low startn signal will be pulsed.

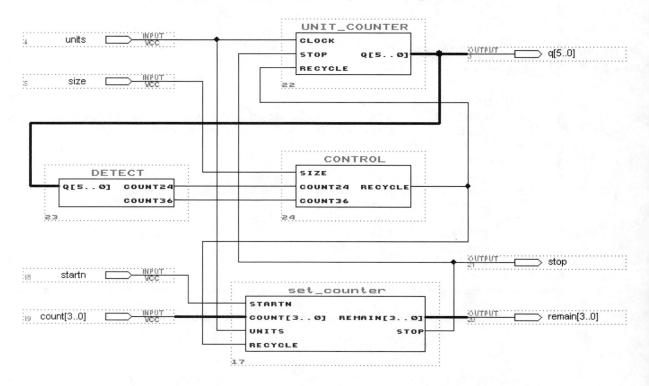

Fig. 14-25 Top-level design file (vary_count.gdf) for Example 14-8

The unit_counter block (see Fig. 14-26) is a sequential circuit that is defined using VHDL. It is simply a 6-bit binary counter that can be synchronously recycled to 000001_2 and asynchronously cleared. Stop will go high when the down counter contained in the set_counter block reaches zero, which will hold the unit_counter at zero with the asynchronous clear. The recycle signal is produced by the control block.

The set_counter block shown in Fig. 14-27 contains a 74190 macrofunction used as a down counter to keep track of the number of sets of units that still remain to be counted. The down counter is triggered on the falling edge of the clocking signal named units when unit_counter is recycled at the end of either a 24- or 36-unit set. The asynchronous startn signal will load in the desired number of sets. When startn is asserted, the output signal stop will go low and the counter will be enabled. When the count on the 74190 reaches zero, stop will go high and the counter will be disabled.

```
ENTITY unit_counter IS
PORT (
      clock                    : IN BIT;
      stop, recycle            : IN BIT;
      q                        : OUT INTEGER RANGE 0 TO 36
);
END unit_counter;

ARCHITECTURE a OF unit_counter IS
BEGIN
      PROCESS (clock, stop)
            VARIABLE cntr      : INTEGER RANGE 0 TO 36;
      BEGIN
            IF (stop = '1')    THEN   cntr := 0;
                  -- asynchronous stop has priority
            ELSIF (clock'EVENT AND clock = '1') THEN
                        -- either recycle or count up
                  IF (recycle = '1')        THEN   cntr := 1;
                  ELSE  cntr := cntr + 1;
                  END IF;
            END IF;
      q <= cntr;              -- output variable cntr on port
      END PROCESS;
END a;
```

Fig. 14-26 VHDL design file for the unit_counter block in Example 14-8

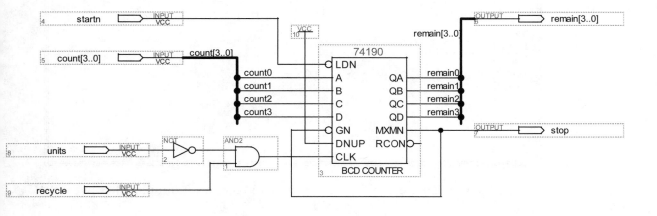

Fig. 14-27 Schematic design file for the set_counter block in Example 14-8

The **detect** block (see Fig. 14-28) is a VHDL-defined combinational circuit. This circuit monitors the output of **unit_counter** to determine when the count reaches the values 24 and 36. The output signals **count24** and **count36** are fed to the **control** block.

```
ENTITY detect IS
PORT (
      q                             : IN INTEGER RANGE 0 TO 36;
      count24                       : OUT BIT;
      count36                       : OUT BIT
);
END detect;

ARCHITECTURE a OF detect IS
CONSTANT   state24       : INTEGER RANGE 0 TO 36 := 24;
CONSTANT   state36       : INTEGER RANGE 0 TO 36 := 36;
BEGIN
      count24 <= '1'     WHEN (q = state24)     ELSE   '0';
      count36 <= '1'     WHEN (q = state36)     ELSE   '0';
END a;
```

Fig. 14-28 VHDL design file for the detect block in Example 14-8

The control block (see Fig. 14-29) is also a combinational circuit defined with VHDL. This circuit determines when the unit_counter should be recycled. The number of units in a set (either 24 or 36 units) is selected with size. A conditional signal assignment statement defines the logic necessary to tell the unit_counter to recycle.

```
ENTITY control IS
PORT (
      size                 : IN BIT;
      count24, count36     : IN BIT;
      recycle              : OUT BIT
);
END control;

ARCHITECTURE a OF control IS
BEGIN
      recycle <=   '1' WHEN (size = '0' AND count24 = '1')
      ELSE   '1'   WHEN (size = '1' AND count36 = '1')
      ELSE   '0';
END a;
```

Fig. 14-29 VHDL design file for the control block in Example 14-8

A sample of the simulation results for Example 14-8 is shown in Fig. 14-30. The top half shows screen dumps with size low and count = 4. This input combination will produce 4 sets of 24 units. The bottom half of the figure illustrates the simulation results when size is high and count = 3. The circuit produced count sequences for 3 sets of 36 units before stop goes high and the counters are disabled.

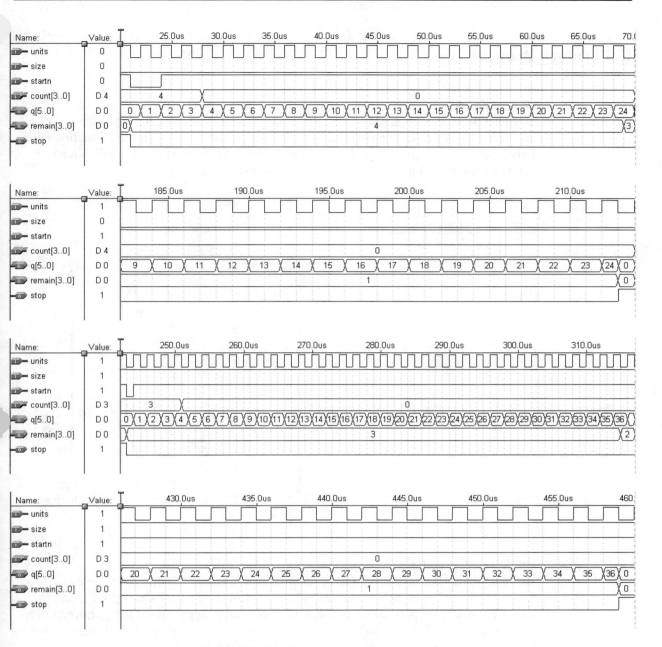

Fig. 14-30 Simulation results for Example 14-8

Laboratory Projects

14V.1   Gray code counter

Design a 4-bit, up/down, recycling Gray code counter using VHDL. The count direction is controlled by a signal called dir, as indicated in the following function table. Label the counter outputs q[3..0]. The circuit also should produce an output signal called index, which goes low whenever the counter state is 0000.

dir	operation
0	Count Up
1	Count Down

Gray code sequence

	q3	q2	q1	q0	
count	0	0	0	0	
up	0	0	0	1	
sequence	0	0	1	1	
	0	0	1	0	
	0	1	1	0	
	0	1	1	1	
	0	1	0	1	
	0	1	0	0	
	1	1	0	0	
	1	1	0	1	
	1	1	1	1	
	1	1	1	0	
	1	0	1	0	
	1	0	1	1	count
	1	0	0	1	down
	1	0	0	0	sequence

14V.2   Up/down BCD counter

Design a mod-10, recycling, BCD up/down counter using VHDL. The counter's function table is given below. Inputs c[1..0] control the counter's function. The counter should also produce an active-low ripple carry output signal called carryn. The carry output signal should only be asserted at 9 when counting up or at 0 when counting down.

c1	c0	operation
0	0	Reset
0	1	Count Down
1	0	Count Up
1	1	Hold Count

14V.3   Mod-60 BCD counter
Design a mod-60, recycling BCD counter using VHDL. The counter should have an active-low, synchronous reset (resn) signal. The count sequence will be 0 through 59_{10} in BCD. Create a hierarchical design with separate VHDL files for the tens digit and the ones digit.

14V.4   Mod-100 binary counter
Design a mod-100, recycling binary counter using VHDL. The counter is triggered with ↓ clocks and should have an active-high count enable called enable. The counter will also output a <u>single</u> active-high pulse (called pulse) during each mod-100 count sequence. The pulse occurs at the <u>end</u> of the count sequence. The pulse width will be controlled by an input signal called w, as shown in the table below. Essentially, w changes the duty cycle of the divide-by-100 output signal.

W	PULSE width
0	5 clock periods
1	10 clock periods

14V.5   Stepper motor sequence controller
Design a half-step sequencer to control a stepper motor using VHDL. The sequencer should produce the appropriate sequence of states to drive the motor either clockwise (CW) or counterclockwise (CCW) <u>without</u> using a binary counter (i.e., produce the half-step count sequence directly). The stepper direction is controlled by an input signal named cw. The stepper enable is called go. The function table is given below. Make sure the sequencer is self-starting.

GO	CW	function
0	X	HALT
1	0	CCW
1	1	CW

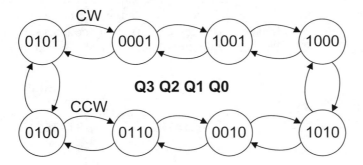

Half-step sequence for stepper motor control

14V.6 Variable frequency divider

Design a variable frequency divider using VHDL. The frequency divider should divide the input frequency by one of four different factors. The divide-by factor is controlled by two mode controls as described by the following function table. The mode controls are used to change the modulus of the counter used for the frequency division. The output waveform will be high for two clock cycles starting at state zero. Hint: Recycle a "buried" up-counter (defined as a VARIABLE) when you detect the desired terminal state (controlled by 4 values of m).

M1	M0	divide by:
0	0	5
0	1	10
1	0	12
1	1	15

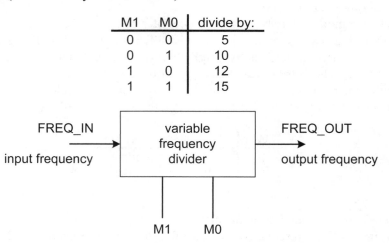

14V.7 Digital lock

Design a digital lock circuit using VHDL. The lock will have a 4-bit data input and an enter signal. **The enter signal is a manual clock signal for the counter.** Use a mod-5 binary counter to keep track of the sequencing through the combination. A sequence of four 4-bit numbers will make up the lock combination (that you will input for your design). Each 4-bit input number will be applied (via switches), and then the manual enter signal (↑clock) will be pulsed. The machine states must be sequenced in the proper order to unlock the lock. The START state is followed by the intermediate states STATE1, then STATE2, then STATE3, and then finally DONE, which "unlocks" the lock. Use an **enumerated** data type for the sequential machine. If an incorrect input combination is "entered" during any counter state, the counter will return to START. The state transition diagram for the digital lock is shown below.

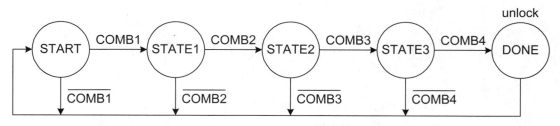

Returns to START if incorrect combination is applied

14V.8   Programmable frequency divider
Design an 8-bit, programmable frequency divider using VHDL. The input signal frequency (freq_in) will be divided by a variable, 8-bit, binary input value (B7 through B0). The output signal (freq_out) that is produced should be a single pulse each time the divider circuit counts through the modulus represented by B7..0. Hint: Detect the counter state 00000001_2 for the output frequency signal, synchronously load in the frequency division factor (b[7..0]) when the counter reaches this state (00000001_2), count down, and repeat.

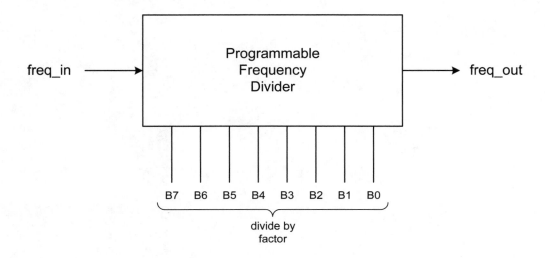

14V.9   State machine
Design the following state machine using VHDL. Make the design self-correcting by forcing any other state to go to 001_2 on the next ↑ clock.

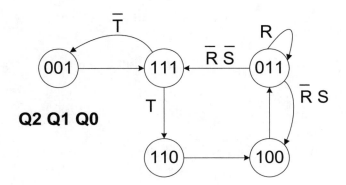

SHIFT REGISTER APPLICATIONS

Objectives

- To apply shift registers in serial and parallel digital data transfer applications.
- To apply shift registers in counter applications.
- To design and implement a shift register application in a PLD.

Suggested Parts			
7404	74160	74166	EPM7128S or EP1C6

Shift Registers

Registers consist of a set of flip-flops used to store and transfer binary data in a digital system. Registers can be classified according to the types of input and output data movement. With the two basic forms of data transfer, serial and parallel, there are the following categories of registers:

1. Parallel-in/parallel-out (PIPO)
2. Serial-in/serial-out (SISO)
3. Parallel-in/serial-out (PISO)
4. Serial-in/parallel-out (SIPO)

Many MSI shift register chips are designed to handle data movement into or out of the register in any desired manner. The input data may be either serial or parallel, and the output data may be serial or parallel. The 74194 (shown in Fig. 15-1) is an MSI, 4-bit, bidirectional, universal shift register with this kind of flexibility. The serial data inputs are labeled **SR SER** (shift-right serial input) and **SL SER** (shift-left serial input). The parallel data inputs are A, B, C, and D. The inputs S1 and S0 control the mode of synchronous operation for the shift register, as shown in the function table in Table 15-1. Since all four register outputs (QA, QB, QC, and QD) are available, the data output may be either serial or parallel. Additionally, this chip has an asynchronous clear input control.

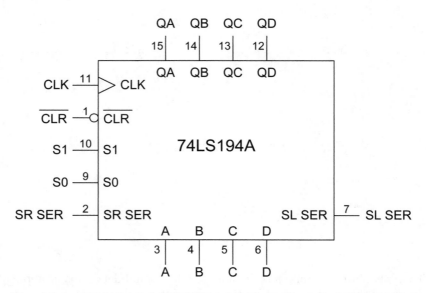

Fig. 15-1 A 74194 4-bit, bidirectional, universal shift register

CLR	Mode		Clock	SER		Parallel inputs				Outputs			
	S1	S0		SL	SR	A	B	C	D	QA_{n+1}	QB_{n+1}	QC_{n+1}	QD_{n+1}
0	X	X	X	X	X	X	X	X	X	0	0	0	0
1	X	X	0	X	X	X	X	X	X	QA_0	QB_0	QC_0	QD_0
1	1	1	↑	X	X	a	b	c	d	a	b	c	d
1	0	1	↑	X	1	X	X	X	X	1	QA_n	QB_n	QC_n
1	0	1	↑	X	0	X	X	X	X	0	QA_n	QB_n	QC_n
1	1	0	↑	1	X	X	X	X	X	QB_n	QC_n	QD_n	1
1	1	0	↑	0	X	X	X	X	X	QB_n	QC_n	QD_n	0
1	0	0	X	X	X	X	X	X	X	QA_0	QB_0	QC_0	QD_0

Table 15-1 74194 function table

Example 15-1

Design an 8-bit universal shift register to be implemented in a PLD. The 8-bit shift register can move data serially or in parallel. The output is to be labeled q[0..7] and the parallel data input is d[0..7]. The serial data movement can be either shifting the data to the left (from q7 toward q0) or to the right (from q0 toward q7). The serial data inputs are sr_ser (shift right serial) and sl_ser (shift left serial). The clocked register function is controlled by s1 and s0, as described in the function table in Table 15-2.

s1	s0	Function	$q0_{n+1}$	$q1_{n+1}$	$q2_{n+1}$	$q3_{n+1}$	$q4_{n+1}$	$q5_{n+1}$	$q6_{n+1}$	$q7_{n+1}$
0	0	HOLD	$q0_n$	$q1_n$	$q2_n$	$q3_n$	$q4_n$	$q5_n$	$q6_n$	$q7_n$
0	1	SHIFT RIGHT	sr_ser	$q0_n$	$q1_n$	$q2_n$	$q3_n$	$q4_n$	$q5_n$	$q6_n$
1	0	SHIFT LEFT	$q1_n$	$q2_n$	$q3_n$	$q4_n$	$q5_n$	$q6_n$	$q7_n$	sl_ser
1	1	LOAD	$d0_n$	$d1_n$	$d2_n$	$d3_n$	$d4_n$	$d5_n$	$d6_n$	$d7_n$

Table 15-2 Function table for Example 15-1

Schematic   An example schematic solution using two 74194 macrofunctions is shown in Fig. 15-2. The asynchronous clear is disabled by defaulting to a high logic level. The results for the simulation of this design are shown in Fig. 15-3.

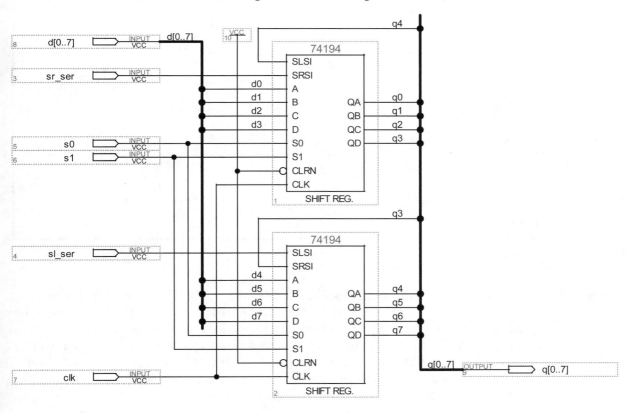

Fig. 15-2 Schematic using 74194 macrofunction for Example 15-1

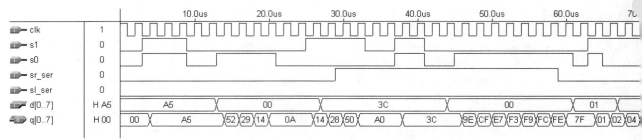

Fig. 15-3 Simulation sample for Example 15-1

```
SUBDESIGN   shift2
(
     clk, s[1..0]                    :INPUT;
     d[0..7], sr_ser, sl_ser         :INPUT;
     q[0..7]                         :OUTPUT;
)
VARIABLE
     register[0..7]                  :DFF;    -- 8-bit register
BEGIN
     register[].clk = clk;

     CASE  s[]  IS
           WHEN  0  =>        -- hold
                 register[0..7].d = register[0..7].q;
           WHEN  1  =>        -- shift right
                 register[1..7].d = register[0..6].q;
                 register0.d = sr_ser;
           WHEN  2  =>        -- shift left
                 register[0..6].d = register[1..7].q;
                 register7.d = sl_ser;
           WHEN  3  =>        -- parallel load
                 register[0..7].d = d[0..7];
     END CASE;

     q[] = register[].q;
                 -- connect register to output port
END;
```

Fig. 15-4 Alternative AHDL solution for Example 15-1

AHDL   An alternative AHDL solution, **shift2.tdf**, is shown in Fig. 15-4. An 8-bit register using D flip-flops is created in the VARIABLE section. The CASE statement determines the necessary input assignments for the register to operate according to the function controls **s[1..0]**. Each input bit (**.d**) is assigned in order to the respective output bit (**.q**). This makes it easy to shift right or left by one bit for each clock cycle when **s[1..0]** is 01_2 or 10_2, respectively. The appropriate serial input bit is also assigned. The output port for the subdesign is assigned to the register outputs.

```
ENTITY  shift3  IS
PORT (
     clk, sr_ser, sl_ser      :IN BIT;
     s                        :IN BIT_VECTOR (1 DOWNTO 0);
     d                        :IN BIT_VECTOR (0 TO 7);
     q                        :OUT BIT_VECTOR (0 TO 7)
);
END shift3;

ARCHITECTURE vhdl OF shift3 IS
BEGIN
   PROCESS (clk)
      VARIABLE  sr   :BIT_VECTOR (0 TO 7); -- register
      BEGIN
        IF (clk'EVENT AND clk = '1')  THEN
           CASE  s  IS
                WHEN  "00"  =>        -- hold
                   sr := sr;
                WHEN  "01"  =>        -- shift right
                   sr(1 TO 7) := sr(0 TO 6);
                   sr(0) := sr_ser;
                WHEN  "10"  =>        -- shift left
                   sr(0 TO 6) := sr(1 TO 7);
                   sr(7) := sl_ser;
                WHEN  "11"  =>        -- parallel load
                   sr:= d;
           END CASE;
         END IF;
      q <= sr;    -- connect register to output port
   END PROCESS;
END vhdl;
```

Fig. 15-5 Alternative VHDL solution for Example 15-1

VHDL   An alternative VHDL solution, **shift3.vhd**, is shown in Fig. 15-5. An 8-bit VARIABLE named **sr** is created to represent the shift register. The CASE statement determines the necessary assignment statements for the register to operate according to the 2-bit function control **s**. For serial shifting, the appropriate input bit is assigned in order, as specified in the truth table. This makes it easy to shift right or left by one bit for each clock cycle when **s** is 01 or 10, respectively. The appropriate serial input bit is also assigned. The output port for the entity is assigned to the register outputs.

Example 15-2

Design an 8-bit, registered barrel shifter using a PLD. The 8-bit barrel shifter can be synchronously parallel-loaded with 8 data inputs (**d0** through **d7**). The register contents can be cyclically rotated from 0 to 7 places under the control of the select inputs (**s[2..0]**), as shown in Table 15-3. The rotated data is stored in the same register.

clk	ld	s2	s1	s0	$q0_{n+1}$	$q1_{n+1}$	$q2_{n+1}$	$q3_{n+1}$	$q4_{n+1}$	$q5_{n+1}$	$q6_{n+1}$	$q7_{n+1}$
↑	1	X	X	X	$d0_n$	$d1_n$	$d2_n$	$d3_n$	$d4_n$	$d5_n$	$d6_n$	$d7_n$
↑	0	0	0	0	$q0_n$	$q1_n$	$q2_n$	$q3_n$	$q4_n$	$q5_n$	$q6_n$	$q7_n$
↑	0	0	0	1	$q1_n$	$q2_n$	$q3_n$	$q4_n$	$q5_n$	$q6_n$	$q7_n$	$q0_n$
↑	0	0	1	0	$q2_n$	$q3_n$	$q4_n$	$q5_n$	$q6_n$	$q7_n$	$q0_n$	$q1_n$
↑	0	0	1	1	$q3_n$	$q4_n$	$q5_n$	$q6_n$	$q7_n$	$q0_n$	$q1_n$	$q2_n$
↑	0	1	0	0	$q4_n$	$q5_n$	$q6_n$	$q7_n$	$q0_n$	$q1_n$	$q2_n$	$q3_n$
↑	0	1	0	1	$q5_n$	$q6_n$	$q7_n$	$q0_n$	$q1_n$	$q2_n$	$q3_n$	$q4_n$
↑	0	1	1	0	$q6_n$	$q7_n$	$q0_n$	$q1_n$	$q2_n$	$q3_n$	$q4_n$	$q5_n$
↑	0	1	1	1	$q7_n$	$q0_n$	$q1_n$	$q2_n$	$q3_n$	$q4_n$	$q5_n$	$q6_n$

Table 15-3 Function table for Example 15-2

```
SUBDESIGN  barrel
(
   clk, s[2..0], ld, d[0..7]            :INPUT;
   q[0..7]                              :OUTPUT;
)
VARIABLE
   reg[0..7]                            :DFF;     -- register
BEGIN
   reg[].clk = clk;

   IF  ld  THEN  reg[0..7].d = d[0..7];        -- parallel load
   ELSE                                        -- shift data
      CASE  s[]  IS                            -- rotate s bits
         WHEN  0  =>  reg[0..7].d = reg[0..7].q;
         WHEN  1  =>  reg[0..7].d = (reg[1..7].q, reg[0].q);
         WHEN  2  =>  reg[0..7].d = (reg[2..7].q, reg[0..1].q);
         WHEN  3  =>  reg[0..7].d = (reg[3..7].q, reg[0..2].q);
         WHEN  4  =>  reg[0..7].d = (reg[4..7].q, reg[0..3].q);
         WHEN  5  =>  reg[0..7].d = (reg[5..7].q, reg[0..4].q);
         WHEN  6  =>  reg[0..7].d = (reg[6..7].q, reg[0..5].q);
         WHEN  7  =>  reg[0..7].d = (reg[7].q, reg[0..6].q);
      END CASE;
   END IF;

   q[] = reg[].q;                       -- connect register to port
END;
```

Fig. 15-6 AHDL solution for Example 15-2

AHDL   An example AHDL solution is given in Fig. 15-6. If ld is asserted and the register is clocked, it will be parallel loaded with the data d[7..0]. Otherwise, the number of bits for the data to be rotated is determined by the CASE statement. The register's input is assigned to be equal to the appropriate output bits for the register. The input bits are mapped in order with the concatenated groups of output bits. The results for the simulation are shown in Fig. 15-7.

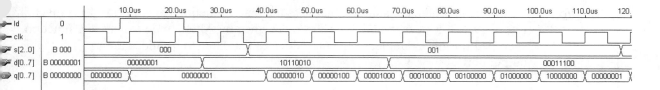

Fig. 15-7 Simulation for Example 15-2

```
ENTITY  barrel  IS
PORT (
   clk, ld         :IN BIT;
   s               :IN BIT_VECTOR (2 DOWNTO 0);
   d               :IN BIT_VECTOR (0 TO 7);
   q               :OUT BIT_VECTOR (0 TO 7)
);
END barrel;

ARCHITECTURE vhdl OF barrel IS
BEGIN
PROCESS (clk)
   VARIABLE  reg  :BIT_VECTOR (0 TO 7);      -- register
   BEGIN
   IF  (clk'EVENT AND clk = '1')     THEN
      IF (ld = '1')  THEN  reg := d;         -- parallel load
      ELSE                                   -- shift data
         CASE  s  IS                         -- rotate s bits
            WHEN  "000"  =>  reg := reg;
            WHEN  "001"  =>  reg := (reg(1 TO 7) & reg(0));
            WHEN  "010"  =>  reg := (reg(2 TO 7) & reg(0 TO 1));
            WHEN  "011"  =>  reg := (reg(3 TO 7) & reg(0 TO 2));
            WHEN  "100"  =>  reg := (reg(4 TO 7) & reg(0 TO 3));
            WHEN  "101"  =>  reg := (reg(5 TO 7) & reg(0 TO 4));
            WHEN  "110"  =>  reg := (reg(6 TO 7) & reg(0 TO 5));
            WHEN  "111"  =>  reg := (reg(7) & reg(0 TO 6));
         END CASE;
      END IF;
   END IF;
   q <= reg;                                 -- connect register to port
END PROCESS;
END vhdl;
```

Fig. 15-8 VHDL solution for Example 15-2

VHDL   A VHDL solution is given in Fig. 15-8. If ld is asserted and the register is clocked, it
will be parallel loaded with the data d. Otherwise, the number of bits for the data to be
rotated is determined by the CASE statement. The register's input is assigned to be
equal to the appropriate output bits for the register. The input bits are mapped in order
with the concatenated groups of output bits. The results for the simulation are shown in
Fig. 15-7.

Schematic An alternate schematic solution that uses the macrofunction named barrlstb is given in Fig. 15-9. This macrofunction has been designed by Altera to do exactly the function specified for this example, so the only devices that have to be added are the input and output ports.

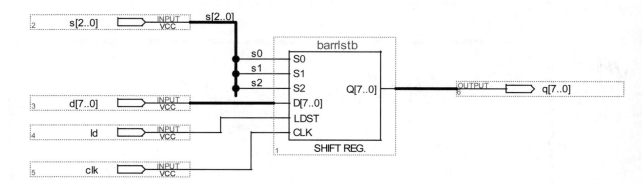

Fig. 15-9 Schematic solution using barrlstb macrofunction for Example 15-2

Feedback Shift Register Counters

A count sequence can be generated with a shift register by using the contents of the register to produce a feedback signal for the serial input to the shift register. This type of counter generally requires very little hardware to construct, and the circuitry required to decode the count sequence can be very simple. Ring counters and Johnson counters are examples of feedback shift register counters.

A ring counter has a modulus equal to the number of flip-flops being used in the shift register. There are two variations of the ring counter. One has a single bit that is high and is moved from one flip-flop in the shift register to the next. At the output end of the serial shift register, one is rotated back to the input of the shift register. The other choice is to rotate a single 0 bit throughout the length of the shift register. Decoding of the ring counter is simply done by noting which bit position contains the single 1 (or single 0). Self-starting ring counters can be easily designed by generating a simple feedback signal that monitors all of the shift register bits <u>except</u> the final bit in the chain. For a ring counter that rotates a single 1, use a NOR function (see Example 14-3). For a ring counter that rotates a single 0, use a NAND function. The fan-in on the appropriate logic gate is always one less than the number of flip-flops in the shift register counter.

The Johnson counter (also called a twisted ring counter) uses the flip-flops a little more efficiently to produce a modulus that is two times the number of flip-flops being used in the shift register. The feedback signal needed for the Johnson sequence is accomplished by merely inverting the single output bit of the serial shift register. Multiple sequences are produced with this simple feedback circuit, but the standard Johnson code sequence includes the state where all flip-flops are low. The Johnson counter sequence can be decoded by monitoring an appropriate pair of bits for each counter state.

A pseudorandom count sequence can be generated by a linear feedback shift register (LFSR). XNORing two or more flip-flop outputs from the shift register produces the feedback for this simple type of shift register counter. A shift register counter using this feedback arrangement with n flip-flops would have a count modulus of $2^n - 1$. The count modulus for any length LFSR counter can be shortened by causing it to skip an appropriate number of states. Table 15-4 lists the proper inputs to the XNOR feedback gate that is generating the serial input to flip-flop Q0 (the first flip-flop in the shift register chain).

Number of flip-flops	Counter modulus	XNOR gate inputs
2	3	Q1, Q0
3	7	Q2, Q1
4	15	Q3, Q2
5	31	Q4, Q2
6	63	Q5, Q4
7	127	Q6, Q5
8	255	Q7, Q5, Q4, Q3
9	511	Q8, Q4
10	1023	Q9, Q6
11	2047	Q10, Q9
12	4095	Q11, Q10, Q9, Q1

Table 15-4 LFSR counter modulus and feedback signals

Example 15-3

Design a self-starting mod-4 ring counter to be implemented in a PLD. The ring counter should output a single 1 that is rotated through a 4-bit shift register to produce the recycling binary pattern: $1000 \rightarrow 0100 \rightarrow 0010 \rightarrow 0001 \rightarrow 1000$.

The desired sequence is listed in the table given in Fig. 15-10. The necessary serial feedback (SER) that will produce this ring counter pattern in a shift register is determined and entered for each desired counter state. Note that the 0000_2 state has been defined to have SER = 1. Thus, the ring counter can start up because the EPM7128 will reset all flip-flops at power-up. The required feedback SER is plotted in the K-map given in Fig. 15-8. The undefined counter states will be assumed to be don't-care conditions. From the K-map and DeMorgan's theorem, the feedback function is:

$$SER = \overline{QA}\ \overline{QB}\ \overline{QC} = \overline{QA + QB + QC}$$

SER	QA	QB	QC	QD	
1	0	0	0	0	*start-up*
0	1	0	0	0	
0	0	1	0	0	
0	0	0	1	0	
1	0	0	0	1	
	1	0	0	0	*recycles*

	QC QD			
QA QB	0 0	0 1	1 1	1 0
0 0	1	1		0
0 1	0			
1 1				
1 0	0			

Fig. 15-10 Sequence table and K-map for Example 15-3

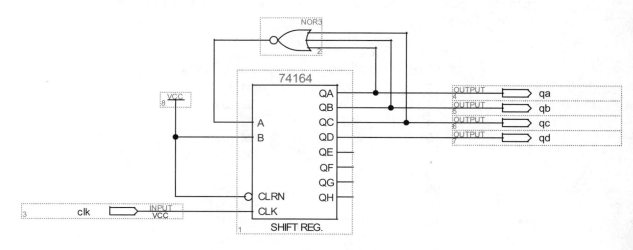

Fig. 15-11 Schematic for Example 15-3

Schematic   Applying the function derived for **SER** results in the circuit design shown in Fig. 15-11. A 74164 macrofunction was used even though it is an 8-bit shift register and only the first 4 bits (**QA** through **QD**) will be used in this application. The compiler will remove unused macrofunction logic to reduce the amount of chip resources needed to implement the design. Examining the report file for this design reveals that only 4 logic cells were used. The serial input to this shift register macrofunction is the result of the ANDing of the two inputs labeled **A** and **B**. Simulation results are shown in Fig. 15-12.

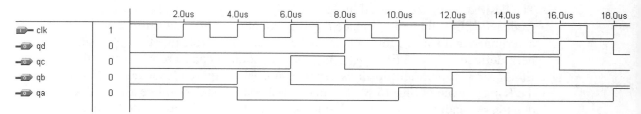

Fig. 15-12 Simulation results for Example 15-3

```
SUBDESIGN  ring4a
(
      clk                       :INPUT;
      qa, qb, qc, qd            :OUTPUT;
)
VARIABLE
      register[0..3]            :DFF;      -- shift register
      ser                       :NODE;     -- feedback signal
BEGIN
      register[].clk = clk;

      ser = !(register0 # register1 # register2);
            -- serial feedback function uses a NOR

      register[0..3].d = (ser, register[0..2].q);
            -- create ring counter by concatenating shift
            -- register with serial feedback function

      (qa, qb, qc, qd) = register[].q;
            -- connect register to output ports
END;
```

Fig. 15-13 AHDL solution for Example 15-3

AHDL   An AHDL design solution is shown in Fig. 15-13. The buried-node, feedback function
ser is defined with the NOR logic expression. By using concatenation, the serial input
is applied to the first flip-flop input while the other three bits of the register are shifted
one position. The register outputs are connected to the output ports for the block. This
circuit can also be designed using a state machine. Simulation results are shown in Fig.
15-12.

```
ENTITY   ring4v   IS
PORT (
      clk                         :IN BIT;
      qa, qb, qc, qd              :OUT BIT
);
END ring4v;

ARCHITECTURE vhdl OF ring4v IS
SIGNAL  ser                :BIT;        -- feedback signal
BEGIN
PROCESS (clk)
      VARIABLE   reg        :BIT_VECTOR (0 TO 3);
                                        -- shift register
      BEGIN
            IF (clk'EVENT AND clk = '1')   THEN
                  reg(0 TO 3)  := (ser & reg(0 TO 2));
                  -- create ring counter by concatenating
                  -- shift register with serial feedback
                  -- function
            END IF;

            ser <= NOT (reg(0) OR reg(1) OR reg(2));
                  -- NOR function for feedback signal

                  -- connect register to output ports
            qa <= reg(0);
            qb <= reg(1);
            qc <= reg(2);
            qd <= reg(3);
END PROCESS;
END vhdl;
```

Fig. 15-14 VHDL solution for Example 15-3

VHDL   A VHDL design solution is shown in Fig. 15-14. By using concatenation, the serial input is applied to the first flip-flop input while the other three bits of the register are shifted one position. The buried-node feedback function **ser** is defined with the NOR logic expression. The register outputs are connected to the output ports for the block. Simulation results are shown in Fig. 15-12.

Example 15-4

Design a self-starting, mod-7 ring counter to be implemented with a PLD. The ring counter should output a single 1 that is rotated through the shift register.

We found in Example 15-3 that a NOR gate will produce the necessary feedback signal for a ring counter to rotate a single 1 through the shift register's flip-flops. This feedback function can be expanded to produce ring counters with more output bits and, therefore, a greater counter modulus. A mod-7 ring counter will require 7 flip-flops in the shift register and a 6-input NOR function for the feedback circuit. Inputs to the NOR will come from the first 6 out of the 7 flip-flop outputs. Only the last flip-flop stage in the serial shift register circuit will be omitted from the NOR's inputs. The serial-input feedback function needed for this ring counter is:

$$\overline{Q0 \ + \ Q1 \ + \ Q2 \ + \ Q3 \ + \ Q4 \ + \ Q5}$$

An example schematic solution is shown in Fig. 15-15. Simulation results are given in Fig. 15-16. HDL solutions are listed in Figs. 15-17 (AHDL) and 15-18 (VHDL).

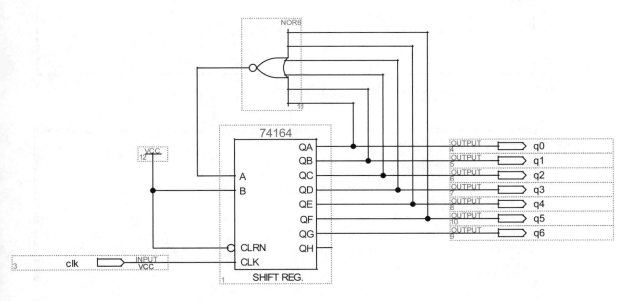

Fig. 15-15 Schematic solution for Example 15-4

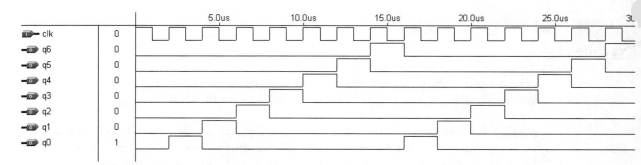

Fig. 15-16 Simulation results for Example 15-4

```
SUBDESIGN   ring7a
(
      clk                 :INPUT;
      q[0..6]             :OUTPUT;
)
VARIABLE
      q[0..6]             :DFF;         -- shift register
      ser                 :NODE;        -- feedback signal
BEGIN
      q[].clk = clk;
      ser = !(q0 # q1 # q2 # q3 # q4 # q5);    -- feedback
      q[0..6].d = (ser, q[0..5].q);            -- concatenate
END;
```

Fig. 15-17 AHDL solution for Example 15-4

```
ENTITY   ring7v   IS
PORT (
      clk         :IN BIT;
      q           :OUT BIT_VECTOR (0 TO 6)
);
END ring7v;
ARCHITECTURE vhdl OF ring7v IS
SIGNAL   ser       :BIT;        -- feedback signal
BEGIN
PROCESS (clk)
      VARIABLE  r :BIT_VECTOR (0 TO 6);   -- register
      BEGIN
            ser <= NOT (r(0) OR r(1) OR r(2) OR r(3)
                  OR r(4) OR r(5));        -- feedback
            IF (clk'EVENT AND clk = '1')   THEN
                  r := (ser & r(0 TO 5));   -- concatenate
            END IF;
            q <= r;
END PROCESS;
END vhdl;
```

Fig. 15-18 VHDL solution for Example 15-4

Laboratory Projects

15.1   Waveform pattern generator
Design a waveform pattern generator using **standard logic devices**. The parallel-in, serial-out shift register will produce any desired 8-bit waveform pattern such as the one illustrated below. The first bit on each pattern cycle should be the LSB. Use an IC counter chip to control the parallel loading/serial shifting sequence. Construct and test the logic circuit by comparing the CLK and SERIAL_OUT waveforms with a two-channel oscilloscope. **Use the Shift/Load signal to trigger the scope.** Note the change in the SERIAL_OUT waveform as the data input switches are changed. Hints: There will be 8 clock cycles needed for each 8-bit pattern sequence: 1 cycle to parallel load the 8-bit pattern and 7 more to serially shift the data toward Q_H for serial output. Use a mod-8 counter to control the loading and shifting sequence.

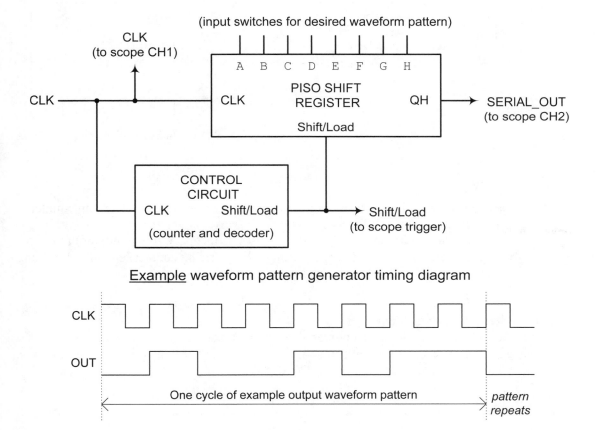

Example waveform pattern generator timing diagram

15.2   Waveform pattern generator
Use an HDL to design Laboratory Project 15.1 and program it into a PLD.

15.3　Serial data buffer

Design a serial data buffer that contains a serial-in, parallel-out shift register and a parallel-in, parallel-out register. The SIPO will accept 8 bits of serial data and then, after 8 clock cycles, automatically transfer (in parallel) the data to the PIPO register. Use a **manual** clock to test the circuit.

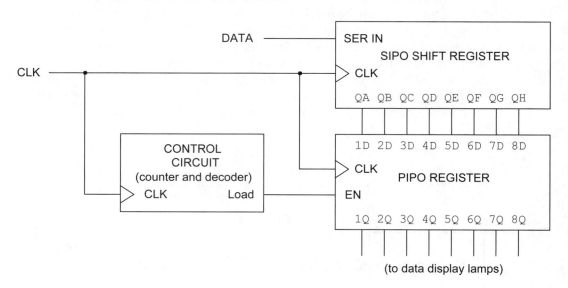

15.4　Mod-10 ring counter

Design a self-starting (and self-correcting) mod-10 ring counter. The ring counter should **rotate a single 0** for its sequence. The ring counter also needs to have an asynchronous, active-low clear (clrn). Hint: The feedback function (gate) must produce a serial feedback that is zero <u>only</u> when the ring counter has shifted the single zero to the last flip-flop.

15.5　Mod-10 Johnson counter

Design a mod-10 Johnson counter. The counter also needs synchronous controls for an active-high reset (reset) and an active-high disable (hold), as shown in the following table. Decode (active-high) state 00000 (zero).

Clock	Reset	Hold	Function
↑	1	X	Clear
↑	0	1	Disable
↑	0	0	Count

15.6   Mod-31 LFSR counter
Design a mod-31 LFSR counter using an HDL. The counter should have two
synchronous controls, an active-low reset (**resetn**), and an active-high count enable
(**enable**).

15.7   Parallel data pipeline
Design a 4-bit data pipeline circuit. A 4-bit data word (**D3 D2 D1 D0**) will be entered
in parallel into the data pipeline when the **LOAD** control is high and the registers are
clocked. Use a **manual** clock to load in one data word at a time into the pipeline. The
data pipeline is five 4-bit words deep. Define a 4-bit register with an HDL and use a
hierarchical design.

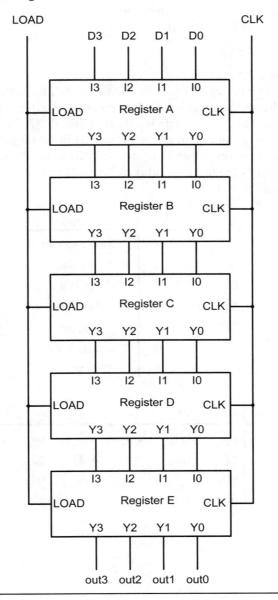

15.8   Special-purpose data register
Design an 8-bit data register that operates according to the following function table. The register function is selected with the controls s[1..0]. The 4-bit data input is labeled i[3..0], and the register output is labeled q[7..0].

s1	s0	Operation	$Q7_{n+1}$	$Q6_{n+1}$	$Q5_{n+1}$	$Q4_{n+1}$	$Q3_{n+1}$	$Q2_{n+1}$	$Q1_{n+1}$	$Q0_{n+1}$
0	0	Load L.S. nibble	$Q7_n$	$Q6_n$	$Q5_n$	$Q4_n$	$I3_n$	$I2_n$	$I1_n$	$I0_n$
0	1	Load M.S. nibble	$I3_n$	$I2_n$	$I1_n$	$I0_n$	$Q3_n$	$Q2_n$	$Q1_n$	$Q0_n$
1	0	Swap nibbles	$Q3_n$	$Q2_n$	$Q1_n$	$Q0_n$	$Q7_n$	$Q6_n$	$Q5_n$	$Q4_n$
1	1	Rotate data right	$Q0_n$	$Q7_n$	$Q6_n$	$Q5_n$	$Q4_n$	$Q3_n$	$Q2_n$	$Q1_n$

Note: L.S. = least significant
M.S. = most significant

15.9   Shift/rotate register
Design an 8-bit data register that can rotate or shift its contents in either direction. The function of the register is controlled by inputs m[2..0], as shown in the following function table. The parallel data inputs are labeled d[7..0], and the register outputs are q[7..0]. The serial data input **ser** is a common input for shifting in either direction. The data can be moved either right (toward q0) or left (toward q7) in the register. A data rotation feeds the last data bit back around to the input of the shift register instead of losing it out the end.

m2	m1	m0	Function
0	0	X	Clear register
0	1	0	Load data
0	1	1	Hold data
1	0	0	Shift right
1	0	1	Shift left
1	1	0	Rotate right
1	1	1	Rotate left

Shift/rotate	Direction	$q7_{n+1}$	$q6_{n+1}$	$q5_{n+1}$	$q4_{n+1}$	$q3_{n+1}$	$q2_{n+1}$	$q1_{n+1}$	$q0_{n+1}$
Shift	Right	ser	$q7_n$	$q6_n$	$q5_n$	$q4_n$	$q3_n$	$q2_n$	$q1_n$
Shift	Left	$q6_n$	$q5_n$	$q4_n$	$q3_n$	$q2_n$	$q1_n$	$q0_n$	ser
Rotate	Right	$q0_n$	$q7_n$	$q6_n$	$q5_n$	$q4_n$	$q3_n$	$q2_n$	$q1_n$
Rotate	Left	$q6_n$	$q5_n$	$q4_n$	$q3_n$	$q2_n$	$q1_n$	$q0_n$	$q7_n$

LIBRARY OF PARAMETERIZED MODULES

Objective

- To use Altera's library of parameterized modules (LPM) in schematic capture design entry.

Suggested Part
   EPM7128S or EP1C6

Altera describes their library of parameterized modules (LPM) as a set of logic functions that use "parameters to achieve scalability, adaptability, and efficient silicon implementation." MAX+PLUS II and Quartus II have a variety of parameterized modules to implement common logic functions including: AND, OR, and XOR gates, counters, and shift registers. The term *scalability* refers to the width of the logic function (i.e., the number of inputs for a logic gate or the number of bits in a counter or shift register). Other common features and controls of counters (up/down, synchronous/asynchronous clear, parallel load, count enable, modulus) and shift registers (serial-in/serial-out, parallel-in/parallel-out, shift direction, synchronous/asynchronous clear) are also parameterized, meaning that they can be included as needed in a specific application. LPM functions can be used in schematic, AHDL, VHDL, Verilog HDL, and EDIF input files. This unit will look at using LPMs only in schematics. See "Schematic Capture of LPMs" in MAXplus Notes or Quartus Notes in the CD-ROM Tutorials folder.

Example 16-1

The top-level design for a serial, synchronous data communications circuit is given in Fig. 16-1. This hierarchical design consists of two major logic blocks, an 8-bit serial data transmitter and an 8-bit serial data receiver. Each of these blocks uses LPM registers and counters in the lower level design files. Examine this case-study design to see how LPMs may be used in schematic files.

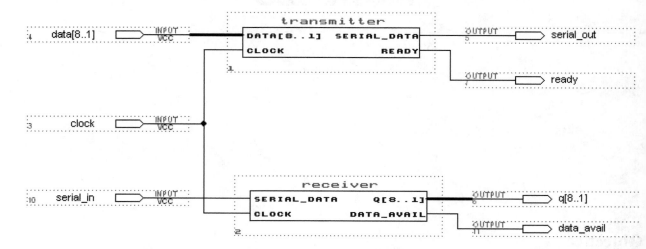

Fig. 16-1 Top-level design for a serial data transmitter/receiver

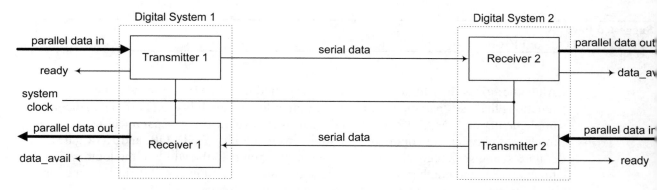

Fig. 16-2 Bidirectional serial data communications circuit

The complete communications circuit will consist of two identical copies of the circuit shown in Fig. 16-1. A pair of data transmitters/receivers will be used for the complete communications circuit to allow for bidirectional data flow between remote digital systems (see Fig. 16-2). Parallel data will be applied to the input of one of the transmitter blocks. This data will be automatically loaded into the transmitter and then shifted out serially. This serial data is to be received by another system that is located some distance away. The remote receiver will input the serial data along with the system clock signal to synchronize the transmitter and receiver together. After all 8 data bits have been received, the parallel output at the receiver will be updated with the new information. This same process can be performed for each system so that serial data can flow in either direction, from transmitter 1 to receiver 2 and from transmitter 2 to receiver 1.

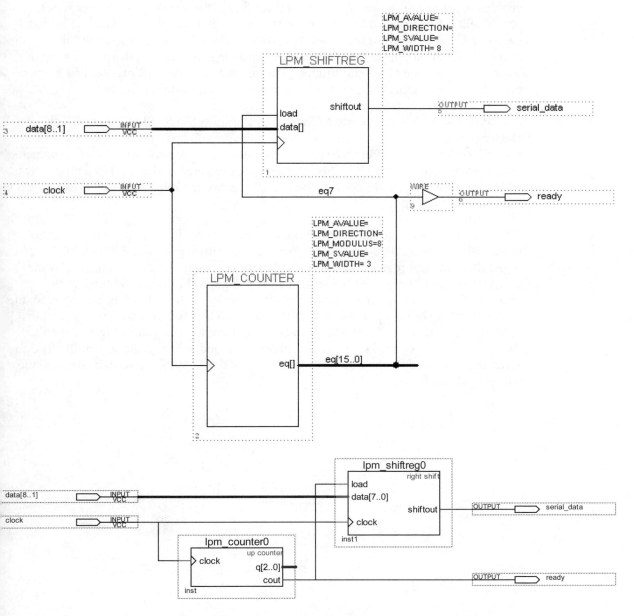

Fig. 16-3 Transmitter block for serial communications circuit.
(Top: MAX+PLUS II; bottom: Quartus II)

The transmitter block is shown in Fig. 16-3. It consists of two LPM modules, an 8-bit parallel-in/serial-out shift register, and a mod-8 binary counter. The counter controls the parallel-load/serial-shift function of the shift register using the signal called ready. This control signal detects (decodes) the terminal state of the mod-8 counter and enables the shift register to parallel load data[8..1]. For the other 7 counter states, ready will be inactive, which will allow the shift register to shift its data one bit for each clock pulse. Each of the data bits in data[8..1] will be output from the shift register's serial output (serial_data). The ready signal indicates that a new 8-bit data word can be applied to the transmitter. The counter bits and shift register bits are not provided on output ports since they are not needed in the application.

An LPM module is entered into a Graphic Design file (MAX+PLUS II) or Block Diagram/Schematic file (Quartus II) in much the same way as primitives or macrofunctions. The difference is that the width and all control features and parameters are programmable for LPMs. This information is selected or declared in dialog boxes when the LPM is entered into the schematic. The two modules used in this example are lpm_counter and lpm_shiftreg.

The receiver block is another schematic file and is shown in Fig. 16-4. It consists of three LPM modules, an 8-bit serial-in/parallel-out shift register, an 8-bit parallel-in/parallel-out shift register, and a mod-8 binary counter. The serial data sent by the transmitter block is received by the first shift register. The counter will count the number of bits received (one data bit per clock cycle). When all 8 bits are received, the data is parallel shifted to the second shift register. The parallel-load function of the second shift register is controlled by the counter terminal state decoding signal called data_avail. This control signal will enable the second shift register to parallel load the serial data received by the first shift register. The data_avail signal indicates that the data output can be read.

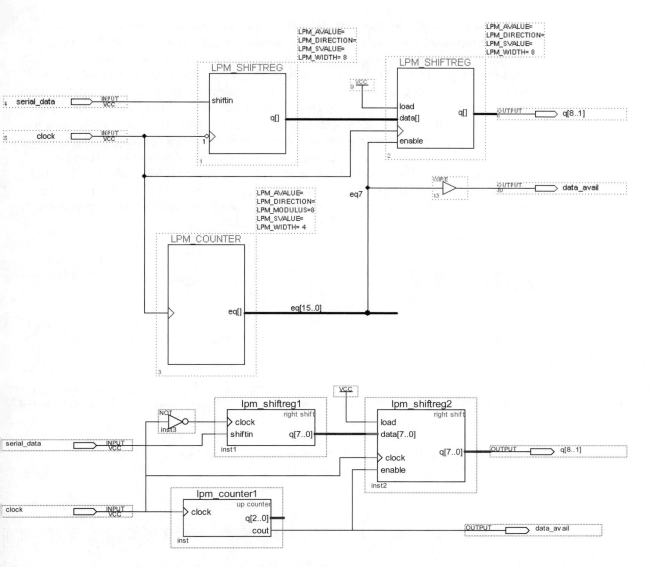

Fig. 16-4 Receiver block for serial communications circuit.
(Top: MAX+PLUS II; bottom: Quartus II)

To verify the serial communications circuit design, a test circuit was created in a separate top-level schematic file. In this simulation test circuit, the serial data input to the receiver is connected directly to the serial data output from the transmitter block in the same chip (see Fig. 16-5). In the actual design, there will be two separate chips, with the transmitter from one connected to the receiver in the other. A sample of the simulation results is shown in Fig. 16-6. The parallel data will be "picked up" by the transmitter on the next ↑ clock after ready goes high. Therefore, the parallel data in can be changed while ready is low but should be stable when ready goes high. One bit of data is transmitted at a time after ready goes high, with the most significant bit shifted first. The least significant bit is shifted when ready is low. The new parallel data is available at the q[8..1] outputs of the receiver when data_avail is low. This occurs every 8 clock cycles. The parallel data could be moved to another register anytime before data_avail goes high.

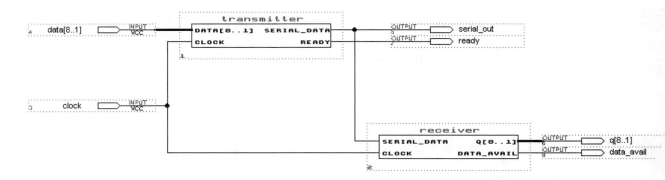

Fig. 16-5 Top-level GDF file for test circuit used in simulation

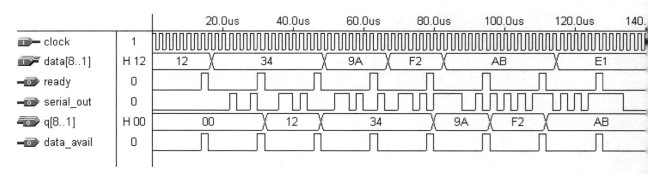

Fig. 16-6 Sample simulation results for serial data communications circuit

Laboratory Projects

16.1   Serial data communications circuit
Create the serial data communications circuit described in Example 16-1. Construct and test the circuit design with two transmitter/receiver chips connected together to provide bidirectional data transmission. Note: Use a common ground (and clock) for the two digital systems.

16.2   Clock divider
Design a logic circuit that will produce clock frequencies of 10 kHz and 1 Hz derived from the on-board oscillator. Use LPMs for the design. Hint: Determine the counter modulus needed to produce the 10-kHz signal and then further divide this frequency with a second counter to produce the 1-Hz signal. Simulate each of these counters separately since the mod numbers will be very large, and then combine them together in a top-level design for the complete circuit. Then test the outputs with a frequency counter. Why will the output signal frequencies differ slightly from the specified values?

16.3   Data word logic unit
Design a logic circuit that can produce the results of four different bit-wise logical operations on two 8-bit data words. The two operands and the 8-bit result are stored in three separate 8-bit registers. The parallel-in/parallel-out registers are named A, B, and C. Registers A and B will store the two operands for the logic function. The two operand registers are parallel loaded from an 8-bit data input bus. Register C is the result register. Under normal operation, each register will be parallel loaded at different times when its respective load control is high and the ↑ CLOCK signal is applied. Use LPMs to create the three registers. There are four logical operations that may be performed, as shown in the following table. Hint: Define a subdesign block using an HDL that will perform the four logic functions.

funct1	funct0	Function
0	0	NOT A
0	1	OR
1	0	AND
1	1	XOR

DECODERS AND DISPLAYS

Objectives

- To apply decoding circuits in digital system applications.
- To implement digital displays using 7-segment devices.

Suggested Parts

7408	7447	74163	EPM7128S or EP1C6	MAN72
330-Ω resistors				

Decoder Circuits

A decoder is used to detect a particular combination of bits applied to the input of the circuit and to display that information in a specified fashion. Logic gates can be used to design any type of decoder circuit. Decoders that are commonly used in logic applications are available as IC chips. For example, the 74138 (a 3-line-to-8-line decoder) shown in Fig. 17-1 is being used to decode a mod-8 binary counter. This decoder chip can be used to identify which of the 8 possible counter states is currently applied to its 3 data input lines (C B A). This chip also has 3 enable inputs (2 active-low G2A G2B and 1 active-high G1), which adds greatly to its flexibility and usefulness. When enabled, only one of the decoder's 8 outputs will be active (low), which will indicate the counter's output state. The truth table for the 74138 is shown in Table 17-1.

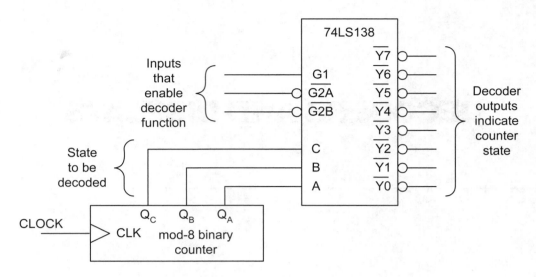

Fig. 17-1 A 74138 decoding a mod-8 binary counter

G1	G2A	G2B	C	B	A	Y0	Y1	Y2	Y3	Y4	Y5	Y6	Y7
1	0	0	0	0	0	0	1	1	1	1	1	1	1
1	0	0	0	0	1	1	0	1	1	1	1	1	1
1	0	0	0	1	0	1	1	0	1	1	1	1	1
1	0	0	0	1	1	1	1	1	0	1	1	1	1
1	0	0	1	0	0	1	1	1	1	0	1	1	1
1	0	0	1	0	1	1	1	1	1	1	0	1	1
1	0	0	1	1	0	1	1	1	1	1	1	0	1
1	0	0	1	1	1	1	1	1	1	1	1	1	0
0	X	X	X	X	X	1	1	1	1	1	1	1	1
X	1	X	X	X	X	1	1	1	1	1	1	1	1
X	X	1	X	X	X	1	1	1	1	1	1	1	1

Table 17-1 Truth table for a 74138 decoder

Decoder/Drivers and 7-Segment Displays

Decoder/driver circuits are available for various kinds of display devices, such as 7-segment displays. A 7-segment display device is commonly used to display the decimal characters 0–9. The display segments are often constructed using light emitting diodes (LEDs) in which the appropriate LED segments are forward-biased (causing them to emit light) for the desired symbol shape. Decoder/driver circuits control the LED biasing for the display of the appropriate characters for the data being input. Series current limiting resistors are employed to protect the individual LED segments from damage caused by too much forward-biased diode current. The pin-out configuration for a typical common-anode 7-segment display is illustrated in Fig. 17-2.

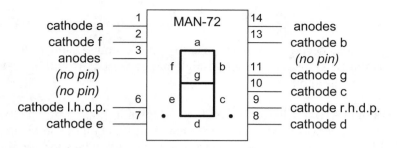

Fig. 17-2 MAN72 (or equivalent) 7-segment common-anode display (top view)

Standard BCD-to-7-segment decoder/driver chips are available to provide the necessary biasing signals for a 7-segment LED display device to produce the decimal characters 0 through 9. Since common-anode and common-cathode 7-segment devices are available, an appropriate decoder/driver chip must be selected to match the display type. The 7447 shown in Fig. 17-3 is designed to be used with a common-anode type device. The BCD input is applied to **DCBA** (A = lsb). The segment driver outputs (labeled **a** through **g**) are active-low since they will be connected to the LED's cathode pin on the corresponding segment. Note that a series resistor is needed for each segment of the display to limit the amount of LED current to a safe level. The active-low lamp test (**LT**) input is used to turn on all 7 segments to check if any are burned out. The active-low ripple-blanking input (**RBI**) is used to blank (turn off) the display if the BCD input is 0000. Both of these functions have been disabled in this schematic by tying them high. The blanking input/ripple-blanking output pin (**BI/RBO**) can be used as either an input or output control. If a low is applied to the pin, the display will be blanked regardless of the BCD input value. Used as an output, this pin will allow all leading zeros in a multi-digit display to be blanked.

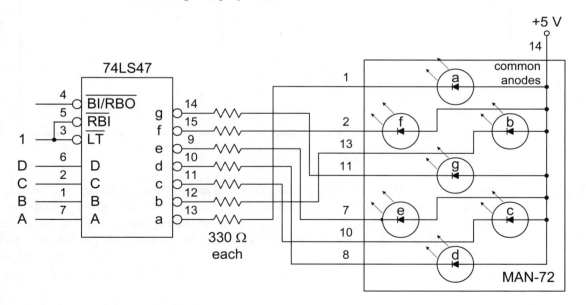

Fig. 17-3 Standard 7447 decoder/driver and 7-segment LED display circuit

Example 17-1

Design a BCD decoder circuit (with active-high outputs) using a PLD that also detects any invalid BCD inputs. An active-high output named **err** will indicate that an invalid BCD input was applied.

AHDL

An example AHDL file for the solution is shown in Fig. 17-4. The truth table design entry technique was used to define the ten valid BCD input combinations. The DEFAULTS statement allows you to specify default values for variables used in TRUTH TABLE, IF/THEN, and CASE statements. The ten **state** outputs are to be low and the **err** output is high except as given in the table. The simulation for this design is shown in Fig. 17-5.

```
SUBDESIGN   BCD_decoder
(
     bcd[3..0]                    :INPUT;
     state[9..0], err             :OUTPUT;
)
BEGIN
     DEFAULTS
             state[] = B"0000000000";        -- active-high
             err = VCC;                      -- active-high
     END DEFAULTS;
     TABLE
             bcd[]  =>      state[], err;
             0      =>      B"0000000001", 0;
             1      =>      B"0000000010", 0;
             2      =>      B"0000000100", 0;
             3      =>      B"0000001000", 0;
             4      =>      B"0000010000", 0;
             5      =>      B"0000100000", 0;
             6      =>      B"0001000000", 0;
             7      =>      B"0010000000", 0;
             8      =>      B"0100000000", 0;
             9      =>      B"1000000000", 0;
     END TABLE;
END;
```

Fig. 17-4 AHDL solution for Example 17-1

VHDL

An example VHDL file for the solution is shown in Fig. 17-6. A CASE statement is used in a PROCESS to define the outputs for the ten valid BCD input combinations. A WHEN OTHERS choice will take care of any invalid BCD input condition and make the ten **state** outputs and the **err** output high. The simulation for this design is shown in Fig. 17-5.

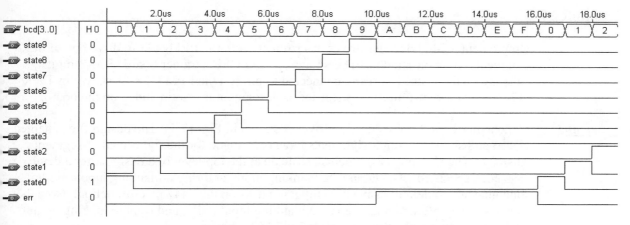

Fig. 17-5 Simulation results for Example 17-1

```
ENTITY  BCD_decoder  IS
PORT (
      bcd            : IN INTEGER RANGE 0 TO 15;
      state          : OUT BIT_VECTOR (9 DOWNTO 0);
      err            : OUT BIT
);
END BCD_decoder;

ARCHITECTURE vhdl OF BCD_decoder IS
BEGIN
   PROCESS (bcd)
   BEGIN
      CASE bcd IS           -- determine input
         WHEN 0 =>          state <= "0000000001";   err <= '0';
         WHEN 1 =>          state <= "0000000010";   err <= '0';
         WHEN 2 =>          state <= "0000000100";   err <= '0';
         WHEN 3 =>          state <= "0000001000";   err <= '0';
         WHEN 4 =>          state <= "0000010000";   err <= '0';
         WHEN 5 =>          state <= "0000100000";   err <= '0';
         WHEN 6 =>          state <= "0001000000";   err <= '0';
         WHEN 7 =>          state <= "0010000000";   err <= '0';
         WHEN 8 =>          state <= "0100000000";   err <= '0';
         WHEN 9 =>          state <= "1000000000";   err <= '0';
         WHEN OTHERS =>     state <= "0000000000";   err <= '1';
            -- takes care of error conditions
      END CASE;
   END PROCESS;
END vhdl;
```

Fig. 17-6 VHDL solution for Example 17-1

Example 17-2

Implement a 7447 decoder/driver macrofunction in the EPM7128 to drive one of the 7-segment, common-anode LED displays on your CPLD trainer board. The 2-digit display on the board is already connected to pins on the EPM7128, as shown in Table 17-2. The current-limiting resistor for each segment is also included on the board.

Schematic   A schematic file for the decoder/driver is shown in Fig. 17-7. The design file is named **7seg** and shows the pin assignments have been made for the right-hand, 7-segment display. The chip pin assignments are made at the top level of a design after a device has been specified. The lamp test, blanking input, and ripple-blanking inputs are left unconnected to default as inactive input controls on the 7447 macrofunction. Note that the 7447 macrofunction has separate blanking input (**BIN**) and ripple-blanking output (**RBON**) ports, unlike the equivalent 7447 MSI chip.

Board →	UP2 and PLDT-2		eSOC	
Segment ↓	Left-hand Digit	Right-hand Digit	Left-hand Digit	Right-hand Digit
a	Pin 58	Pin 69	Pin 27	Pin 36
b	Pin 60	Pin 70	Pin 28	Pin 37
c	Pin 61	Pin 73	Pin 29	Pin 40
d	Pin 63	Pin 74	Pin 30	Pin 41
e	Pin 64	Pin 76	Pin 31	Pin 44
f	Pin 65	Pin 75	Pin 33	Pin 45
g	Pin 67	Pin 77	Pin 34	Pin 48
Decimal Point	Pin 68	Pin 79	Pin 35	Pin 49

Table 17-2 EPM7128SLC84 pin assignments for 2-digit, 7-segment displays on UP2, PLDT-2, and eSOC trainer boards

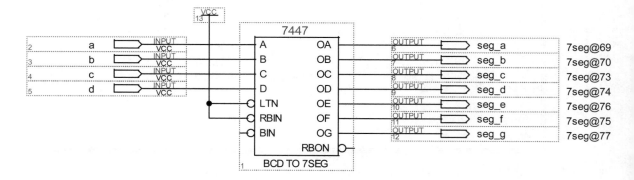

Fig. 17-7 Schematic for Example 17-2

The simulation results are shown in Fig. 17-8. The 7447 is designed to drive common-anode, 7-segment displays and will, therefore, output a low to light the appropriate segments and thus produce the desired decimal characters.

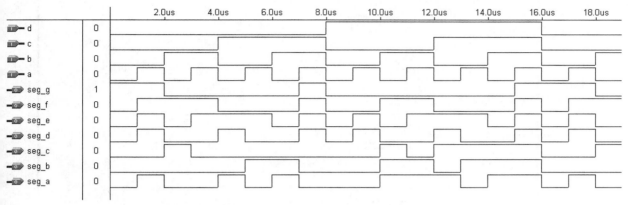

Fig. 17-8 Simulation results for Example 17-2

Example 17-3

Design a memory chip decoder using a PLD. The decoder should produce individual chip select signals (cs6 through cs0) for seven different memory chips. The decoder's function table and specific address range for each chip is given in Table 17-3. The 16-bit addresses (a15 through a0) are given in hexadecimal in the table.

Address Range (hexadecimal)	Chip Selects						
	cs6	cs5	cs4	cs3	cs2	cs1	cs0
0000–07FF	1	1	1	1	1	1	0
0800–0FFF	1	1	1	1	1	0	1
1000–17FF	1	1	1	1	0	1	1
1800–1FFF	1	1	1	0	1	1	1
8000–8FFF	1	1	0	1	1	1	1
A000–AFFF	1	0	1	1	1	1	1
C000–FFFF	0	1	1	1	1	1	1

Table 17-3 Decoder function table for Example 17-3

AHDL   An example AHDL solution is given in Fig. 17-9. The chip select outputs are active-low, so the DEFAULTS statement declares them to be high (inactive) unless otherwise indicated in the TABLE. Each chip select output signal will be low when the appropriate address range is applied to the decoder. The X's in the table indicate that the address bit can be either 0 or 1 for the specified address range. The compiler will automatically determine which of the address input bits need to be decoded to distinguish the address ranges from each other. The simulation results are shown in Fig. 17-10. Notice that the compiler has dropped out the input bits that don't matter.

```
SUBDESIGN  mem_decoder
(
      a[15..0]    :INPUT;
      cs[6..0]    :OUTPUT;
)
BEGIN
      DEFAULTS
            cs[] = B"1111111";
      END DEFAULTS;

      TABLE
            a[]                      =>    cs[];
            B"00000XXXXXXXXXXX"       =>    B"1111110";
            B"00001XXXXXXXXXXX"       =>    B"1111101";
            B"00010XXXXXXXXXXX"       =>    B"1111011";
            B"00011XXXXXXXXXXX"       =>    B"1110111";
            B"1000XXXXXXXXXXXX"       =>    B"1101111";
            B"1010XXXXXXXXXXXX"       =>    B"1011111";
            B"11XXXXXXXXXXXXXX"       =>    B"0111111";
                  -- X indicates "don't care" inputs
      END TABLE;
END;
```

Fig. 17-9 AHDL solution for Example 17-3

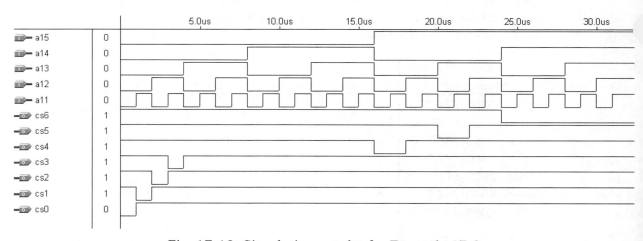

Fig. 17-10 Simulation results for Example 17-3

VHDL   An example VHDL solution is given in Fig. 17-11. The 16-bit address port is declared to be an INTEGER data type with a value range of 0 through 65535 ($2^{16} - 1$). The 7-bit chip select output port is a BIT_VECTOR data type. Each chip select output signal will be low when the appropriate address range is applied to the decoder. An IF/THEN statement is used in the PROCESS to determine the value of **a** and specify the appropriate output for **cs**. The integer values for each of the given address ranges is given in hexadecimal. A hexadecimal integer value is specified by preceding the value with the base (16) and enclosing it with a pair of # characters. The compiler will automatically determine which of the address input bits need to be decoded to distinguish the address ranges from each other. The simulation results are shown in Fig. 17-10. Notice that the compiler has dropped out the input bits that don't matter.

```
ENTITY  mem_decoder  IS
PORT (   a               : IN INTEGER RANGE 0 TO 65535;
         cs              : OUT BIT_VECTOR (6 DOWNTO 0) );
END mem_decoder;

ARCHITECTURE decoder OF mem_decoder IS
BEGIN
   PROCESS (a)
   BEGIN
           -- determine input address range in hex
      IF    a >= 16#0000# AND a <= 16#07FF#   THEN   cs <= "1111110";
      ELSIF a >= 16#0800# AND a <= 16#0FFF#   THEN   cs <= "1111101";
      ELSIF a >= 16#1000# AND a <= 16#17FF#   THEN   cs <= "1111011";
      ELSIF a >= 16#1800# AND a <= 16#1FFF#   THEN   cs <= "1110111";
      ELSIF a >= 16#8000# AND a <= 16#8FFF#   THEN   cs <= "1101111";
      ELSIF a >= 16#A000# AND a <= 16#AFFF#   THEN   cs <= "1011111";
      ELSIF a >= 16#C000# AND a <= 16#FFFF#   THEN   cs <= "0111111";
      ELSE                                           cs <= "1111111";
      END IF;
   END PROCESS;
END decoder;
```

Fig. 17-11 VHDL solution for Example 17-3

Example 17-4

Design a binary-to-BCD-code converter using a PLD. The code converter will have a 5-bit input (00000_2 through 11111_2) and a 2-digit output (00 through 31_{10} in BCD).

AHDL

An example AHDL solution is given in Fig. 17-12. Two separate IF/THEN statements are used to define the desired outputs for each of the two digits. The most significant digit output will be determined by the binary input being less than or equal to 9, less than or equal to 19, less than or equal to 29, or equal to 30–39. The first IF clause that is true will determine the value to assign to the MSD output. The least significant digit of the decimal input value determines the least significant digit. The set of appropriate input values for each output condition is tested in each IF clause. The simulation results are shown in Fig. 17-13.

```
SUBDESIGN  bin2bcd2
(
      bin[4..0]                    :INPUT;
      msd[1..0], lsd[3..0]    :OUTPUT;
)
BEGIN
              -- determine most significant digit
      IF         bin[] <= 9            THEN  msd[] = 0;
      ELSIF      bin[] <= 19           THEN  msd[] = 1;
      ELSIF      bin[] <= 29           THEN  msd[] = 2;
      ELSE                                   msd[] = 3;
      END IF;

              -- determine least significant digit
      IF       (bin[] == 0) # (bin[] == 10) # (bin[] == 20)
            # (bin[] == 30)            THEN    lsd[] = 0;
      ELSIF    (bin[] == 1) # (bin[] == 11) # (bin[] == 21)
            # (bin[] == 31)            THEN    lsd[] = 1;
      ELSIF    (bin[] == 2) # (bin[] == 12) # (bin[] == 22)
                                       THEN    lsd[] = 2;
      ELSIF    (bin[] == 3) # (bin[] == 13) # (bin[] == 23)
                                       THEN    lsd[] = 3;
      ELSIF    (bin[] == 4) # (bin[] == 14) # (bin[] == 24)
                                       THEN    lsd[] = 4;
      ELSIF    (bin[] == 5) # (bin[] == 15) # (bin[] == 25)
                                       THEN    lsd[] = 5;
      ELSIF    (bin[] == 6) # (bin[] == 16) # (bin[] == 26)
                                       THEN    lsd[] = 6;
      ELSIF    (bin[] == 7) # (bin[] == 17) # (bin[] == 27)
                                       THEN    lsd[] = 7;
      ELSIF    (bin[] == 8) # (bin[] == 18) # (bin[] == 28)
                                       THEN    lsd[] = 8;
      ELSE                                     lsd[] = 9;
      END IF;
END;
```

Fig. 17-12 AHDL solution for Example 17-4

Fig. 17-13 Simulation results for Example 17-4

```
ENTITY  bin2bcd2  IS
PORT (        bin            :  IN   INTEGER RANGE 0 TO 31;
        msd                  :  OUT  INTEGER RANGE 0 TO 3;
        lsd                  :  OUT  INTEGER RANGE 0 TO 9 );
END bin2bcd2;


ARCHITECTURE  vhdl  OF  bin2bcd2  is
BEGIN
    PROCESS (bin)
    BEGIN
            -- determine most significant digit
        IF     bin <= 9          THEN   msd <= 0;
        ELSIF  bin <= 19         THEN   msd <= 1;
        ELSIF  bin <= 29         THEN   msd <= 2;
        ELSE                            msd <= 3;
        END IF;

            -- determine least significant digit
        IF      (bin = 0 OR bin = 10 OR bin = 20 OR bin = 30)
                                 THEN   lsd <= 0;
        ELSIF   (bin = 1 OR bin = 11 OR bin = 21 OR bin = 31)
                                 THEN   lsd <= 1;
        ELSIF   (bin = 2 OR bin = 12 OR bin = 22)
                                 THEN   lsd <= 2;
        ELSIF   (bin = 3 OR bin = 13 OR bin = 23)
                                 THEN   lsd <= 3;
        ELSIF   (bin = 4 OR bin = 14 OR bin = 24)
                                 THEN   lsd <= 4;
        ELSIF   (bin = 5 OR bin = 15 OR bin = 25)
                                 THEN   lsd <= 5;
        ELSIF   (bin = 6 OR bin = 16 OR bin = 26)
                                 THEN   lsd <= 6;
        ELSIF   (bin = 7 OR bin = 17 OR bin = 27)
                                 THEN   lsd <= 7;
        ELSIF   (bin = 8 OR bin = 18 OR bin = 28)
                                 THEN   lsd <= 8;
        ELSE                            lsd <= 9;
        END IF;
    END PROCESS;
END vhdl;
```

Fig. 17-14 VHDL solution for Example 17-4

VHDL   An example VHDL solution is given in Fig. 17-14. The input and output ports are declared to be an INTEGER data type. Two separate IF/THEN statements are used to define the desired outputs for each of the two digits. The most significant digit output will be determined by the binary input being less than or equal to 9, less than or equal to 19, less than or equal to 29, or equal to 30–39. The first IF clause that is true will determine the value to assign to the MSD output. The least significant digit of the decimal input value determines the least significant digit. The set of appropriate input values for each output condition is tested in each IF clause. The simulation results are shown in Fig. 17-13.

Schematic   An alternative schematic solution is shown in Fig. 17-15. A 74185 binary-to-bcd converter macrofunction is used in the design file. This macrofunction can handle up to a 6-bit binary input. The input labeled **GN** is an active-low enable. The additional input bit is applied to the **E** input, and another output bit would be produced at **Y6**. Using multiple 74185 macrofunctions can create larger binary-to-BCD converters, but the circuit arrangement is not obvious. For example, Fig. 17-16 shows an 8-bit binary-to-BCD converter.

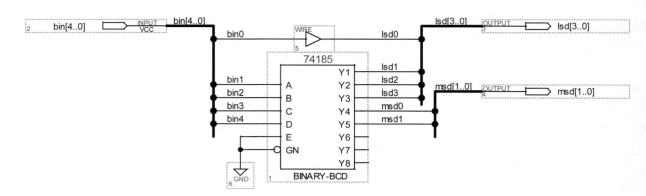

Fig. 17-15 Schematic solution for Example 17-4

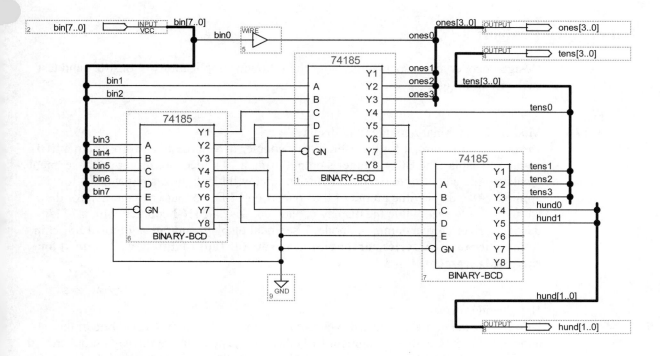

Fig. 17-16 An 8-bit binary-to-BCD converter using the 74185 macrofunction

Laboratory Projects

Design decoder and display circuits for the following applications. Construct and test each circuit design.

17.1   Modified 4-bit binary counter and display
Design a control circuit for the 4-bit binary counter in a 74163 to convert it into a BCD counter. Display the BCD counter's output using a 7447 decoder/driver and 7-segment display. Add a control to the decoder/driver that will blank the display when a low is applied. Also display the output of the counter on LEDs so that you can monitor the count progress even while the display is blanked. Use a 74163 counter chip; a 7447 decoder/driver chip; a common-anode, 7-segment display; and <u>one</u> additional SSI chip. **Remember to use a series current limiting resistor (approximately 330 ohms) for <u>each</u> LED segment.**

17.2   Hex decoder/driver
Design a hexadecimal decoder/driver circuit using a PLD that will drive one of the <u>attached</u> common-anode, 7-segment LED displays. The resultant display output should be the equivalent hexadecimal value of 0 through F. The input to the decoder/driver is a 4-bit binary value produced by a mod-16 binary counter macrofunction. To prevent ambiguous display characters, use lowercase "**b**" (for 1011) and "**d**" (for 1101), and light the a-segment for a **6** (0110). Assign the clock input to the counter to an available global clock pin.

17.3   Mod-100 BCD counter and 7-segment display
Design a mod-100 BCD counter that drives a 2-digit, 7-segment display. The count sequence will be 0 through 99. Blank leading zeros in the tens digit of the display. Assign the clock input to the counter to an available global clock pin.

17.4   Mod-16 counter and decoder
Design a mod-16, up/down binary counter and decoder with active-low outputs using a PLD. The count direction is controlled by a signal named dir (dir = 0 for count up). The decoder is to have an active-low enable named en. Use macrofunctions 74191 (counter) and 74138 (decoder). The decoder outputs are named y[15..0]. Assign the clock input to the counter to an available global clock pin.

17.5   Binary-to-BCD converter and display
Design a mod-64 binary counter and binary-to-BCD converter using a PLD. The converter should output the equivalent BCD value for the 6-bit binary input. Display the converter output on the attached 2-digit, 7-segment display. The count sequence will be 00 through 63. Do <u>not</u> blank leading zeros in the display. Assign the clock input to the counter to an available global clock pin.

17.6   Memory decoder

Design a memory chip decoder using a PLD. The decoder should produce individual chip select signals for six memory chips. The decoder should also be enabled by either of two active-low, memory-control strobe signals (memr and memw). The memory should be disabled if the two strobe signals are active simultaneously. The specific address range to be decoded for each memory chip is given below. The 16-bit addresses are given in hexadecimal in the table. Hint: Create a "buried" node whose logic equation describes the function of the memory-control signals.

Address Range (hexadecimal)	Chip Selects					
	CS5	CS4	CS3	CS2	CS1	CS0
0000–03FF	1	1	1	1	1	0
0400–07FF	1	1	1	1	0	1
0800–0BFF	1	1	1	0	1	1
0C00–0FFF	1	1	0	1	1	1
E800–EBFF	1	0	1	1	1	1
EC00–EFFF	0	1	1	1	1	1

17.7   State decoder

Design a logic circuit using a PLD that will decode the 9 specified states given in the following truth table. The inputs to the decoder are in binary and represent 0 to 99_{10}. The outputs are labeled y[9..1].

State (decimal)	y9	y8	y7	y6	y5	y4	y3	y2	y1
10	0	0	0	0	0	0	0	0	1
20	0	0	0	0	0	0	0	1	0
30	0	0	0	0	0	0	1	0	0
40	0	0	0	0	0	1	0	0	0
50	0	0	0	0	1	0	0	0	0
60	0	0	0	1	0	0	0	0	0
70	0	0	1	0	0	0	0	0	0
80	0	1	0	0	0	0	0	0	0
90	1	0	0	0	0	0	0	0	0

17.8   Binary-to-7-segment display decoder/driver

Design a binary-to-7-segment display decoder/driver using a PLD. The decoder/driver will accept a 4-bit binary input (representing zero through fifteen) and display the value using the on-board 2-digit, common-anode, 7-segment LED displays. The display for the ones digit will show the appropriate decimal character of 0 through 9, but the tens digit will either be blank or show a one (for 10 through 15). Note that all 7 segments (a through g) on the ones digit will be driven, but that only the b and c segments on the tens digit will be and they will be controlled by the same function.

ENCODERS

Objective

- To apply encoder circuits in digital system applications.

Suggested Parts				
7447	74148	EPM7128S or EP1C6	MAN72	Hex keypad
Resistors: 330 Ω, 1 kΩ				

Encoder Circuits

Input data to a logic system often comes from switches. This switch input information must be encoded into a representative binary form that can be processed by the system. Encoders have several data lines for the inputs that are being applied. The encoded output will be a binary number that will be used by the digital system to represent the specific input condition. Simple types of encoders can handle only one active input at a time. A priority encoder has an established order of precedence for the input lines so that the input with the highest priority will be encoded when multiple inputs are active simultaneously.

In Fig. 18-1, the eight pushbutton switches are encoded using a 74148, an MSI encoder chip. Each of the switch inputs to the 74148 (labeled 0 through 7) are active-low. Every SPST switch must be connected to a pull-up resistor to provide a logic one input to the 74148 when the normally open switch is not pressed. Remember that an open input to any logic device is not desirable. The 74148 is a priority encoder, so the greatest input value will be encoded if multiple inputs are active simultaneously. The truth table for the 74148 is shown in Table 18-1. The inverters have been added to the outputs from the 74148 because the encoded output that is produced by this chip happens to be the inverted binary value. The enable input (EI) and enable output (EO) pins can be used to encode more than 8 switches by cascading multiple chips together. The encoder chip has been permanently enabled with EI tied low in the schematic of Fig. 18-1. The active-low strobe output pin (GS) will indicate that an input has been applied and the encoded result is available at the output.

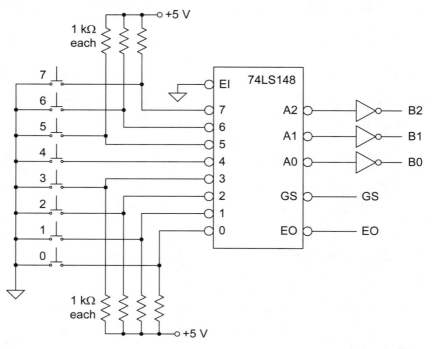

Fig. 18-1 Encoding pushbuttons with a 74148, 8-line-to-3-line priority encoder chip

EI	0	1	2	3	4	5	6	7	EO	GS	A2	A1	A0
1	X	X	X	X	X	X	X	X	1	1	1	1	1
0	1	1	1	1	1	1	1	1	0	1	1	1	1
0	0	1	1	1	1	1	1	1	1	0	1	1	1
0	X	0	1	1	1	1	1	1	1	0	1	1	0
0	X	X	0	1	1	1	1	1	1	0	1	0	1
0	X	X	X	0	1	1	1	1	1	0	1	0	0
0	X	X	X	X	0	1	1	1	1	0	0	1	1
0	X	X	X	X	X	0	1	1	1	0	0	1	0
0	X	X	X	X	X	X	0	1	1	0	0	0	1
0	X	X	X	X	X	X	X	0	1	0	0	0	0

Table 18-1 Truth table for a 74148 priority encoder

Example 18-1

Design a 16-input priority encoder circuit using the 74148 macrofunction in a PLD. The encoder should also produce an active-high output signal (called flag) to indicate that one or more of the inputs is active.

A solution is shown in Fig. 18-2. There are 16 active-low inputs that will be encoded into the corresponding binary output value (out[3..0]). If any of the higher eight inputs (sw15 through sw8) is active, the resulting high output for out3 (produced by EON) will disable the other 74148, which handles the encoding for the lower eight inputs. The active-low inputs on the ORs (equivalent to a NAND function according to DeMorgan's theorem and called the BOR primitive in MAX+PLUS II or Quartus II) will detect if an active-low output occurs for either 74148. Simulation results for this design are shown in Fig. 18-3.

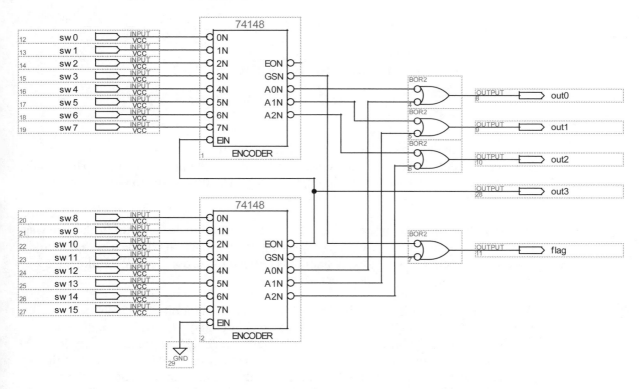

Fig. 18-2 Schematic for Example 18-1

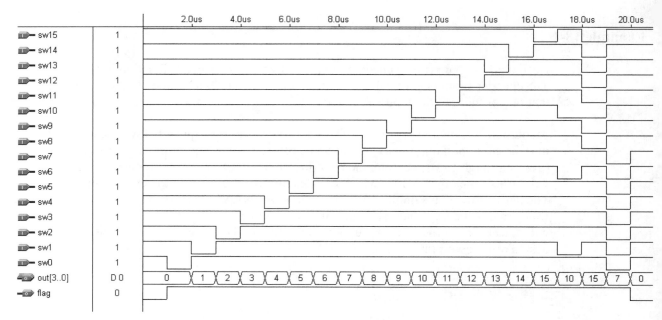

Fig. 18-3 Simulation results for Example 18-1

Example 18-2

Design an 8-input priority encoder circuit using an HDL. The inputs are active-low. The encoder output will be equal to the binary value of the pressed switch. The circuit should also produce an active-high output signal (key_press) that indicates that an input switch was pressed.

AHDL An example solution is shown in Fig. 18-4. The truth table design entry technique was used to define the encoder's outputs. The key_press function will be asserted if any input is low (active). The priority feature is defined using don't-care conditions for lower priority inputs to the encoder.

VHDL An example solution is shown in Fig. 18-5. The eight input bits are given a BIT_VECTOR data type so that each bit can be individually tested. A conditional signal assignment statement was used to define the encoder's outputs. Priority is achieved by the order of the expression tests made after the WHEN clause. The first true result that is encountered will control the value assignment for output. Since output is an INTEGER data type with a RANGE of 0 to 7, the compiler will automatically assign three bits to output. Since the key_press function is to be asserted if any input is low (active), it is very easy to define when key_press should be high (inactive). This is done with another conditional signal assignment statement.

Simulation results for either version of this design are shown in Fig. 18-6. Note that a high output for key_press indicates that a switch has been pressed and a valid binary output is produced by the encoder.

```
SUBDESIGN  encoder8
(
     sw[7..0]                          :INPUT;
     out[2..0], key_press              :OUTPUT;
)
BEGIN
     TABLE
             sw[]             =>    out[], key_press;
             B"11111111"   =>    B"000", 0;  -- no input
             B"11111110"   =>    B"000", 1;
             B"1111110X"   =>    B"001", 1;
             B"111110XX"   =>    B"010", 1;
             B"11110XXX"   =>    B"011", 1;
             B"1110XXXX"   =>    B"100", 1;
             B"110XXXXX"   =>    B"101", 1;
             B"10XXXXXX"   =>    B"110", 1;
             B"0XXXXXXX"   =>    B"111", 1;
             -- listed from lowest to highest priority
     END TABLE;
END;
```

Fig. 18-4 AHDL file for Example 18-2

```
ENTITY  encoder8  IS
PORT (      sw           : IN BIT_VECTOR (7 DOWNTO 0);
            output       : OUT INTEGER RANGE 0 TO 7;
            key_press    : OUT BIT );
END encoder8;

ARCHITECTURE vhdl OF encoder8 IS
BEGIN
output <=   7 WHEN sw(7) = '0' ELSE
            6 WHEN sw(6) = '0' ELSE
            5 WHEN sw(5) = '0' ELSE
            4 WHEN sw(4) = '0' ELSE
            3 WHEN sw(3) = '0' ELSE
            2 WHEN sw(2) = '0' ELSE
            1 WHEN sw(1) = '0' ELSE
            0 ;   -- listed in order of priority

key_press <= '0' WHEN sw = "11111111" ELSE '1';
END vhdl;
```

Fig. 18-5 VHDL file for Example 18-2

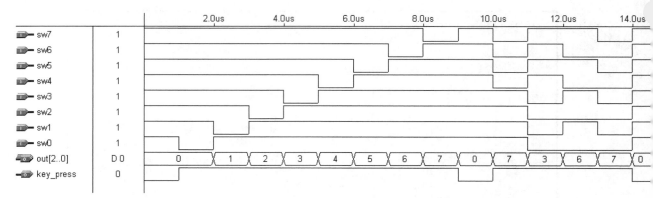

Fig. 18-6 Simulation results for Example 18-2

Scanning Encoder

A scanning encoder can be utilized when there are many switch inputs (more than is practical with cascaded 74148 chips) to be encoded in a digital system. Standard functional blocks such as counters, decoders, and encoders can be combined to implement a scanning encoder. The schematic in Fig. 18-7 illustrates a scanning encoder system for a matrix of 64 SPST pushbutton switches. The scanning encoder will output a 6-bit binary number for Z5 Z4 Z3 Z2 Z1 Z0 that is equivalent to a pressed switch's decimal label.

The scan counter (74163) is used as a mod-8 binary counter that controls the repetitive scanning of the 8 columns of switches. The column scanning decoder (74138) decodes the scan counter's output to determine which switch matrix column is currently being scanned. Only one column at a time is scanned with the active-low output produced by the scanning decoder. A closed switch will short one of the rows to one of the columns. Each switch represents a unique combination of a row and column. A closed switch on a particular column is indicated by a low input to the 8-input row encoder (74148) <u>when</u> the appropriate column with the pressed switch is scanned with a low from the decoder. When the closed switch is detected by a low input to the encoder, the GS output (Scan Disable) of the encoder will go low. A low on Scan Disable will stop the counter (and the scanning of the switch columns) so that the binary code for the switch may be read out as the 6 bits labeled Z5 Z4 Z3 Z2 Z1 Z0. Note that inverters are used to change the inverted binary encoder output into the standard binary value for the corresponding row.

As long as there is no pressed switch in the column that is currently being scanned, all rows will be pulled high with the resistors. With all highs into the encoder, the GS output (Scan Disable) will be high and the counter will be enabled. This allows the counter to step to the next state when it is clocked, and the decoder output will then change to scan the next column. Any pressed switch in a column that is <u>not</u> currently being scanned (with a low from the decoder) will have no effect on the encoder or counter since both sides of the switch will be high. The counting and column scanning will proceed until a closed switch is detected in the currently scanned column. A pressed switch will stop the counter only when that specific column is scanned.

Releasing the switch will then allow the count to continue. For example, if switch "21" (located in column 5) is pressed, row 2 will go low when the counter reaches state 101 ($Z2\ Z1\ Z0$). The low on input 2 of the encoder will produce a 010 for $Z5\ Z4\ Z3$. This 6-bit number 010101 is the binary equivalent of the decimal number 21.

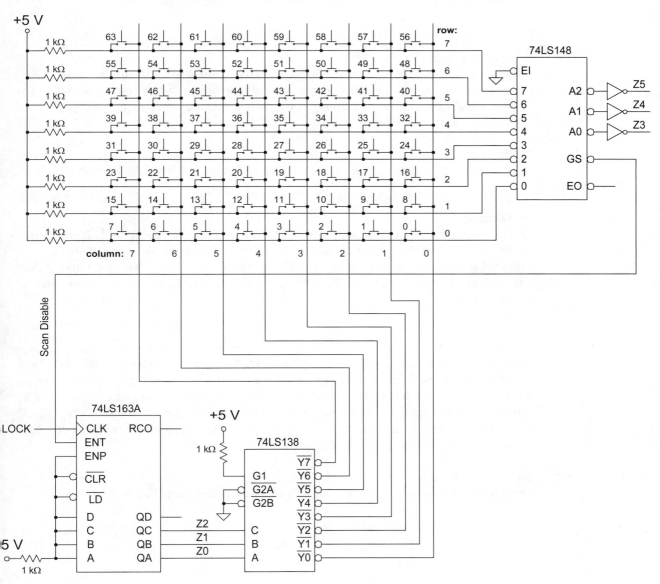

Fig. 18-7 Scanning encoder system

Laboratory Projects

Design encoder circuits for the following applications. Construct and test each circuit design.

18.1   Encoder and display
Design an octal-to-binary switch encoder and 7-segment display circuit using a 74148 priority encoder chip, a 7447 decoder/driver chip, and any other necessary devices. The display should be blanked when there is no switch input being applied.

18.2   16-line priority encoder
Implement a 16-line priority encoder with active-low switch inputs using a PLD.

18.3   BCD encoder
Design a decimal-to-BCD priority encoder (8421 BCD output) using a PLD. The ten inputs are all active-low. The encoder should produce an active-low output signal (strobe) to indicate that at least one of the ten inputs is applied. The circuit also should have an active-high, encoder enable (en) input. When disabled, the encoder output should be 0000.

18.4   Scanning encoder
Design a 16-input scanning encoder with a PLD. Connect a hexadecimal keypad (4 × 4 pushbutton switches) for inputs to the scanning encoder and produce the appropriate binary output for each button. Note: The buttons may not be arranged in a convenient order, thus requiring that either a custom encoder or a code conversion block be designed (that translates the row × column combination into the correct binary number).

18.5   HDL 74148 encoder
Design an octal-to-binary encoder using an HDL that functions like a 74148.

MULTIPLEXERS

Objective

- To apply multiplexer circuits in digital system applications.

Suggested Parts				
7408	7447	74151	74157	74163
EPM7128S or EP1C6		MAN72	330-Ω resistors	

<u>Multiplexer Circuits</u>

A multiplexer (also called a data selector) is a logic block that steers selected input data to its output. This logic function has multiple data inputs from which to choose, but only one of the inputs will appear on the output. Control signals called select lines are used to determine which data input will be routed to the output. Because of its ability to output different data inputs dependent on a set of control lines, a multiplexer can also easily be used to synthesize a combinational logic function. MSI multiplexer chips such as the 74151 (see Fig. 19-1) are available. This chip is a one-of-eight or 8-channel multiplexer. The truth table for this multiplexer is given in Table 19-1. Three select lines are necessary to choose one of the eight possible inputs for the data output. For added flexibility, this chip has both a normal data output and an inverted data output, as well as an active-low strobe or enable control input.

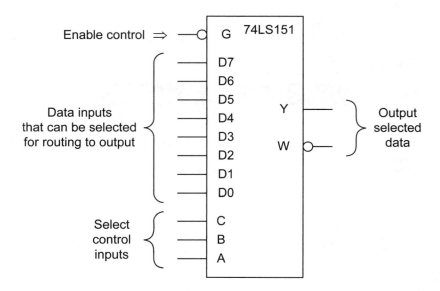

Fig. 19-1 A 74151 8-channel multiplexer

G	C	B	A	Y	W
1	X	X	X	0	1
0	0	0	0	D0	D0
0	0	0	1	D1	D1
0	0	1	0	D2	D2
0	0	1	1	D3	D3
0	1	0	0	D4	D4
0	1	0	1	D5	D5
0	1	1	0	D6	D6
0	1	1	1	D7	D7

Table 19-1 Truth table for a 74151 8-channel multiplexer

Example 19-1

Design a 4-channel multiplexer that will output the selected waveform produced by a 4-bit binary counter.

A schematic solution is shown in Fig. 19-2. A 74163 macrofunction is used to create the 4-bit binary counter. The 4-channel multiplexer function is carried out by a 74151 macrofunction (using only half of the 8-channel multiplexer). The counter's four outputs are the data inputs to the multiplexer. Selection of the desired counter signal is controlled by sel1 and sel0. Simulation results are shown in Fig. 19-3.

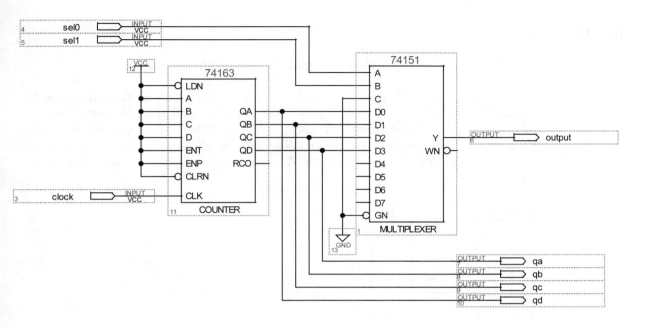

Fig. 19-2 Schematic design for Example 19-1

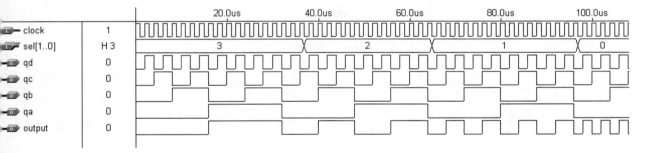

Fig. 19-3 Simulation results for Example 19-1

Example 19-2

Create a 16-channel multiplexer using the 74151 macrofunction.

A schematic solution is shown in Fig. 19-4. A 16-channel multiplexer will require four select lines (d c b a). The most significant select (d) is used to enable one of the two 74151 multiplexers and disable the other. Only one of the multiplexers will be enabled at a time, so when the two outputs are ORed together, the final output will only depend on the one multiplexer that is enabled. A sample of the simulation results for this design is shown in Fig. 19-5.

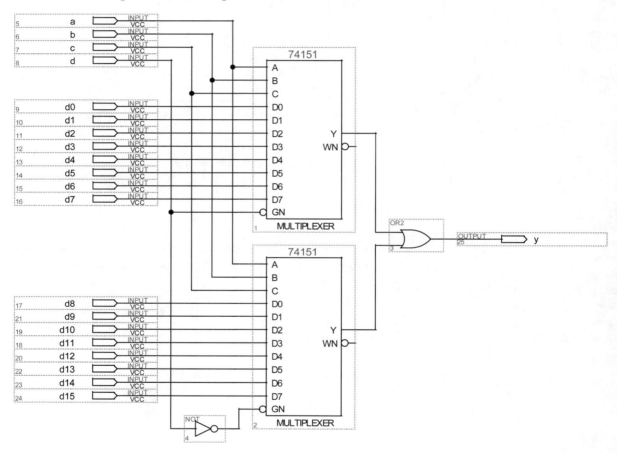

Fig. 19-4 Schematic design for Example 19-2

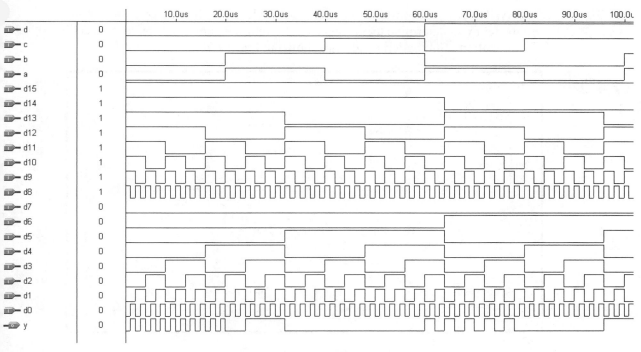

Fig. 19-5 Simulation sample for Example 19-2

Example 19-3

Design a dual 4-channel multiplexer using an HDL. The function table for this circuit is listed in Table 19-2. The 2-bit data input words are labeled a, b, c, and d and the 2-bit output word is y. An active-low enable control is labeled EN, and the two selection controls are labeled s1 and s0.

en	s1	s0	y1	y0
0	0	0	a1	a0
0	0	1	b1	b0
0	1	0	c1	c0
0	1	1	d1	d0
1	X	X	0	0

Table 19-2 Function table for Example 19-3

__AHDL__   An AHDL file solution is shown in Fig. 19-6. If the en input is low, the CASE
statement will determine the necessary 2-bit multiplexer output for each select input
combination. Simulation results are shown in Fig. 19-7.

```
SUBDESIGN  dual_mux4
(
      en, s[1..0]                                :INPUT;
      a[1..0], b[1..0], c[1..0], d[1..0]   :INPUT;
      y[1..0]                                    :OUTPUT;
)
BEGIN
      IF  !en  THEN              -- active-low enable
            CASE  s[]  IS        -- select input
                  WHEN 0  =>  y[] = a[];
                  WHEN 1  =>  y[] = b[];
                  WHEN 2  =>  y[] = c[];
                  WHEN 3  =>  y[] = d[];
            END CASE;
      ELSE  y[] = 0;             -- disabled
      END IF;
END;
```

Fig. 19-6 AHDL design file for Example 19-3

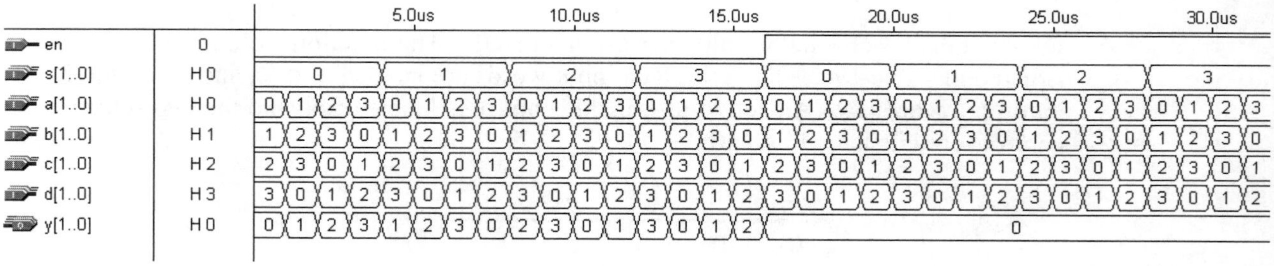

Fig. 19-7 Simulation results for Example 19-3

```
ENTITY dual_mux4 IS
PORT (    en              : IN BIT;
          s               : IN INTEGER RANGE 0 TO 3;
          a, b, c, d      : IN BIT_VECTOR (1 DOWNTO 0);
          y               : OUT BIT_VECTOR (1 DOWNTO 0) );
END dual_mux4;

ARCHITECTURE vhdl OF dual_mux4 IS
BEGIN
      PROCESS (en, s, a, b, c, d)
      BEGIN
            IF en = '0' THEN        -- active-low enable
                CASE   s  IS        -- select input
                    WHEN 0  =>  y <= a;
                    WHEN 1  =>  y <= b;
                    WHEN 2  =>  y <= c;
                    WHEN 3  =>  y <= d;
                END CASE;
            ELSE   y <= "00";       -- disabled
            END IF;
      END PROCESS;
END vhdl;
```

Fig. 19-8 VHDL design file for Example 19-3

VHDL
A VHDL file solution is shown in Fig. 19-8. If the en input is low, the CASE
statement will determine the necessary 2-bit multiplexer output for each select input
combination. Simulation results are shown in Fig. 19-7.

Laboratory Projects

Design multiplexer circuits for the following applications. Use standard logic devices or a PLD. Construct and test each circuit design.

19.1 Serial data word generator
Design a logic circuit using a one-of-eight multiplexer to output an 8-bit serial data word. The multiplexer will output the 8-bit data word (whose bit pattern is defined with 8 logic switches) and then the serial output will be blanked (low) for 8 more clock cycles. This pattern continues repetitively. View the serial output and clock on an oscilloscope while changing the data input on the logic switches. Trigger the scope with an appropriate signal from the control circuit.

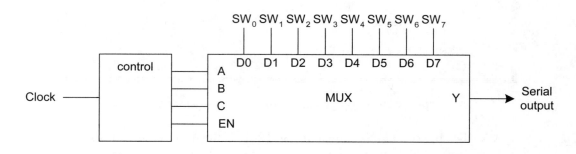

19.2   Variable frequency divider

Design a circuit that will select (multiplex) a specified frequency to be output
(freq_select). A 128-kHz clock signal will be divided into a number of different
frequencies by two cascaded 74163 binary counter macrofunctions as shown in the
logic diagram below. The desired frequency will be selected by a 74151 one-of-eight
multiplexer, as indicated in the following function table. The frequency selection is
determined by the state of S2 S1 S0. Use a frequency counter to measure the signal
frequency output by the multiplexer.

S2	S1	S0	Output frequency
0	0	0	500 Hz
0	0	1	1.0 kHz
0	1	0	2.0 kHz
0	1	1	4.0 kHz
1	0	0	8.0 kHz
1	0	1	16.0 kHz
1	1	0	32.0 kHz
1	1	1	64.0 kHz

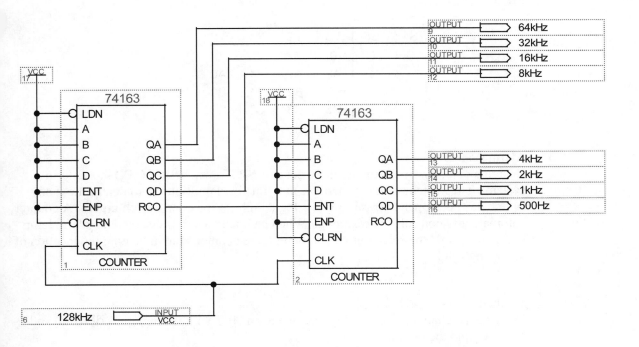

19.3   Multiplexed BCD display

Design a quad, 2-channel (2-line-to-1-line) multiplexer to route the outputs from two BCD counters (A[3..0] and B[3..0]) to a BCD decoder/driver and single-digit, 7-segment display. Each counter has a separate clock signal. Only one of the two 4-bit numbers input to the multiplexer will be displayed on the 7-segment display, as indicated by the following function table. The gating control G will produce an invalid BCD output (1111) from the MUX when it is disabled.

		MUX Outputs			
G	S	Y3	Y2	Y1	Y0
1	0	A3	A2	A1	A0
1	1	B3	B2	B1	B0
0	X	1	1	1	1

19.4   Quad, 3-channel MUX

Design a multiplexer that can select one of three 4-bit binary words to be output. The inputs are A3 A2 A1 A0, B3 B2 B1 B0, and C3 C2 C1 C0. The multiplexer's outputs are Y3 Y2 Y1 Y0 and the select controls are S1 S0. The function table for this MUX is given below. The output from the MUX will be 0000 when S1 = S0 = 0 (i.e., the MUX is disabled).

S1	S0	Y3	Y2	Y1	Y0
0	0	0	0	0	0
0	1	A3	A2	A1	A0
1	0	B3	B2	B1	B0
1	1	C3	C2	C1	C0

19.5   Alarm system

Design a detector circuit to monitor a set of 8 SPST switches (s[7..0]) in an alarm system. The switches are scanned one at a time by a multiplexer to determine if any switch has been opened (resulting in a logic high for the open switch input). A counter automatically controls the scanning. When an open switch is detected, an alarm lamp will go high and the scanning will stop, with the counter state indicating the location of the open switch.

19.6   16-channel, 1-bit MUX

Design a 16-channel, 1-bit multiplexer using an HDL. Label the inputs d[15..0] and sel[3..0] and the output y.

DEMULTIPLEXERS

Objective

- To apply demultiplexer circuits in digital system applications.

Suggested Parts				
7404	74138	74151	74163	EPM7128S or EP1C6
DIP switch with 8 SPSTs		1-kΩ resistor		

<u>Demultiplexer Circuits</u>

A demultiplexer is also called a data distributor since it has several possible destinations to which the input data may be sent. The single output line that will receive the data is controlled by the specific select code applied to the demultiplexer. The 74138 (see Fig. 20-1 and Table 20-1) is an example of an MSI demultiplexer chip. This chip can function as either a decoder or a demultiplexer. A decoder can be used as a demultiplexer by connecting the DMUX select lines to the data input lines (of the decoder) and applying the DMUX data to the enable input (of the decoder). One bit of input data may be sent to any one of eight possible output destinations with the 74138. Data that is input to one of the **G2** enables will not be inverted by the DMUX chip. The **G2B** input pin has been chosen for the data input pin in the schematic of Fig. 20-1. The other two enable pins may be utilized as enable controls for the DMUX.

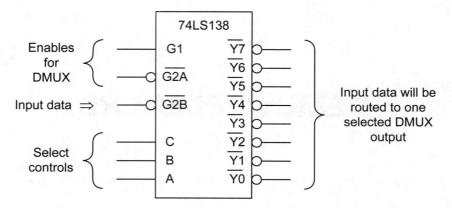

Fig. 20-1   A 74138, 8-channel demultiplexer chip

G1	G2A	C	B	A	Y0	Y1	Y2	Y3	Y4	Y5	Y6	Y7
1	0	0	0	0	data	1	1	1	1	1	1	1
1	0	0	0	1	1	data	1	1	1	1	1	1
1	0	0	1	0	1	1	data	1	1	1	1	1
1	0	0	1	1	1	1	1	data	1	1	1	1
1	0	1	0	0	1	1	1	1	data	1	1	1
1	0	1	0	1	1	1	1	1	1	data	1	1
1	0	1	1	0	1	1	1	1	1	1	data	1
1	0	1	1	1	1	1	1	1	1	1	1	data
0	X	X	X	X	1	1	1	1	1	1	1	1
X	1	X	X	X	1	1	1	1	1	1	1	1

Table 20-1   Truth table for a 74138 demultiplexer

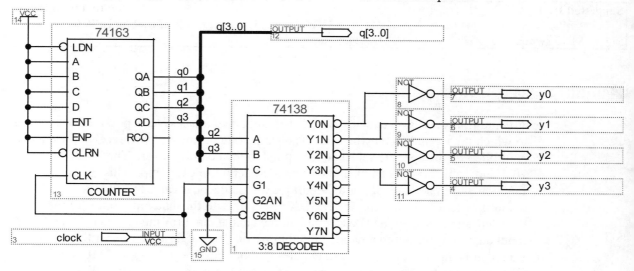

Fig. 20-2   Circuit for Example 20-1

Example 20-1

Simulate the circuit given in Fig. 20-2 and describe its operation. The 74138 is used as a demultiplexer.

Simulation results are shown in Fig. 20-3. One of the four demultiplexer outputs will produce a series of four clock pulses, and then the next demultiplexer will do the same until all four have done so. The pulsing continues through each output in turn. The two least significant counter bits of the 74163 are used to count the four clock pulses for each demultiplexer output. The two most significant counter bits are used to select each of the DMUX outputs in sequence. The inverters will cause the inverted DMUX outputs to be inverted again so that the pulses are "in-phase" with the clock input signal.

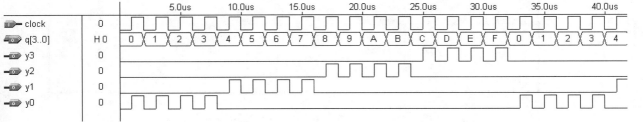

Fig. 20-3 Simulation results for Example 20-1

Example 20-2

Design a 2-bit, 4-channel demultiplexer using an HDL. The function table for this circuit is listed in Table 20-2. The 2-bit input data i[1..0] can be routed to any of the 4 output channels a[1..0], b[1..0], c[1..0], or d[1..0]. The selection controls are s[1..0], and the DMUX also has an enable control.

enable	s1	s0	a1 a0	b1 b0	c1 c0	d1 d0
0	X	X	0 0	0 0	0 0	0 0
1	0	0	i1 i0	0 0	0 0	0 0
1	0	1	0 0	i1 i0	0 0	0 0
1	1	0	0 0	0 0	i1 i0	0 0
1	1	1	0 0	0 0	0 0	i1 i0

Table 20-2 Function table for Example 20-2

AHDL   An AHDL solution is shown in Fig. 20-4. If the DMUX is enabled, the CASE statement identifies which of the 2-bit outputs is to receive the 2-bit input data. The DEFAULTS statement sets each 2-bit output equal to zero otherwise. Simulation results are shown in Fig. 20-5.

```
SUBDESIGN  dmux2_4
(
      enable, s[1..0], i[1..0]            :INPUT;
      a[1..0], b[1..0], c[1..0], d[1..0]  :OUTPUT;
            -- four 2-bit DMUX outputs
)
BEGIN
      DEFAULTS        -- DMUX output = 00 when deselected
            a[] = 0;
            b[] = 0;
            c[] = 0;
            d[] = 0;
      END DEFAULTS;
      IF   enable  THEN
            CASE  s[]   IS     -- selects DMUX output
                  WHEN  0  =>  a[] = i[];
                  WHEN  1  =>  b[] = i[];
                  WHEN  2  =>  c[] = i[];
                  WHEN  3  =>  d[] = i[];
            END CASE;
      END IF;
END;
```

Fig. 20-4 AHDL file for Example 20-2

Fig. 20-5 Simulation results for Example 20-2

VHDL   A VHDL solution is shown in Fig. 20-6. If the DMUX is enabled, the CASE statement identifies which of the 2-bit outputs is to receive the 2-bit input data while the others output 00. If the DMUX is disabled, all outputs will be 00. Simulation results are shown in Fig. 20-5.

```
ENTITY dmux2_4 IS
PORT ( enable        : IN BIT;
         s, i         : IN BIT_VECTOR (1 DOWNTO 0);
         a, b, c, d   : OUT BIT_VECTOR (1 DOWNTO 0) );
                -- four 2-bit DMUX outputs
END dmux2_4;

ARCHITECTURE vhdl OF dmux2_4 IS
BEGIN
    PROCESS (enable, s, i)
    BEGIN
       IF  enable = '1' THEN
          CASE  s  IS           -- selects DMUX output
             WHEN  "00"  =>
                a <= i;    b <= "00"; c <= "00"; d <= "00";
             WHEN  "01"  =>
                a <= "00"; b <= i;    c <= "00"; d <= "00";
             WHEN  "10"  =>
                a <= "00"; b <= "00"; c <= i;    d <= "00";
             WHEN  "11"  =>
                a <= "00"; b <= "00"; c <= "00"; d <= i;
          END CASE;
       ELSE      a <= "00"; b <= "00"; c <= "00"; d <= "00";
                    -- not enabled
       END IF;
    END PROCESS;
END vhdl;
```

Fig. 20-6 VHDL file for Example 20-2

Laboratory Projects

Design demultiplexer circuits for the following applications. Construct and test each circuit design.

20.1 Clock DMUX

Design a demultiplexer circuit to route a clock signal to one of three different counters. The counters each produce a different modulus, as shown in the following table. The sel[1..0] controls determine which counter is to receive the clock signal. One of the select combinations (00) does not route the clock to any of the counters.

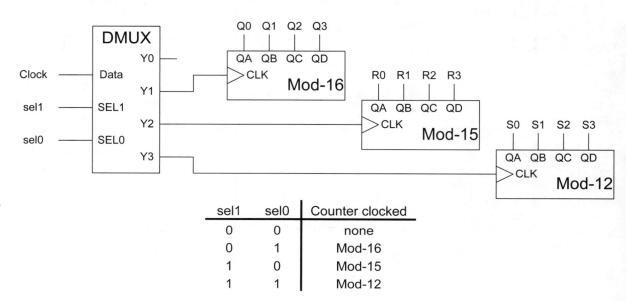

sel1	sel0	Counter clocked
0	0	none
0	1	Mod-16
1	0	Mod-15
1	1	Mod-12

20.2 BCD counter demultiplexer

Design and construct a circuit to route the output from a BCD counter to the selected 7-segment display on the PLD trainer board. An enable and a select will control a 4-bit, 2-channel demultiplexer for the displays, as shown in the following function table. Blank the display that is not being used. Hint: A 7447 will blank the display if the data input is 1111.

| Controls | | Left display | Right display |
G	S		
0	0	Counter	Blank
0	1	Blank	Counter
1	X	Blank	Blank

20.3 Alarm indicator

Implement the alarm circuit given in the block diagram below using standard logic devices for each of the blocks. The switches are to be placed on windows and doors that we wish to monitor. An alarm condition occurs if any of the switches are opened due to the corresponding window or door being opened. The MUX will sequentially check each of the switches and output a signal that is transmitted to the DMUX (that we will assume is some distance away). The DMUX will control a set of lamps to indicate which switch has been opened. All lamps will be off if none of the switches are open. A flashing lamp will indicate an alarm. Use a 200-Hz clock for the counter. Note: If the DMUX is powered with a separate power source (because it is located some distance from the MUX circuit), make sure that you have a common ground.

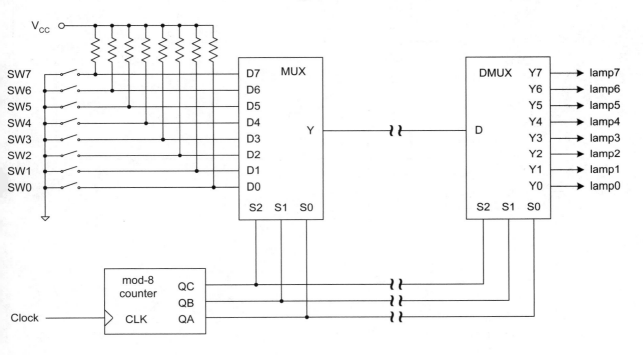

20.4 8-channel, 1-bit DMUX

Design an 8-channel, 1-bit demultiplexer using an HDL.

20.5   2-channel data transmitter

Design and construct the data transmitter given in the block diagram below using a PLD. The 8-bit data input will be split so that D[7..4] will be transmitted to channel 2 of the oscilloscope and D[3..0] will be transmitted to channel 1. Use the counter MSB to trigger the oscilloscope.

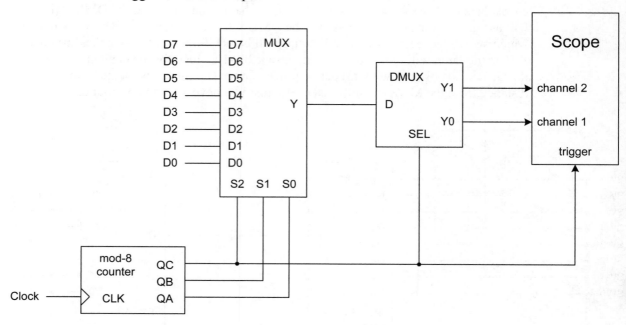

MAGNITUDE COMPARATORS

Objective

- To apply magnitude comparators in digital system applications.

Suggested Parts

7485	74161	EPM7128S or EP1C6

Magnitude Comparators

Magnitude comparators are used to determine the magnitude relationships between two quantities. A typical comparator will indicate whether two input values are equivalent or, if not, which of the values is larger. Logic gates can be used to implement various types of comparator circuits. MSI comparator chips such as the 7485, 4-bit comparator shown in Fig. 21-1 can be easily used in a variety of magnitude comparator applications. This comparator chip determines the magnitude relationship between the two binary values A3 A2 A1 A0 and B3 B2 B1 B0. The outputs produced are A<B, A>B, and A=B. The truth table for this chip is shown in Table 21-1. The three cascade inputs allow multiple 7485 chips to be cascaded together to compare binary quantities that are more than 4 bits long. If the cascade feature is not used, the A=B input will normally be tied high and the other two cascade inputs (A<B and A>B) are tied low. An 8-bit magnitude comparator circuit constructed with two 7485 chips is shown in Fig. 21-2. The two comparator chips are cascaded together by connecting the outputs from the comparator that is monitoring the least significant 4 bits from each number to the cascade inputs on the comparator that is monitoring the most significant 4 bits. The lower nibbles will affect the 8-bit comparator's output only when the higher nibbles are equivalent. This cascading technique can be expanded to compare the magnitudes of larger numbers (bigger than 8 bits), but the propagation delays can get rather long.

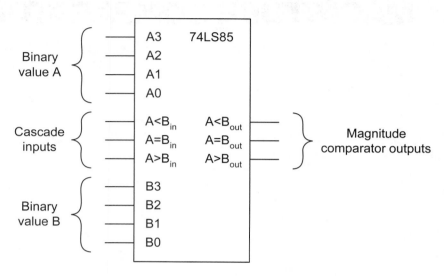

Fig. 21-1 A 7485, 4-bit magnitude comparator chip

Comparing inputs				Cascading inputs			Outputs		
A3, B3	A2, B2	A1, B1	A0, B0	$A<B_{in}$	$A>B_{in}$	$A=B_{in}$	$A<B_{out}$	$A>B_{out}$	$A=B_{out}$
A3<B3	X	X	X	X	X	X	1	0	0
A3>B3	X	X	X	X	X	X	0	1	0
A3=B3	A2<B2	X	X	X	X	X	1	0	0
A3=B3	A2>B2	X	X	X	X	X	0	1	0
A3=B3	A2=B2	A1<B1	X	X	X	X	1	0	0
A3=B3	A2=B2	A1>B1	X	X	X	X	0	1	0
A3=B3	A2=B2	A1=B1	A0<B0	X	X	X	1	0	0
A3=B3	A2=B2	A1=B1	A0>B0	X	X	X	0	1	0
A3=B3	A2=B2	A1=B1	A0=B0	1	0	0	1	0	0
A3=B3	A2=B2	A1=B1	A0=B0	0	1	0	0	1	0
A3=B3	A2=B2	A1=B1	A0=B0	0	0	1	0	0	1

Table 21-1 Function table for a 7485

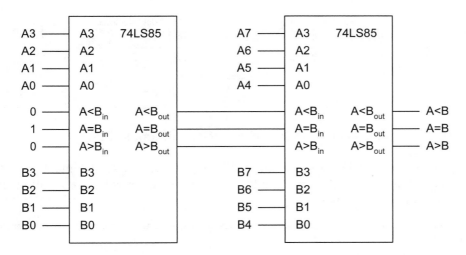

Fig. 21-2 An 8-bit magnitude comparator circuit using two 7485 chips

Example 21-1

Design a 4-bit magnitude comparator using an HDL.

AHDL

An example AHDL solution is shown in Fig. 21-3. The IF statement tests for the magnitude relationship between the two 4-bit input variables. Simulation results for this design are shown in Fig. 21-4.

```
SUBDESIGN   compare
(
      a[3..0], b[3..0]          :INPUT;
      agtb, altb, aeqb          :OUTPUT;
)

BEGIN
      DEFAULTS
              agtb = GND;
              altb = GND;
              aeqb = GND;
      END DEFAULTS;

            -- compare a and b inputs
      IF      a[] < b[]   THEN   altb = VCC;
      ELSIF   a[] > b[]   THEN   agtb = VCC;
      ELSE                       aeqb = VCC;
      END IF;
END;
```

Fig. 21-3 AHDL file for Example 21-1

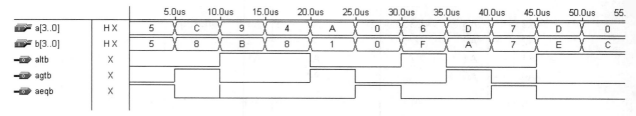

Fig. 21-4 Simulation results for Example 21-1

VHDL   An example VHDL solution is shown in Fig. 21-5. The IF statement tests for the magnitude relationship between the two 4-bit input variables. Simulation results for this design are shown in Fig. 21-4.

```
ENTITY compare IS
PORT (
      a, b                 : IN INTEGER RANGE 0 TO 15;
      agtb, altb, aeqb  : OUT BIT
);
END compare;

ARCHITECTURE vhdl OF compare IS
BEGIN
      PROCESS (a, b)
      BEGIN           -- compare a and b inputs
        IF     a < b   THEN
                altb <= '1';  agtb <= '0';  aeqb <= '0';
        ELSIF  a > b   THEN
                altb <= '0';  agtb <= '1';  aeqb <= '0';
        ELSE
                altb <= '0';  agtb <= '0';  aeqb <= '1';
        END IF;
      END PROCESS;
END vhdl;
```

Fig. 21-5 VHDL file for Example 21-1

Laboratory Projects

Design magnitude comparator circuits for the following applications. Construct and test each circuit design.

21.1 Count detector
Design a comparator circuit in which the single output (count_detect) will be high if the 4-bit value produced by a binary counter is greater than a lower limit (low_limit) and less than an upper limit (hi_limit). Low_limit and hi_limit are each 4-bit input values set by switches.

21.2 Adjustable range detector
Design a logic circuit that will compare a 5-bit input value (value[4..0]) to one of four specified input ranges selected by the control r[1..0]. The comparator should have three outputs to indicate that the input value is either less than (ltr) or greater than (gtr) the range of values in the selected window or within the range (rng) of window values.

R1	R0	Selected range of window values
0	0	16
0	1	15–17
1	0	14–18
1	1	13–19

21.3 Variable modulus counter
Design a recycling counter circuit that can have any selected count modulus from **2 through 16**. The desired count modulus will be determined by a 4-bit input value (mod = n[3..0]). Mod-16 will be selected by n[3..0] = 0 0 0 0.

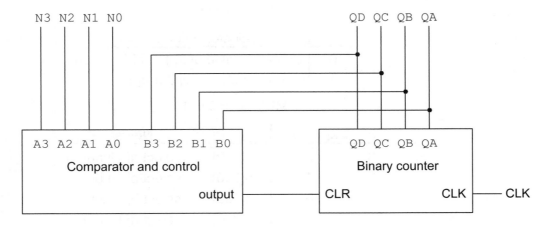

21.4   Variable self-stopping counter
Design a self-stopping counter circuit that can count up to any selected 4-bit binary value and then stop. The desired binary value at which to stop the counter will be determined by a 4-bit input (n[3..0]). The counter should also have a manual, active-low **restartn** control signal that will asynchronously reset the counter to 0 so that the counter can again cycle through its self-stopping count sequence.

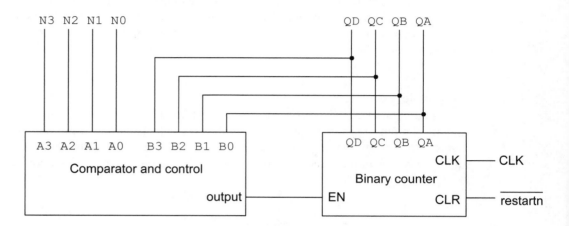

21.5   Number selector
Design a logic circuit that will produce a 4-bit output (y[3..0]) that is equal to either the larger or smaller of two 4-bit inputs (a[3..0] and b[3..0]). The selection of the larger or smaller value is specified by the control signal F, as shown in the following function table. Note that the number selector circuit will output the common value when the a and b inputs are equal. Hint: This circuit is basically a multiplexer in which the output data (y[3..0]) are selected by a function that is dependent upon the control F and the result of a magnitude comparison between a[3..0] and b[3..0] (see the MUX control table below).

Function table

F	Selector output:
0	smaller value of a[ ] or b[ ]
1	larger value of a[ ] or b[ ]

MUX control table

F	a[ ] > b[ ]	y[3..0]	Notes:
0	0	a[3..0]	select a[ ] input
0	1	b[3..0]	select b[ ] input
1	0	b[3..0]	select b[ ] input
1	1	a[3..0]	select a[ ] input

DIGITAL/ANALOG AND ANALOG/DIGITAL CONVERSION

Objectives

- To construct a digital-to-analog conversion (DAC) circuit using a standard commercial DAC IC chip.
- To construct an analog-to-digital conversion (ADC) circuit using a standard commercial ADC IC chip.

Suggested Parts

    AD557   ADC0804   EPM7128S or EP1C6

    Resistors: 1.1 kΩ, 3.3 kΩ, 10 kΩ, 10 kΩ (10-turn) potentiometer   Capacitor: 150 pF

Digital-to-Analog Conversion

Digital system outputs often must be interfaced to analog devices. One type of interfacing involves converting a digital data word into a representative analog signal (either a current or a voltage). Various digital-to-analog converter chips are available to perform this type of conversion. An example of a complete D/A converter in a single IC chip is the AD557 manufactured by Analog Devices. This 8-bit D/A converter is powered by a single 5-volt power supply and has a full-scale output of 2.55 volts. The resolution or incremental analog step size of the DAC is dependent on the number of digital input bits. The output voltage step size for this device is 10 mV. Fig. 22-1 shows how to use the AD557 to produce an analog output from 0 to 2.55 volts.

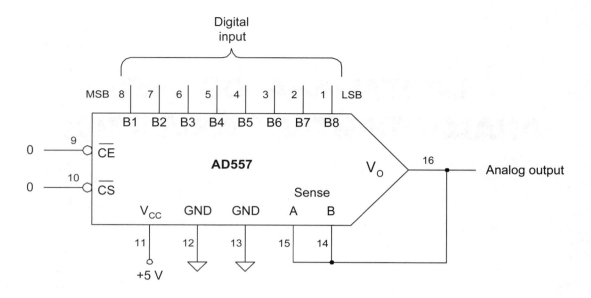

Fig. 22-1 AD557 digital-to-analog conversion IC

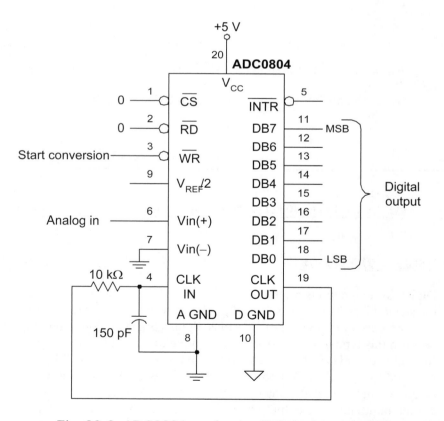

Fig. 22-2 ADC0804 analog-to-digital conversion IC

Analog-to-Digital Conversion

For a digital system to be able to process analog information, the analog signal must first be digitized or converted from analog to digital. The analog input signal is then represented by a digital value in the digital system. There are various analog-to-digital converter chips available to perform this type of conversion. The ADC0804 manufactured by National Semiconductor is an example of an 8-bit successive approximation converter contained in a single IC chip. This device will handle an analog input range from 0 to 5 volts and is powered by a single 5-volt power supply. The quantization error of an ADC is dependent on the number of digital output bits. With a resolution of 8 bits and a reference voltage of 5 volts, the ADC0804 will have a quantization error of $V_{REF}/2^8 \approx 19.5$ mv. Fig. 22-2 shows how to connect the ADC0804 so that it will digitize the analog input when start conversion goes low.

The ADC0804 ADC chip can also be operated in free-running mode by connecting the "end-of-conversion" output signal named INTR (interrupt) to the "start-conversion" input signal named WR (write). (See Fig. 22-3.) It may be necessary to <u>momentarily</u> short the WR pin to ground in order to initially start the conversion process, but the ADC should then operate continuously. $V_{in(-)}$ and $V_{REF}/2$ can be changed to modify the ADC's zero and span for the analog input signal's range and the desired step size. The analog differential input voltage ($V_{in(+)} - V_{in(-)}$) is the actual signal that is converted to a representative digital output value. Therefore, the analog input voltage that produces an output of 00000000 (zero) can be adjusted above ground by applying a DC voltage to the $V_{in(-)}$ pin. The input voltage span can also be adjusted by applying a DC voltage to the $V_{REF}/2$ pin. The analog input voltage span (V_{REF}) will be equal to two times the voltage on the $V_{REF}/2$ pin. The new quantization error factor is equal to $V_{REF} \div 2^8$.

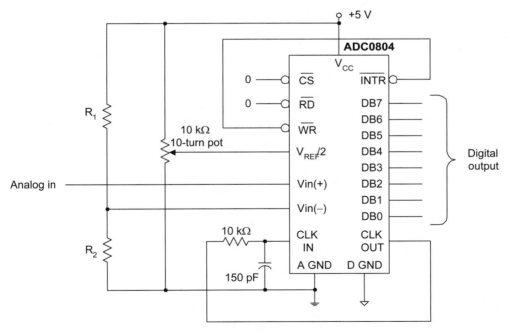

Fig. 22-3 Free-running analog-to-digital conversion circuit with span adjust

Laboratory Projects

22.1   Digital-to-analog converter
        Construct a D/A converter using an Analog Devices AD557 IC chip. Determine a
        procedure to test the operation of the DAC. Enter your test data into a spreadsheet.
        Use the spreadsheet to calculate the theoretical output and the full-scale error for the
        test results. Graph the test results for the DAC.

22.2   Analog-to-digital converter
        Construct an A/D converter using a National ADC0804 IC chip. Determine a
        procedure to test the operation of the ADC. Enter your test data into a spreadsheet.
        Use the spreadsheet to calculate the theoretical output and the full-scale error for the
        test results. Graph the test results for the ADC.

22.3   Free-running ADC with span adjust
        Design a free-running A/D converter (using a National ADC0804) that produces a
        digital output of 00000000 for analog input voltages ≤ 0.5 V and has a resolution of 15
        mV. Test your design. Enter your test data into a spreadsheet. Use the spreadsheet to
        calculate the theoretical output and the full-scale error for the test results. Graph the
        test results for the ADC. See Fig. 22-3.

22.4 Digital voltmeter

Construct a simple 0–5 V DC digital voltmeter using the ADC0804 and a PLD to convert the binary output into BCD, which will be displayed on two 7-segment displays. The PLD will be programmed to convert a 6-bit binary number to a 2-digit BCD number. Note that the 2 least significant A/D output bits are left unconnected (using only 6 bits of resolution). Calibrate the digital voltmeter by applying 5 V to the analog in (measured with a DVM) and adjusting the 10-turn potentiometer until the 7-segment display reads 5.0 (the decimal point is assumed to be in the middle). Test the accuracy of the digital voltmeter with several different values for analog in. It may be necessary to readjust the calibration for your digital voltmeter.

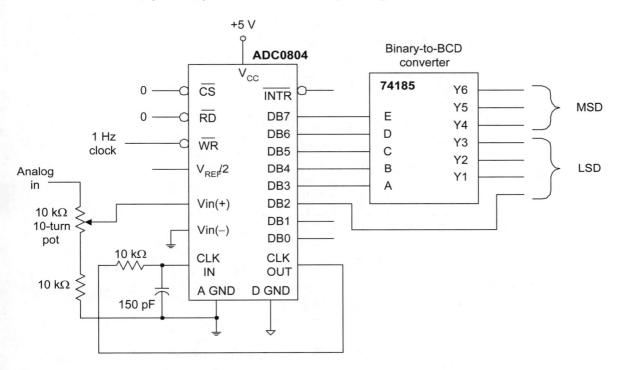

22.5   Digitized sine-wave generator
Construct a digitized sine-wave generator using an AD557 D/A converter, a PLD, and a mod-36 binary counter. The sine-wave output will be produced by the D/A using data generated by the PLD. A mod-36 counter will provide 36 counts per cycle of the sine wave. How many degrees are there per count? Calculate (with a spreadsheet) the D/A digital data needed for each step (count) to generate the desired analog output. The amplitude of the sine wave should be 1.0 volt, and the DC offset should be 1.5 volts. The formula for the instantaneous output voltage is:

$$V_{out} \;=\; 1.5 + 1.0 \sin \theta$$

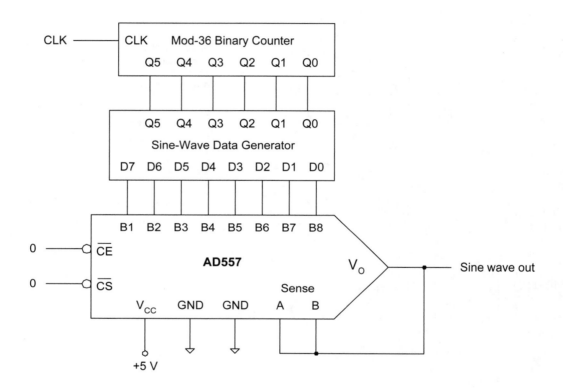

22.6   Reconstructing a digitized signal
Use the A/D converter to digitize a sine-wave input signal and then reconvert the representative digital signal into an analog signal with the DAC. Connect the input of the D/A converter to the output of the A/D converter. Make sure the MSB out is connected to the MSB in. Adjust the input sine wave to 2.5 V_{p-p} with a DC offset of 1.25 volts (i.e., the sine wave goes from 0 to 2.5 V). Adjust the $V_{REF}/2$ voltage using the potentiometer so that the analog input span on the ADC is 0 to 2.5 V. Use an oscilloscope to compare the analog input and output waveforms. Set the analog input signal frequency to approximately 200 Hz and observe the resultant analog output signal. Sketch the input and output waveforms. Increase the input signal frequency and note the effect on the resultant output signal.

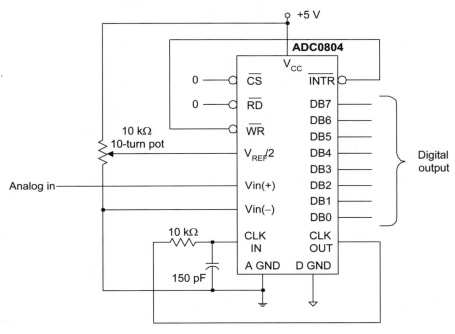

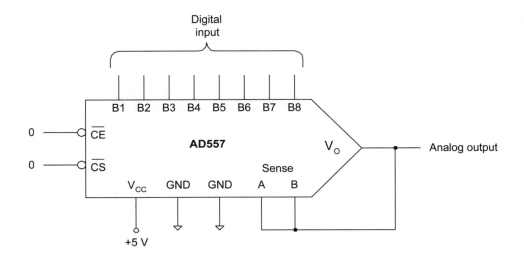

MEMORY SYSTEMS

Objectives

- To construct a random access memory (RAM) circuit using a semiconductor RAM chip.
- To read and write data in a RAM memory.
- To combine multiple RAM chips to expand word size and/or memory capacity.

Suggested Parts			
7404	74138	74244	2114

Memory Devices and Systems

Memory devices are used in digital systems to store digital information. A specific storage location in memory is identified with a unique binary value called an address. Accessing data stored at a specified address is referred to as a read operation. Storing new data at a specified address is referred to as a write operation.

Random access memory (RAM) is the term used frequently for memory that can be read from or written into with equal ease. Ordinary semiconductor RAM devices are said to be volatile because the information stored in the device is lost if the electrical power for the memory is removed. Semiconductor RAM may be either static, which does not need the stored data to be periodically refreshed, or dynamic, which does require the data to be periodically rewritten into the memory cells. Static RAM memory chips have the following types of pins: address pins that are used to select a specific memory location, data pins that are used to input the data into or output the data from the addressed memory location, a chip select pin to enable a specific chip (or set of chips) in a memory system, and a Read/Write pin to control the chip's read or write function (read = 1 and write = 0). The block diagram for a 2114 static RAM memory chip containing 1024 4-bit words is shown in Fig. 23-1.

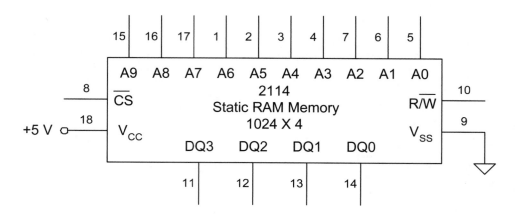

Fig. 23-1 Block diagram for a typical static RAM chip

Read only memory (ROM) often refers to a broad category of memory devices that normally have their data permanently stored in them while they are used in a digital system. There are various subtypes of ROM devices, some of which can have the stored data erased and replaced with new information.

Many different memory devices (with different part numbers) are available that differ in word size and memory capacity. The memory chip's word size is the number of bits that are accessed simultaneously in the chip with a given address. The memory capacity for a chip is the total number of words (2^n, where n = number of address bits) that can be addressed on the chip. Several memory chips can be interconnected to expand the total system memory. This expansion can be in word size, total number of addressable words, or both.

Tristate Bus Drivers

In addition to high and low output levels, a tristate output device also has a high impedance output condition. This type of output structure is normally used to connect several possible sources of digital information to a common bus, such as a data bus in a memory system. Only one source of information will be enabled at a time and allowed to place data on the bus. Most memory chips today have built-in tristate output buffers for the data pins that are enabled when the chip is selected and a read operation is performed. The source of data for a write operation must be removed from the data bus (i.e., the output placed in the tristate mode) when a write operation is not being performed. The output for a device in the tristate mode will be a high impedance (acts like an open circuit) when the device is disabled. Separate tristate buffer or bus driver chips are available to accomplish this task. The 74244 shown in Fig. 23-2 is an example of a tristate buffer. It contains a total of eight buffers in one chip. The buffers are arranged in two sets of four buffers each. Each set of buffers has a common active-low tristate enable.

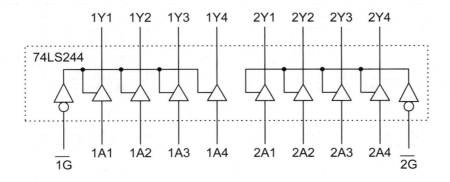

Fig. 23-2 A 74244 octal buffer with tristate output

Example 23-1

Design a 256-word RAM memory system in which each word is 8 bits. Use 1024-bit RAM memory chips that are arranged as 256 × 4 memory devices.

It will be necessary to use two of these 256 × 4 memory chips in order to double the word size for the specified memory system. The schematic for this 256 × 8 memory is shown in Fig. 23-3. The chips are permanently enabled with a 0 on the common (active-low) chip select line. Both chips receive the same address information to access a 4-bit word in each. The two 4-bit words from each chip are used to double the word size for the memory system. RAM 0 provides the least significant 4 bits, while RAM 1 provides the most significant 4 bits of the 8-bit data word. The octal tristate buffer chip (74244) is necessary so that external data (from some data source such as switches) can be stored in the memory system during a memory write cycle. During a memory write, the data from the switches is placed on the data bus and then is written into the addressed memory location. During a memory read cycle, the tristate buffers are disabled so that the data placed on the data bus comes from the memory chips.

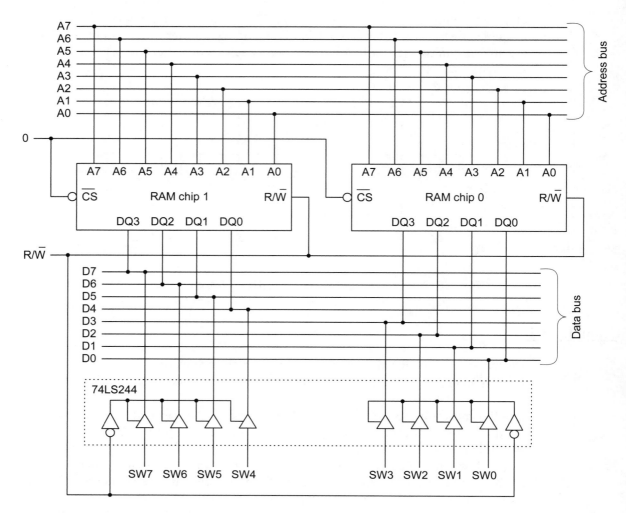

Fig. 23-3 Expanding word size for 256 X 8 RAM memory system in Example 23-1

Example 23-2

Design a 512-word RAM memory system in which each word is 4 bits. Use 1024-bit RAM memory chips that are arranged as 256 X 4 memory devices.

It will be necessary to use two of these 256 X 4 RAM memory chips in order to double the word capacity for the specified memory system. The schematic for this 512 X 4 memory is shown in Fig. 23-4. Another address line (A8) will be necessary to double the word capacity that is provided by only one 256 X 4 chip. The A8 address line is decoded using an inverter so that only one chip is selected at a time. The other eight address lines are connected to each of the chip's address pins. If A8 is low, then RAM 0 will be accessed; if A8 is high, then RAM 1 will be accessed. The corresponding data pins on each chip are tied to the four data bus lines. The tristate data output for each of the RAM chips will be enabled when the CS pin is low. The decoding gate (inverter) will allow only one of the chips to be enabled at a time. Only one-half (either half) of the octal tristate buffer chip will be needed since the data bus is only 4 bits wide in this memory system.

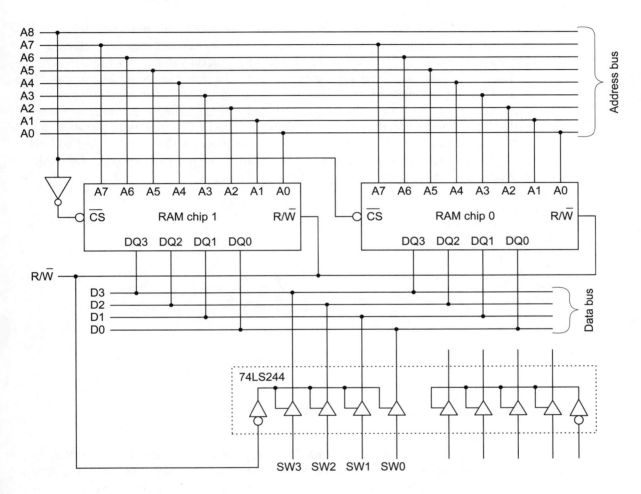

Fig. 23-4 Expanding the memory capacity for a 512 **X** 4 RAM memory system (Example 23-2)

Laboratory Projects

23.1   RAM memory chip

Test a 2114 (1024 X 4) memory chip by writing 4-bit data words to some selected memory locations and then verifying the data storage by reading the same selected addresses. Use a 74244 as the data bus buffer (enabled only during a write operation) for a set of 4 logic switches that provide the data to be stored in the RAM memory. Use a set of 8 logic switches to provide the address bus information for A0 through A7. Connect the remaining two address pins (A8 and A9) to ground so that only one-fourth of the 2114 is being tested. Monitor the data bus with LEDs. Test your memory system by writing the following sample hexadecimal data in the specified hex address (A9...A0) locations and then reading it back from the memory. Remember A9 = A8 = 0. Also check to see if the memory chips are volatile.

Address	Data
000	5
004	C
005	0
008	F
00B	6
00E	9
010	A
015	2
01F	1
020	7

23.2   Memory word-size expansion

Use two 2114 chips to design a 1024 X 8 memory system. Construct and test your design. Test your memory system by writing the following sample hexadecimal data in the specified hex address locations and then reading it back from the memory.

Address	Data
000	23
004	45
005	67
008	89
00B	AB
00E	CD
010	EF
015	01
01F	CC
020	33

23.3   Memory capacity expansion

Use two 2114 chips to design a 2048 x 4 memory system. Construct and test your design. Test your memory system by writing the following sample hexadecimal data in the specified hex address (A10…A0) locations and then reading it back from the memory.

Address	Data
000	1
400	2
007	3
407	4
00A	5
40A	6
010	7
410	8
017	9
417	A
01A	B
41A	C
020	D
420	E

23.4   Memory address decoding

Design a decoding circuit for a 2048 x 4 memory system. One K of the 4-bit words is at hex addresses 1800–1BFF. The other half of the memory is at locations 6800–6BFF. Assume the system has 16 address bits (A15…A0).

APPENDIX

CD-ROM Contents

MAX+PLUS II Student Edition
Quartus II Web Edition
MAXplus Tutorial Files
       MAXplus AHDL
       MAXplus Notes
       MAXplus Schematics
       MAXplus VHDL
Quartus Tutorial Files
       Quartus AHDL
       Quartus Notes
       Quartus Schematics
       Quartus VHDL

The Student Edition of MAX+PLUS II and the Web Edition of Quartus II are free versions of the commercial software and can be found on the enclosed CD-ROM. After installation of the hardware development software, you will need to request a software license from Altera via their web site www.altera.com. These software packages contain all of the tools necessary to design and develop CPLD/FPGA solutions for logic circuit design. MAX+PLUS II is an easy-to-use, mature development tool, while Quartus II provides some additional advanced features and can compile newer Altera PLDs. The tutorial files provide step-by-step procedures for design entry using schematic capture and hardware description languages, simulation, and device programming with Altera's MAX+PLUS II or Quartus II. The tutorials are provided in PowerPoint and Adobe PDF formats.

LOGIC CIRCUIT TESTER

Suggested Parts				
74ACT11004	74HC00	NE555	LM393	LEDs
SPST and SPDT switches		Resistors: 330 Ω, 1 kΩ, 16 kΩ, 24 kΩ, 62 kΩ, 100 kΩ*		
Capacitors: 0.01 μf*		* Plus desired resistors and capacitors for 555 clock		

Digital Test Equipment

An inexpensive digital testing system having many of the capabilities of a commercially available system can be constructed with parts listed under "Suggested Parts" above. The basic logic circuit tester described here may be either temporarily breadboarded as needed or mounted more permanently on some type of circuit board.

Lamp Monitor

A light emitting diode (LED) can be easily used as a lamp monitor for digital signals. A driver circuit using an inverter from a 74ACT11004 can be used to turn on the LED without loading down the monitored gate's output (see Fig. A-1).

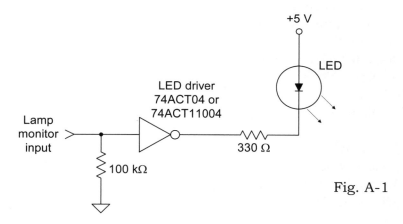

Fig. A-1

Logic Switches

An SPST toggle switch can be conveniently used for logic inputs in digital circuit testing. The schematic in Fig. A-2 shows how to wire a simple logic switch.

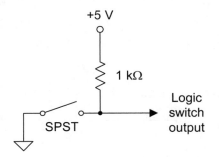

Fig. A-2

Manual Clock (Pushbutton)

A pushbutton or momentary switch can be easily debounced, thereby making it suitable to manually clock digital circuits. Use a simple NAND latch as shown in Fig. A-3.

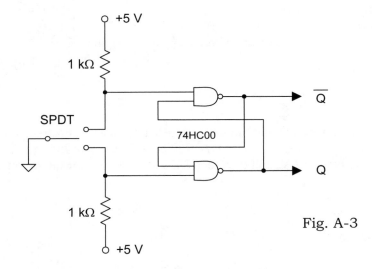

Fig. A-3

Clock

A 555 timer chip can be conveniently used to produce a TTL compatible square wave for clocking digital circuits. The frequency may be varied by changing the timing components R_A, R_B, and C. A 555 clock circuit schematic and the equations for determining the output frequency are given in Fig. A-4.

$$\texttt{Frequency = 1.44/(R_A + 2R_B)C}$$
$$\texttt{Duty cycle = ((R_A + R_B)/(R_A + 2R_B)) × 100\%}$$

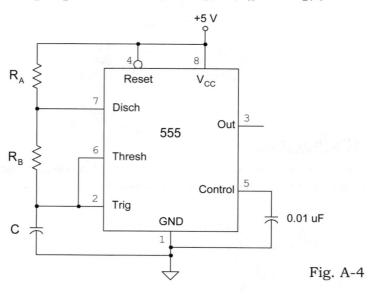

Fig. A-4

Logic Probe

A TTL voltage-compatible logic probe can be easily constructed using two analog comparators, as shown in Fig. A-5. The red LED will light for input voltages above approximately 2 V, and the green LED should light for input voltages below 0.8 V.

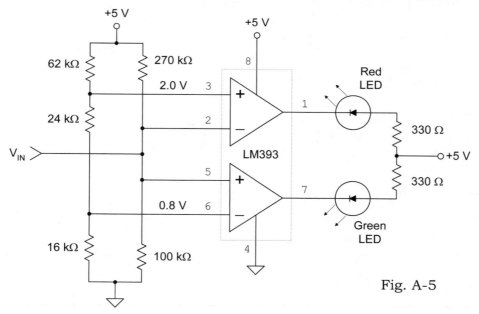

Fig. A-5

AHDL LANGUAGE ELEMENTS

Names

- Symbolic names specify internal and external nodes and groups, constants, state machine variables, state bits, state names, and instances
- Subdesign names are user-defined names for lower-level design files and must be the same as the TDF filename
- Port names are symbolic names that identify the input or output of a logic block
- Start with an alphabet character or slash unless quoted ' '
- Can contain numeric characters or underscore or dash (if quoted); cannot contain spaces
- Are not case sensitive
- May be up to 32 characters long
- Cannot contain any reserved keywords unless quoted

Reserved keywords

AND	FUNCTION	OUTPUT
ASSERT	GENERATE	PARAMETERS
BEGIN	GND	REPORT
BIDIR	HELP_ID	RETURNS
BITS	IF	SEGMENTS
BURIED	INCLUDE	SEVERITY
CASE	INPUT	STATES
CLIQUE	IS	SUBDESIGN
CONNECTED_PINS	LOG2	TABLE
CONSTANT	MACHINE	THEN
DEFAULTS	MOD	TITLE
DEFINE	NAND	TO
DESIGN	NODE	TRI_STATE_NODE
DEVICE	NOR	VARIABLE
DIV	NOT	VCC
ELSE	OF	WHEN
ELSIF	OPTIONS	WITH
END	OR	XNOR
FOR	OTHERS	XOR

Reserved identifiers

CARRY	JKFF	SRFF
CASCADE	JKFFE	SRFFE
CEIL	LATCH	TFF
DFF	LCELL	TFFE
DFFE	MCELL	TRI
EXP	MEMORY	USED
FLOOR	OPENDRN	WIRE
GLOBAL	SOFT	X

(continued)

AHDL LANGUAGE ELEMENTS (continued)

Symbols

% %	enclose comments
--	begin comments (to end of line)
( )	enclose port names in Subdesign section; enclose highest priority operations in Boolean and arithmetic expressions
[ ]	enclose the range of a group name
' '	enclose quoted symbolic names
" "	enclose digits in nondecimal numbers
.	separate symbolic names of variables from port names
..	separate MSB from LSB in a range
;	end AHDL statements and sections
,	separate members of sequential groups and lists
:	separate symbolic names from types in declarations
=	assign values in Boolean equations; assign values to state machine states
=>	separate inputs from outputs in truth table statements
+	addition operator
−	subtraction operator
==	numeric or string equality operator
!	NOT operator
!=	not equal to operator
>	greater than comparator
>=	greater than or equal to comparator
<	less than comparator
<=	less than or equal to comparator
&	AND operator
!&	NAND operator
$	XOR operator
!$	XNOR operator
#	OR operator
!#	NOR operator

Numbers

- Default base for numbers is decimal
- Binary values (series of 0's, 1's, X's) are enclosed in double quotes and prefixed with B
- Hexadecimal values (series from 0 to 9, A to F) are enclosed in double quotes and prefixed with H
- Numbers cannot be assigned to single nodes in Boolean equations; use VCC and GND

VHDL LANGUAGE ELEMENTS

Reserved words

ABS	FOR	PACKAGE
ACCESS	FUNCTION	PORT
AFTER	GENERATE	PROCEDURE
ALIAS	GENERIC	PROCESS
ALL	GUARDED	RANGE
AND	IF	RECORD
ARCHITECTURE	IN	REGISTER
ARRAY	INOUT	REM
ASSERT	IS	REPORT
ATTRIBUTE	LABEL	RETURN
BEGIN	LIBRARY	SELECT
BLOCK	LINKAGE	SEVERITY
BODY	LOOP	SIGNAL
BUFFER	MAP	SUBTYPE
BUS	MOD	THEN
CASE	NAND	TO
COMPONENT	NEW	TRANSPORT
CONFIGURATION	NEXT	TYPE
CONSTANT	NOR	UNITS
DISCONNECT	NOT	UNTIL
DOWNTO	NULL	USE
ELSE	OF	VARIABLE
ELSIF	ON	WAIT
END	OPEN	WHEN
ENTITY	OR	WHILE
EXIT	OTHERS	WITH
FILE	OUT	XOR

(continued)

VHDL LANGUAGE ELEMENTS (continued)

Identifiers

- An identifier is the name of an object
- Objects are named entities that can be assigned a value and have a specific data type
- Objects include signals, variables, and constants
- Must start with an alphabet character and end with an alphabet or a numeric character
- Can contain numeric or underscore characters and cannot contain spaces
- Are not case sensitive
- May be up to 32 characters long
- Cannot contain any reserved words

Symbols

--	begins comment (to end of line)
( )	encloses port names in entity declaration; encloses highest priority operations in Boolean and arithmetic expressions
' '	encloses scalar values
" "	encloses array values
;	ends VHDL statements and declarations
,	separates objects
:	separates object identifier names from mode and data type in declarations
<=	assigns values in signal assignment statements
:=	assigns values in variable assignment statements or to constants
=>	separates signal assignment statements from WHEN clause in CASE statements
+	addition operator
−	subtraction operator
=	equality operator
/=	inequality operator
>	greater than comparator
>=	greater than or equal to comparator
<	less than comparator
<=	less than or equal to comparator
&	concatenation operator

Synthesis Data Types

BIT	object can only have single-bit values of '0' or '1'
STD_LOGIC	object with multi-value logic including '0', '1', 'X', 'Z'
INTEGER	objects with whole number (decimal) values, e.g., 54, −21
BIT_VECTOR	objects with arrays of bits such as "10010110"
STD_LOGIC_VECTOR	objects with arrays of multi-value logic, e.g., "01101XX"

7-SEGMENT DISPLAYS

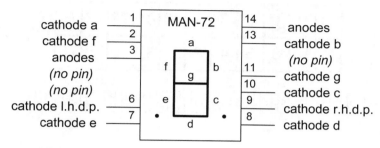

MAN72 (or equivalent), 7-segment, common-anode display (top view)

Board →	UP2 and PLDT-2		eSOC	
Segment ↓	Left-hand Digit	Right-hand Digit	Left-hand Digit	Right-hand Digit
a	Pin 58	Pin 69	Pin 27	Pin 36
b	Pin 60	Pin 70	Pin 28	Pin 37
c	Pin 61	Pin 73	Pin 29	Pin 40
d	Pin 63	Pin 74	Pin 30	Pin 41
e	Pin 64	Pin 76	Pin 31	Pin 44
f	Pin 65	Pin 75	Pin 33	Pin 45
g	Pin 67	Pin 77	Pin 34	Pin 48
Decimal Point	Pin 68	Pin 79	Pin 35	Pin 49

EPM7128SLC84 pin assignments for 2-digit, 7-segment displays
on UP2, PLDT-2, and eSOC trainer boards

CPLD BOARD HEADERS
(UP2 AND PLDT-2)

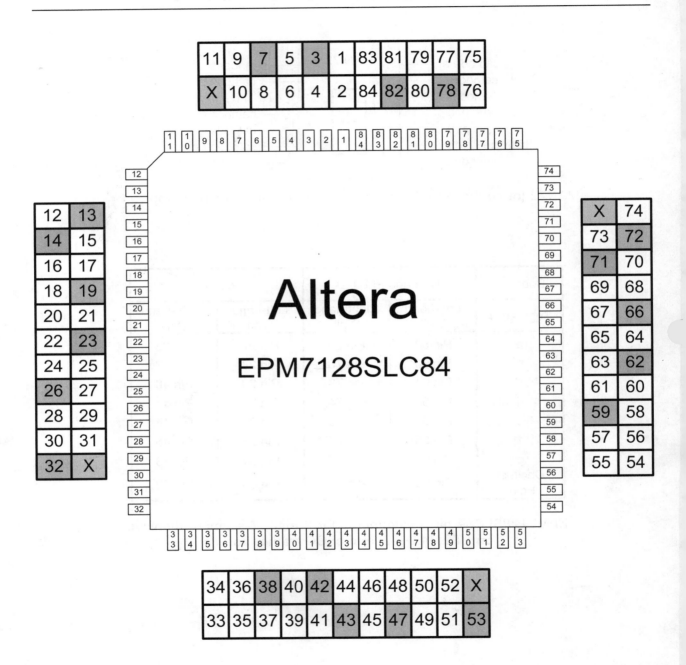

Note: Shaded pins are not available for user input or output.

LOGIC GATE PIN-OUTS

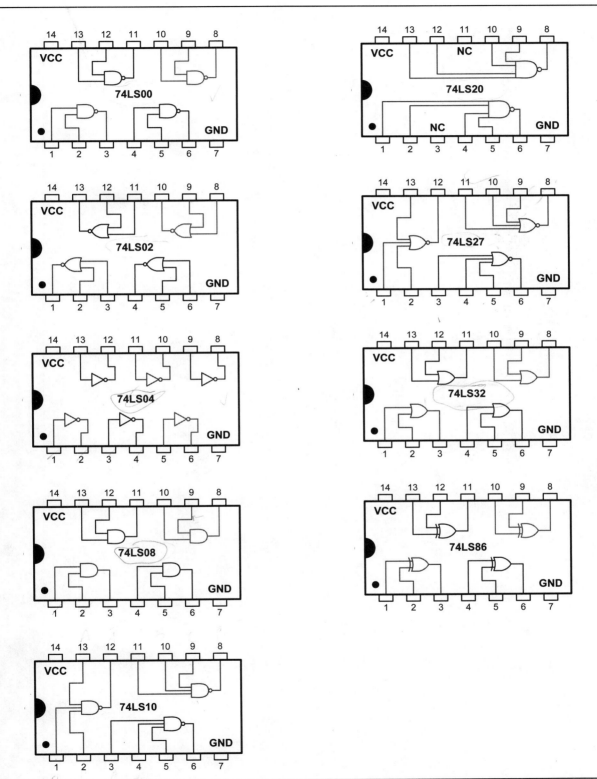